Teacher's Edition

PRENTICE HALL

SCIENCE EXPLORER

Earth's Waters

PRENTICE HALL
Needham, Massachusetts
Upper Saddle River, New Jersey

ISBN 0-13-434565-7
3 4 5 6 7 8 9 10   05 04 03 02 01 00 99

PRENTICE HALL

SCIENCE EXPLORER

GET READY FOR A CONTENT-RICH, HANDS-ON EXPLORATION!

PRENTICE HALL
SCIENCE EXPLORER
Earth's Waters

PRENTICE HALL
SCIENCE EXPLORER
Motion, Forces and Energy

PRENTICE HALL
SCIENCE EXPLORER
Animals

15 Books In All

Chart your own course.

15 motivational hardcover books make it easy for you to create your own curriculum; meet local, state, and national guidelines; and teach your favorite topics in depth.

Prepare your students with rich, motivating content...

Science Explorer is crafted for today's middle grades student, with accessible content and in-depth coverage of all the important concepts.

...and a wide variety of inquiry activities.

Motivational student- and teacher-tested activities reinforce key concepts and allow students to explore science concepts for themselves.

Check your compass regularly.

Science Explorer gives you more ways to regularly check student performance than any other program available.

Utilize a variety of tools.

Integrated science sections in every chapter and Interdisciplinary Explorations in every book allow you to make in-depth connections to other sciences and disciplines. Plus, you will find a wealth of additional tools to set your students on a successful course.

Chart the course you want with 15 motivating books that easily match your curriculum.

Each book in the series contains:
- Integrated Science sections in every chapter
- Interdisciplinary Explorations for team teaching at the end of each book
- Comprehensive skills practice and application—assuring that you meet the National Science Education Standards and your local and state standards

For custom binding options, see your local sales representative.

EXPLORATION TOOLS: BASIC PROCESS SKILLS

Observing

Measuring

Calculating

Classifying

Predicting

Inferring

Graphing

Creating data tables

Communicating

LIFE SCIENCE TITLES

From Bacteria to Plants
1 Living Things
2 Viruses and Bacteria
3 Protists and Fungi
4 Introduction to Plants
5 Seed Plants

Animals
1 Sponges, Cnidarians, and Worms
2 Mollusks, Arthropods, and Echinoderms
3 Fishes, Amphibians, and Reptiles
4 Birds and Mammals
5 Animal Behavior

Cells and Heredity
1 Cell Structure and Function
2 Cell Processes and Energy
3 Genetics: The Science of Heredity
4 Modern Genetics
5 Changes Over Time

Human Biology and Health
1 Healthy Body Systems
2 Bones, Muscles, and Skin
3 Food and Digestion
4 Circulation
5 Respiration and Excretion
6 Fighting Disease
7 The Nervous System
8 The Endocrine System and Reproduction

Environmental Science
1 Populations and Communities
2 Ecosystems and Biomes
3 Living Resources
4 Land and Soil Resources
5 Air and Water Resources
6 Energy Resources

 Integrated Science sections in every chapter

Posing questions

Forming operational definitions

Developing hypotheses

Controlling variables

Interpreting data

Interpreting graphs

Making models

Drawing conclusions

Designing experiments

 Integrated Science sections in every chapter

Place your students in the role of science explorer through a variety of inquiry activities.

Motivational student- and teacher-tested activities reinforce key concepts and allow students to explore science concepts for themselves. More than 350 activities are provided for each book in the Student Edition, Teacher's Edition, Teaching Resources, Integrated Science Lab Manual, Inquiry Skills Activity Book, Interactive Student Tutorial CD-ROM, and *Science Explorer* Web Site.

STUDENT EDITION ACTIVITIES

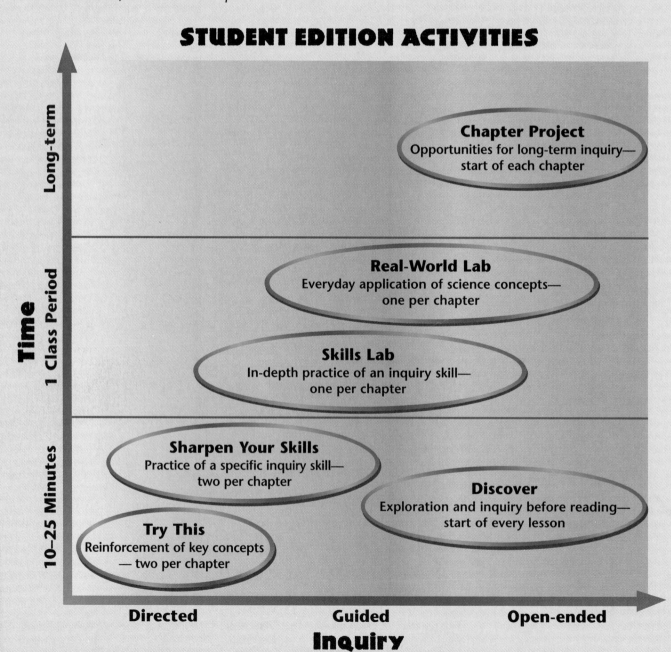

Time

Long-term

Chapter Project
Opportunities for long-term inquiry—
start of each chapter

1 Class Period

Real-World Lab
Everyday application of science concepts—
one per chapter

Skills Lab
In-depth practice of an inquiry skill—
one per chapter

10–25 Minutes

Sharpen Your Skills
Practice of a specific inquiry skill—
two per chapter

Discover
Exploration and inquiry before reading—
start of every lesson

Try This
Reinforcement of key concepts
— two per chapter

Directed   Guided   Open-ended

Inquiry

Check your compass regularly with integrated assessment tools.

Prepare for state exams with traditional and performance-based assessment.

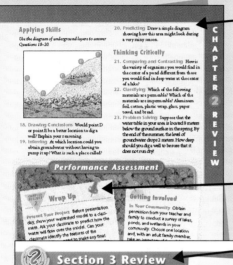

- **Comprehensive Chapter Reviews** include a wide range of question types that students will encounter on standardized tests. Types include multiple choice, enhanced true/false, concept mastery, visual thinking, skill application, and critical thinking. Also includes Chapter Project "Wrap Up."

- **Chapter Projects** contain rubrics that allow you to easily assess student progress.

- **Section Reviews** provide "Check your Progress" opportunities for the Chapter Project, as well as review questions for the section.

Additional *Science Explorer* assessment resources:

- **Assessment Resources with CD-ROM**
- **Resource Pro® with Planning Express® CD-ROM**
- **Standardized Test Practice Book**
- **On-line review activities** at www.phschool.com
  See page T9 for complete product descriptions.

Self-assessment opportunities help students keep themselves on course.

- **Caption Questions** throughout the text assess critical thinking skills.

- **Checkpoint Questions** give students an immediate content check as new concepts are presented.

- **Interactive Student Tutorial CD-ROM** provides students with electronic self-tests, review activities, and Exploration activities.

- **Got It! Video Quizzes** motivate and challenge students with engaging animations and interactive questions.

- **www.science-explorer.phschool.com** provides additional support and on-line test prep.

Utilize a wide variety of tools.

Easy-to-manage, book-specific teaching resources

15 Teaching Resource Packages, each containing a Student Edition, Teacher's Edition, Teaching Resources with Color Transparencies, Guided Reading Audiotape, Materials Kit Order form, and Correlation to the National Science Education Standards.

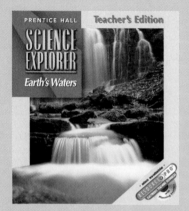

15 Teacher's Editions with a three-step lesson plan—*Engage/Explore, Facilitate,* and *Assess*—that is ideal for reaching all students. Chapter planning charts make it easy to find resources, as well as to plan for block scheduling and team teaching.

15 Teaching Resource Books with Color Transparencies offer complete support organized by chapter to make it easy for you to find what you need—when you need it.

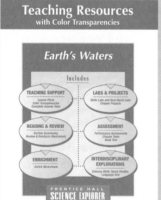

15 Guided Reading Audiotapes (English and Spanish) provide section summaries for students who need additional support.

15 Explorer Videotapes allow students to explore concepts through spectacular short videos containing computer animations. Available in Spanish.

Program-wide print resources

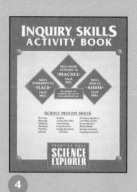

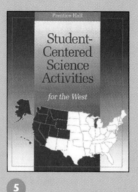

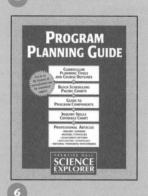

1. **Materials Kits**—Prentice Hall and Science Kit, Inc. have collaborated to develop a Consumable Kit and Nonconsumable Kit for each book. Ordering software makes it easy to customize!

2&3. **Integrated Science Laboratory Manual with Teacher's Edition**—74 in-depth labs covering the entire curriculum, with complete teaching support.

4. **Inquiry Skills Activity Book**—additional activities to teach, practice, and assess a wide range of inquiry skills.

5. **Student-Centered Science Activities**—five activity books for the Northeast, Southeast, Midwest, Southwest, and West.

6. **Program Planning Guide**—course outlines, block scheduling pacing charts, correlations, and more.

7. **Product Testing Activities by *Consumer Reports***—19 student-oriented testing activities turn students into real-world explorers.

Additional print resources...
8. **Reading in the Content Area**—with Literature Connections
9. **Standardized Test Practice**—review and self-tests to prepare for statewide exams.
10. **15 Prentice Hall Interdisciplinary Explorations**
11. **How to Assess Student Work**
12. **How to Manage Instruction in the Block**
13. ***Cobblestone, Odyssey, Calliope,* and *Faces* Magazines**

Program-wide technology resources

1. **Resource Pro® CD-ROM**—the ultimate management tool with easy access to blackline masters and lab activities for all 15 books. Planning Express® software lets you customize lesson plans by day, week, month, and year. Also includes Computer Test Bank software.

2. **Assessment Resources with CD-ROM**—*Computer Test Bank* software with Dial-A-Test® provides you with unparalleled flexibility in creating tests.

3. *Science Explorer* **Web Site**—activities and teaching resources for every chapter at www.science-explorer.phschool.com

4. **Interactive Student Tutorial CD-ROMs**—provide students with self-tests, helpful hints, and Explorations. Tests are scored instantly and provide complete explanations to all answers.

5. **An Odyssey of Discovery CD-ROMs**—interactive labs encourage students to hypothesize and experiment. (Life and Earth Science).

6. **Interactive Earth CD-ROM**—explore global trends, search the media library, and zoom in on a 3-D globe.

7. **Mindscape CD-ROMs**—*The Animals!™, Oceans Below,* and *How Your Body Works* bring science alive with compelling videoclips, 3-D animations, and interactive databases.

8. **A.D.A.M. The Inside Story**—take an entertaining tour of each body system, designed for middle grades students.

9. **Interactive Physics**—explore physics concepts with computer simulations that encourage what-if questions.

10. **Explorer Videotapes and Videodiscs**—explore and visualize concepts through spectacular short documentaries containing computer animations (Spanish audio track).

11. **Got It! Video Quizzes**—make in-class review fun and prepare students for book tests and state assessments.

12. **Event-Based Science**—series of NSF-funded modules that engage students with inquiry-based projects. Includes video.

Options for Pacing *Earth's Waters*

The Pacing Chart below suggests one way to schedule your instructional time. The **Science Explorer** program offers many other aids to help you plan your instructional time, whether regular class periods or **block scheduling**. Refer to the Chapter Planning Guide before each chapter to view all program resources with suggested times for Student Edition activities.

Pacing Chart

	Days	Blocks		Days	Blocks
Nature of Science: Life in a Sunless World	1	1/2	**Chapter 4 Ocean Motions**		
Chapter 1 Earth: The Water Planet			Chapter 4 Project Protecting a Shoreline	Ongoing	Ongoing
Chapter 1 Project Every Drop Counts	Ongoing	Ongoing	1 Wave Action	2–3	1–2
1 How Is Water Important?	3–4	2	2 Integrating Space Science: Tides	1–2	1
2 Integrating Chemistry: The Properties of Water	4–5	3–4	3 Ocean Water Chemistry	2–3	1–2
3 The Water Cycle	1–2	1	4 Currents and Climate	2–3	1–2
Chapter 1 Review and Assessment	1	1/2	Chapter 4 Review and Assessment	1	1/2
Chapter 2 Fresh Water			**Chapter 5 Ocean Zones**		
Chapter 2 Project Build a Watershed	Ongoing	Ongoing	Chapter 5 Project At Home in the Sea	Ongoing	Ongoing
1 Streams and Rivers	4–5	2–3	1 Exploring the Ocean	4–5	2–3
2 Ponds and Lakes	2–3	1–2	2 Integrating Life Science: Life at the Ocean's Edge	2–3	1–2
3 Integrating Life Science: Wetland Environments	2–3	1–2	3 Integrating Life Science: The Neritic Zone and Open Ocean	2–3	1–2
4 Glaciers and Icebergs	1–2	1/2–1	4 Resources From the Ocean	3–5	2–3
5 Water Underground	3–4	1–2	Chapter 5 Review and Assessment	1	1/2
Chapter 2 Review and Assessment	1	1/2	Interdisciplinary Exploration: The Mississippi	2–3	1–2
Chapter 3 Freshwater Resources					
Chapter 3 Project A Precious Resource	Ongoing	Ongoing			
1 Water to Drink	3–4	2–3			
2 Balancing Water Needs	3–4	2–3			
3 Freshwater Pollution	2	1			
4 Integrating Physics: Water As an Energy Resource	2	1			
Chapter 3 Review and Assessment	1	1/2			

RESOURCE PRO

The Resource Pro® CD-ROM is the ultimate scheduling and lesson planning tool. Resource Pro® allows you to preview all the resources in the *Science Explorer* program, organize your chosen materials, and print out any teaching resource. You can follow the suggested lessons or create your own, using resources from anywhere in the program.

Thematic Overview of *Earth's Waters*

The chart below lists the major themes of *Earth's Waters*. For each theme, the chart supplies a big idea, or concept statement, describing how a particular theme is taught in a chapter.

	Chapter 1	Chapter 2	Chapter 3	Chapter 4	Chapter 5
Energy	Water molecules gain or lose energy when water changes state. The sun is the source of energy that drives the water cycle.		Hydroelectric power plants capture the energy of moving water and change it into electrical energy.	Waves form when winds transmit their energy to water.	The feeding relationships in a habitat make up a food web.
Patterns of Change	Water moves from Earth's surface to the atmosphere and back to Earth's surface in the water cycle.	Rivers shape the land through erosion and deposition. Glaciers change the land.	Water shortages occur when there is too little water or too great a demand.	Waves shape a beach through erosion and deposition.	
Scale and Structure	Water has a unique structure that gives it unusual properties.	Water soaks down through permeable materials until it reaches a layer of impermeable materials.			Earth consists of several layers, and the outer layer, the crust, is made up of moving plates.
Systems and Interactions	Water is naturally recycled through the water cycle.	Fresh water on Earth's surface forms streams and rivers; collects in lakes and wetlands; forms glaciers; and moves underground.	Water pollution can affect surface water, groundwater, and even rain.	Tides are causes by the interactions of Earth, the moon, and the sun.	The interaction of Earth's plates forms many seafloor features.
Unity and Diversity		Rivers, ponds, lakes, and wetlands provide habitats for many living things.	Students test and compare various types of water.		The ocean floor has features similar to those of continents.
Stability	For millions of years, the total amount of water on Earth has remained fairly constant.			On average, ocean water salinity is about 35 parts per thousand.	
Modeling		Students design and build a watershed model. Students explore the water-holding properties of different soil types.	Students design and build a model of a water treatment plant. Students investigate desalination using a distillation model.	Students build an ocean beach model to investigate erosion.	Students create models of marine habitats and organisms.

Inquiry Skills Chart

The Prentice Hall *Science Explorer* program provides comprehensive teaching, practice, and assessment of science skills, with an emphasis on the process skills necessary for inquiry. The chart lists the skills covered in the program and cites the page numbers where each skill is covered.

Basic Process SKILLS				
	Student Text: Projects and Labs	Student Text: Activities	Student Text: Caption and Review Questions	Teacher's Edition: Extensions
Observing	36, 40–41, 70–71, 78–79, 82–83, 112–113, 138–139	16, 23, 59, 61, 68, 86, 97, 105, 114, 116, 127, 162, 172, 186		186
Inferring	36, 82–83, 138–139, 155	25, 32, 50, 65, 134, 146, 156, 166, 171, 186	74, 77, 81, 89, 103, 111, 131, 154, 173, 179	64, 117, 171, 186
Predicting	40–41	29, 42, 58, 90, 93, 122, 186	29, 39, 58, 77, 87, 111, 143, 179	85, 87, 124, 158, 186
Classifying		53, 99, 169, 187	22, 66, 77, 143, 179	187
Making Models	40–41, 46–47, 78– 79, 95, 112–113, 138–139, 144–145, 176	40–41, 46–47, 78–79, 95, 112–113, 138–139, 144–145, 176		50, 149, 167, 187
Communicating	14–15, 78–79, 112–113, 144–145	19, 28, 57, 119, 149, 158, 181, 185, 187	38, 76, 110, 142, 178	187
Measuring	70-71, 112-113, 132-133	188–189, 183		52, 60, 188–189
Calculating	36, 46–47	20, 80, 183	39, 143	
Creating Data Tables	14–15, 132–133, 155	196-198		27, 58, 196–198
Graphing	14–15, 132–133	124, 146, 196–198	143	21, 151, 198
Advanced Process SKILLS				
Posing Questions		190	179	190
Developing Hypotheses	30–31	106, 190	93, 111	190
Designing Experiments	112–113, 132–133	191	111	26, 191
Controlling Variables	30–31, 40–41, 132–133	191		88, 191
Forming Operational Definitions	78–79, 82–83, 176	191		191

	Student Text: Projects and Labs	Student Text: Activities	Student Text: Caption and Review Questions	Teacher's Edition: Extensions
Advanced Process SKILLS *(continued)*				
Interpreting Data	14–15, 46–47, 144–145, 155	152, 191 26, 69, 102, 136, 191	17, 39, 84, 128 17, 143	191
Drawing Conclusions	78-79	34, 45, 67, 72, 174, 182, 187		
Critical Thinking SKILLS				
Comparing and Contrasting	78–79	94, 192	27, 39, 60, 77, 111, 123, 140, 143	27, 49, 54, 103, 118, 192
Applying Concepts	36, 70–71, 82–83, 138–139, 176	131, 192	24, 29, 39, 43, 52, 67, 94, 115, 126, 143, 174	136, 166, 173, 192
Interpreting Diagrams, Graphs Photographs, and Maps		192	21, 22, 44, 56, 63, 69, 73, 99, 107, 117, 118, 121, 125, 128, 135, 147, 153, 154, 163, 165, 167, 170, 179	33, 192
Relating Cause and Effect		193	34, 35, 39, 58, 91, 98, 101, 111, 121, 128, 137, 143, 168, 179	129, 153, 193
Making Generalizations		193	39, 51, 126, 160, 179	193
Making Judgments		92, 96, 175, 193	64, 67, 94, 104, 111, 161, 174	193
Problem Solving		193	77, 108	193
Information Organizing SKILLS				
Concept Maps		194	76, 110	194
Compare/ Contrast Tables		194	178	27, 58, 108, 135, 161, 167, 194
Venn Diagrams		195		195
Flowcharts	78-79	195	142	195
Cycle Diagrams		195	38	195

The *Science Explorer* program provides additional teaching, reinforcement, and assessment of skills in the Inquiry Skills Activities Book and the Integrated Science Laboratory Manual.

Throughout the *Science Explorer* program, every effort has been made to keep the materials and equipment *affordable, reusable,* and *easily accessible.*

The *Science Explorer* program offers an abundance of activity options so you can pick and choose those activities that suit your needs. To help you order supplies at the beginning of the year, the Master Materials List cross-references the materials by activity. If you prefer to create your list electronically, use the electronic order forms at:
www.science–explorer.phschool.com

There are two kits available for each book of the *Science Explorer* program, a Consumable Kit and a Nonconsumable Kit. These kits are produced by **Science Kit and Boreal Laboratories,** the leader in providing science kits to schools. Prentice Hall and Science Kit collaborated throughout the development of *Science Explorer* to ensure that the equipment and supplies in the kits precisely match the requirements of the program activities.

The kits provide an economical and convenient way to get all of the materials needed to teach each book. For each book, Science Kit also offers the opportunity to buy equipment and safety items individually. For a current listing of kit offerings or additional information about materials to accompany *Science Explorer*, please, contact Science Kit at:
1-800-828-7777
or at their Internet site at:
www.sciencekit.com

Master Materials List

Consumable Materials

*	Description	Quantity per class	Textbook Section(s)	*	Description	Quantity per class	Textbook Section(s)
SS	Agar, Pkg, 0.5 oz.	10	5-4 (TT)	SS	Guava Juice or other Fruit Juice	5	5-4 (TT)
SS	Aluminum Foil, Roll 12″x25′	1	3-2 (Lab)	SS	Ice Cubes, bucket	2	1-3 (DIS), 2-4 (DIS) 3-2 (Lab), 4-3 (Lab), 4-4 (DIS)
SS	Bag, Plastic Small (Sandwich)	15	1-3 (Lab)				
SS	Bags, Plastic Clear Trash Pkg/15	1	3-1 (DIS), 3-4 (DIS)				
SS	Baking Soda 454 g (2 cups)	1	1-2 (TT)	SS	Labels from Household Products	5	5-4 (DIS)
C	Balloons, Round 15″ Pkg/5	1	1-1 (DIS)	C	Lid, Plastic for 40 oz. Bowl	5	5-3 (DIS)
SS	Box of Common Materials	5	5-2 (DIS)	C	Marker, Black, Permanent	5	1-1 (DIS), 4-4 (Lab), 5-3 (DIS)
SS	Box, Covered with Holes	5	5-1 (DIS)				
SS	Bulb, 100 W, Incandescent	1	1-2 (Lab), 1-3 (TT)				
				C	Mixed Pond Culture (Coupon Fulfill. No. 28026-01)	1	2-2 (DIS)
SS	Cardboard, Corrugated 32x32 cm	5	2-4 (DIS)	SS	Newspapers	5	2-3 (TT), 2-5 (TT), 3-1 (TT), 4-4 (Lab)
SS	Cards, Index Blank 3x5 Pkg/100	1	1-2 (Lab)				
C	Chalk, White Pkg/12	1	4-4 (Lab)				
C	Cheesecloth, 2-m piece	1	2-5 (Lab)				
C	Clay, Modeling (Cream) lb. (water resistant)	11	2-5 (TT), 4-4 (Lab)	SS	Oil, Vegetable 16 oz.	2	1-2 (DIS), 1-2 (TT), 5-4 (Lab)
C	Clay, Powder 1 lb.	1	2-5 (Lab)				
SS	Cotton Balls, Pkg/300	1	5-4 (Lab)	SS	Paper Towel Roll (120 sheets)	1	1-2 (DIS), 1-2 (Lab), 2-1 (TT), 5-4 (Lab)
SS	Cup, Paper 200 mL	160	1-1 (SYS), 2-3 (DIS), 3-1 (Lab) 5-4 (Lab)				
				SS	Paper, Construction, Blue (sheet)	1	4-4 (Lab)
SS	Cup, Plastic Clear 2 oz. each	30	1-2 (TT)	SS	Paper, Construction, Red (sheet)	1	4-4 (Lab)
SS	Cup, Plastic Clear 300 mL each	10	1-2 (DIS), 1-2 (TT), 4-4 (DIS)	C	Pebbles/Gravel 1 kg (2-1/2 Cups)	10	1-3 (Lab), 2-1 (DIS), 2-4 (DIS), 2-5 (DIS), 2-5 (Lab), 4-1 (DIS)
SS	Detergent, Household 14.7 oz.	1	3-1 (Lab)				
SS	Egg, Uncooked	10	4-3 (DIS)				
C	Feathers, Turkey Pkg/6	1	5-4 (Lab)	C	Pencil, Wax Marking, Black	5	3-1 (Lab)
C	Fertilizer, Granular, 8 oz.	1	3-3 (TT)	SS	Pencil, with Eraser	10	2-1 (Lab), 4-3 (Lab), 5-1 (Lab)
SS	Filters, Coffee Box/100	1	3-3 (DIS)				
SS	Flour, 2 lb (7 cups)	1	5-3 (DIS)				
SS	Food Coloring	1	5-4 (TT)	C	pH Test Paper-Wide Range 100/Vial 1/4″ x 2″	5	3-1 (Lab)
C	Food Coloring, Dark Red 30 mL in Dropper Bottle	5	1-2 (TT), 2-1 (Lab), 3-3 (DIS), 4-4 (DIS)	SS	Plastic Wrap Roll, 50 sq. ft.	1	1-3 (TT)
				SS	Plates, Paper 9″, Pkg/50	1	3-3 (DIS)
SS	Graph Paper (sheet)	10	4-2 (SYS), 5-1 (Lab)	SS	Pond or Aquarium Water	5	3-3 (TT)
				SS	Rain Gutter Section	5	2-1 (Lab)

KEY: **DIS**: Discover; **SYS**: Sharpen Your Skills; **TT**: Try This; **Lab**: Lab   **Quantities based on 5 lab groups per class.**

* Items designated **C** are in the Consumable Kit, **NC** are in the Nonconsumable Kit, and **SS** are School Supplied.

Master Materials List

Consumable Materials (cont.)

*	Description	Quantity per class	Textbook Section(s)	*	Description	Quantity per class	Textbook Section(s)
C	Rheoscopic Fluid, Kalliroscope 32 oz.	2	4-4 (Lab)	C	Straws, Plastic Pkg/200	1	2-5 (TT), 5-1 (DIS)
SS	Salt, Non-Iodized 737 g	1	1-2 (TT), 3-2 (Lab), 4-3 (DIS), 4-3 (Lab)	C	String, Cotton 430 ft	1	1-2 (TT), 4-1 (TT), 5-3 (DIS)
C	Sand, Fine 2.5 kg (7-1/2 Cups)	12	1-3 (TT), 2-1 (DIS), 2-4 (DIS), 2-5 (DIS), 2-5 (Lab), 2-5 (TT), 4-1 (DIS)	SS	Sugar, 1 Cup	5	5-4 (TT)
				SS	Tape, Masking 3/4″ x 60 yd.	1	1-2 (TT), 5-3 (DIS)
				C	Tongue Depressor (Wood Slats)	5	4-1 (DIS)
				SS	Toothpicks, Round Pkg/250	1	3-4 (TT)
				C	Twist Tie 10 cm, Plastic	15	1-3 (Lab)
SS	Soil and Grass Clump	5	2-1 (DIS)	SS	Water, Distilled, 200mL	1	3-1 (Lab)
C	Soil, Potting 4 lb. (12-1/2 Cups)	2	2-3 (TT)	SS	Water, Mineral, 200mL	1	3-1 (Lab)
C	Sticks, Craft Pkg/50	1	5-4 (Lab)	SS	Water, Spring, 200mL	1	3-1 (Lab)
C	Straw, Flexible Plastic (Wrapped)	10	4-4 (Lab)	SS	Wax Paper, Roll 75 sq. ft.	1	1-2 (DIS)

Nonconsumable Materials

*	Description	Quantity per class	Textbook Section(s)	*	Description	Quantity per class	Textbook Section(s)
NC	Aquarium, Plastic Medium	5	4-1 (TT), 4-4 (DIS)	NC	Cork, Size 7	20	3-4 (DIS), 4-1 (TT)
NC	Ball, Foam 2″ Diameter	5	3-4 (TT)	NC	Cup, Plastic Measuring 500 mL	5	3-2 (DIS), 3-2 (SYS)
SS	Ball, Table Tennis	5	5-2 (DIS)	NC	Cylinder, Graduated, Polypropylene, 100 x 1 mL	5	1-1 (SYS), 4-3 (Lab), 5-4 (Lab)
SS	Ball, Tennis	5	3-4 (DIS)				
NC	Beaker, Pyrex Low Form, 250ml, Double Scale	20	2-1 (Lab), 2-5 (Lab), 3-1 (), 3-2 (Lab), 4-3 (DIS), 4-3 (Lab)	NC	Cylinder, Polypropylene, 25mL	5	3-1 (Lab)
				NC	Dish, Plastic Petri Top + Bottom 100 mm	10	1-2 (Lab)
SS	Bottle, Plastic, 1 liter	5	1-1 (SYS)	NC	Dropper, Plastic	10	1-1 (SYS), 1-2 (DIS), 1-2 (Lab), 3-2 (DIS), 4-4 (DIS), 5-4 (Lab)
NC	Bowl, Small Plastic, 40 oz.	10	1-1 (SYS), 1-3 (TT), 3-1 (TT) 3-2 (DIS)				
SS	Bucket, Large	5	5-3 (DIS)	NC	Flask, Pyrex Erlenmeyer, 500 mL, Narrow Mouth	5	3-2 (Lab)
NC	Can, Watering, w/Sprinkler Head	5	2-1 (DIS), 2-3 (TT), 2-5 (DIS)	NC	Funnel, Plastic 5″	15	2-5 (Lab), 2-5 (TT)

KEY: **DIS**: Discover; **SYS**: Sharpen Your Skills; **TT**: Try This; **Lab**: Lab
* Items designated **C** are in the Consumable Kit, **NC** are in the Nonconsumable Kit, and **SS** are School Supplied.

Nonconsumable Materials (cont.)

*	Description	Quantity per class	Textbook Section(s)
SS	Glass, Drinking	5	1-3 (DIS)
SS	Hole Punch	1	4-4 (Lab)
NC	Jar, Clear Styrene, 850 mL	15	2-5 (DIS), 2-5 (Lab), 3-3 (TT), 3-4 (DIS)
NC	Jar, Plastic, 89 mm, 8 oz.	5	1-3 (TT)
SS	Lamp	5	1-2 (Lab), 1-3 (TT)
SS	Large Trash Barrels	2	3-1 (DIS)
NC	Lid, Metal 63 mm for 850-mL Styrene Jar	10	3-3 (TT)
NC	Magnifying Glass	5	2-2 (DIS), 2-5 (Lab)
NC	Marbles, 9/16″ Pkg/6	1	3-4 (DIS)
NC	Meter Stick, Wood, Plain Ends	5	2-1 (Lab), 5-3 (DIS)
NC	Pan, Aluminum Foil 11 x 21 x 6 cm (bread pan)	5	2-3 (TT), 2-5 (TT)
NC	Pan, Aluminum Foil 13 x 10 x 2	5	2-1 (DIS), 2-1 (Lab), 2-3 (DIS), 3-2 (Lab), 4-1 (DIS), 5-2 (DIS), 5-4 (Lab)
NC	Pan, Aluminum Foil 22.5 cm Diameter	5	3-4 (TT)
SS	Paper Clips, Box/100	1	5-3 (DIS)
NC	Pitcher, 2 qt. with Lid	5	1-2 (TT), 3-1 (DIS), 5-2 (DIS)
NC	Rubber Bands, #10 1 oz. Pkg (Approx. 257)	1	2-5 (Lab)
SS	Rock, Small	1	1-3 (TT), 5-2 (DIS)
NC	Rubber Bands,#33 32 oz. Pkg Approx. 50)	1	1-3 (TT)
SS	Ruler, Plastic	5	1-2 (DIS), 3-1 (Lab), 4-3 (Lab), 4-4 (Lab)
SS	Saucepan, cooking	5	5-4 (TT)
SS	Scissors, General Purpose, 6″	5	1-2 (DIS), 3-4 (TT), 5-3 (DIS)
SS	Shallow Pan, Cooking	5	5-4 (TT)
NC	Slide, Microscope Plastic, 25 x 75 mm	1	2-2 (DIS)
SS	Sponge, 15 x 7.5 x 1.8 cm	10	2-3 (DIS), 2-3 (TT), 3-3 (DIS)
NC	Spool, Plastic	5	3-4 (DIS)
NC	Spoons, Plastic Pkg/24	1	1-2 (TT), 2-1 (TT), 3-2 (DIS), 3-2 (Lab), 4-3 (Lab)

*	Description	Quantity per class	Textbook Section(s)
NC	Spray Bottle, 16 oz. Trigger	5	3-4 (DIS)
NC	Stirring Rod, Glass, 5 x 150mm	5	3-2 (Lab)
NC	Stopper, Rubber Size 7, 1-Hole Ea.	5	3-2 (Lab)
NC	Stopper, Size 2 Rubber, Solid, 1lb.	1	3-1 (Lab)
NC	Stopwatch	5	1-2 (Lab), 2-1 (Lab), 2-5 (Lab), 3-2 (DIS)
NC	Streak Plate, 50x50x3 mm	5	2-1 (DIS)
NC	Test Tube Support, Wood	5	3-1 (Lab)
NC	Test Tube, 27ml	20	3-1 (Lab)
NC	Thermometer, Metal-10° to 230°F/-20° to 110° C	5	4-3 (Lab)
SS	Thumbtacks, Pkg/100	1	4-3 (Lab)
NC	Tray, Plastic, Baking 10″x14″	5	4-4 (Lab)
NC	Tubing, Rigid 6″ x 1/4″OD, Smooth Ends	5	3-2 (Lab)
NC	Tubing, Vinyl Plastic, 3/16″ ID x 1/16″ Wall (1ft.)	10	3-1 (TT), 3-2 (Lab)
NC	Washer, Metal 3/4″ OD x 5/16″ ID, Zinc Plated, Flat	75	4-1 (TT)
NC	Wood, Block 2 x 4 x 6	20	2-1 (Lab)

Equipment

*	Description	Quantity per class	Textbook Section(s)
SS	Apron, Vinyl	30	(Lab)
SS	Balance, Triple Beam, Single Pan	5	1-3 (Lab), 4-3 (Lab)
SS	Goggles, Chemical Splash-Class Set	30	(Lab), (TT)
SS	Hot Plate, Variable Heat Control,	5	3-1 (Lab), 3-2 (Lab), 4-3 (Lab)
SS	Microscope	1	2-2 (DIS)
SS	Mitten, Oven	5	3-1 (Lab), 3-2 (Lab), 4-3 (Lab), 5-4 (TT)

KEY: **DIS**: Discover; **SYS**: Sharpen Your Skills; **TT**: Try This; **Lab**: Lab
* Items designated **C** are in the Consumable Kit, **NC** are in the Nonconsumable Kit, and **SS** are School Supplied.

PRENTICE HALL
SCIENCE EXPLORER

Earth's Waters

Program Resources

Student Edition
Annotated Teacher's Edition
Teaching Resources Book with Color Transparencies
Earth's Waters Materials Kits

Program Components

Integrated Science Laboratory Manual
Integrated Science Laboratory Manual, Teacher's Edition
Inquiry Skills Activity Book
Student-Centered Science Activity Books
Program Planning Guide
Guided Reading English Audiotapes
Guided Reading Spanish Audiotapes and Summaries
Product Testing Activities by Consumer Reports™
Event-Based Science Series (NSF funded)
Prentice Hall Interdisciplinary Explorations
Cobblestone, Odyssey, Calliope, and *Faces* Magazines

Media/Technology

Science Explorer Interactive Student Tutorial CD-ROMs
Odyssey of Discovery CD-ROMs
Resource Pro® (Teaching Resources on CD-ROM)
Assessment Resources CD-ROM with Dial-A-Test®
Internet site at www.science-explorer.phschool.com
Life, Earth, and Physical Science Videodiscs
Life, Earth, and Physical Science Videotapes
Got It! Video Quizzes

Science Explorer Student Editions

From Bacteria to Plants

Animals

Cells and Heredity

Human Biology and Health

Environmental Science

Inside Earth

Earth's Changing Surface

Earth's Waters

Weather and Climate

Astronomy

Chemical Building Blocks

Chemical Interactions

Motion, Forces, and Energy

Electricity and Magnetism

Sound and Light

Staff Credits

The people who made up the *Science Explorer* team—representing editorial, editorial services, design services, field marketing, market research, marketing services, on-line services/multimedia development, product marketing, production services, and publishing processes—are listed below. Bold type denotes core team members.

Kristen E. Ball, **Barbara A. Bertell,** Peter W. Brooks, **Christopher R. Brown, Greg Cantone,** Jonathan Cheney, **Patrick Finbarr Connolly,** Loree Franz, Donald P. Gagnon, Jr., **Paul J. Gagnon, Joel Gendler,** Elizabeth Good, Kerri Hoar, **Linda D. Johnson,** Katherine M. Kotik, Russ Lappa, Marilyn Leitao, David Lippman, **Eve Melnechuk, Natania Mlawer,** Paul W. Murphy, **Cindy A. Noftle,** Julia F. Osborne, Caroline M. Power, Suzanne J. Schineller, **Susan W. Tafler,** Kira Thaler-Marbit, Robin L. Santel, Ronald Schachter, **Mark Tricca,** Diane Walsh, Pearl B. Weinstein, Beth Norman Winickoff

ISBN 0-13-434484-7
2 3 4 5 6 7 8 9 10   05 04 03 02 01 00 99

Cover: This waterfall in North Yorkshire, England, illustrates the force and beauty of water in motion.

2 ◆ H

Teacher's Edition ISBN 0-13-434565-7

Program Authors

Michael J. Padilla, Ph.D.
Professor
Department of Science Education
University of Georgia
Athens, Georgia

Michael Padilla is a leader in middle school science education. He has served as an editor and elected officer for the National Science Teachers Association. He has been principal investigator of several National Science Foundation and Eisenhower grants and served as a writer of the National Science Education Standards.
  As lead author of *Science Explorer*, Mike has inspired the team in developing a program that meets the needs of middle grades students, promotes science inquiry, and is aligned with the National Science Education Standards.

Ioannis Miaoulis, Ph.D.
Dean of Engineering
College of Engineering
Tufts University
Medford, Massachusetts

Martha Cyr, Ph.D.
Director, Engineering
  Educational Outreach
College of Engineering
Tufts University
Medford, Massachusetts

Science Explorer was created in collaboration with the College of Engineering at Tufts University. Tufts has an extensive engineering outreach program that uses engineering design and construction to excite and motivate students and teachers in science and technology education.
  Faculty from Tufts University participated in the development of *Science Explorer* chapter projects, reviewed the student books for content accuracy, and helped coordinate field testing.

CHAPTER PROJECT

Book Authors

Barbara Brooks Simons
Science Writer
Boston, Massachusetts

Thomas R. Wellnitz
Science Instructor
The Paideia School
Atlanta, Georgia

Contributing Writers

Greg Hutton
Science and Health Curriculum
  Coordinator
School Board of Sarasota County
Sarasota, Florida

Jeffrey C. Callister
Science Instructor
Newburgh Free Academy
Newburgh, New York

Jan Jenner, Ph.D.
Science Writer
Talladega, Alabama

Reading Consultant

Bonnie B. Armbruster, Ph.D.
Department of Curriculum
  and Instruction
University of Illinois
Champaign, Illinois

Interdisciplinary Consultant

Heidi Hayes Jacobs, Ed.D.
Teacher's College
Columbia University
New York, New York

Safety Consultants

W. H. Breazeale, Ph.D.
Department of Chemistry
College of Charleston
Charleston, South Carolina

Ruth Hathaway, Ph.D.
Hathaway Consulting
Cape Girardeau, Missouri

H ◆ 3

Tufts University Program Reviewers

Content Reviewers

Teacher Reviewers

Stephanie Anderson
Sierra Vista Junior
    High School
Canyon Country, California

John W. Anson
Mesa Intermediate School
Palmdale, California

Pamela Arline
Lake Taylor Middle School
Norfolk, Virginia

Lynn Beason
College Station Jr. High School
College Station, Texas

Richard Bothmer
Hollis School District
Hollis, New Hampshire

Jeffrey C. Callister
Newburgh Free Academy
Newburgh, New York

Judy D'Albert
Harvard Day School
Corona Del Mar, California

Betty Scott Dean
Guilford County Schools
McLeansville, North Carolina

Sarah C. Duff
Baltimore City Public Schools
Baltimore, Maryland

Melody Law Ewey
Holmes Junior High School
Davis, California

Sherry L. Fisher
Lake Zurich Middle
    School North
Lake Zurich, Illinois

Melissa Gibbons
Fort Worth ISD
Fort Worth, Texas

Debra J. Goodding
Kraemer Middle School
Placentia, California

Jack Grande
Weber Middle School
Port Washington, New York

Steve Hills
Riverside Middle School
Grand Rapids, Michigan

Carol Ann Lionello
Kraemer Middle School
Placentia, California

Jaime A. Morales
Henry T. Gage Middle School
Huntington Park, California

Patsy Partin
Cameron Middle School
Nashville, Tennessee

Deedra H. Robinson
Newport News Public Schools
Newport News, Virginia

Bonnie Scott
Clack Middle School
Abilene, Texas

Charles M. Sears
Belzer Middle School
Indianapolis, Indiana

Barbara M. Strange
Ferndale Middle School
High Point, North Carolina

Jackie Louise Ulfig
Ford Middle School
Allen, Texas

Kathy Usina
Belzer Middle School
Indianapolis, Indiana

Heidi M. von Oetinger
L'Anse Creuse Public School
Harrison Township, Michigan

Pam Watson
Hill Country Middle School
Austin, Texas

Activity Field Testers

Nicki Bibbo
Russell Street School
Littleton, Massachusetts

Connie Boone
Fletcher Middle School
Jacksonville Beach, Florida

Rose-Marie Botting
Broward County
    School District
Fort Lauderdale, Florida

Colleen Campos
Laredo Middle School
Aurora, Colorado

Elizabeth Chait
W. L. Chenery Middle School
Belmont, Massachusetts

Holly Estes
Hale Middle School
Stow, Massachusetts

Laura Hapgood
Plymouth Community
    Intermediate School
Plymouth, Massachusetts

Sandra M. Harris
Winman Junior High School
Warwick, Rhode Island

Jason Ho
Walter Reed Middle School
Los Angeles, California

Joanne Jackson
Winman Junior High School
Warwick, Rhode Island

Mary F. Lavin
Plymouth Community
    Intermediate School
Plymouth, Massachusetts

James MacNeil, Ph.D.
Concord Public Schools
Concord, Massachusetts

Lauren Magruder
St. Michael's Country
    Day School
Newport, Rhode Island

Jeanne Maurand
Glen Urquhart School
Beverly Farms, Massachusetts

Warren Phillips
Plymouth Community
    Intermediate School
Plymouth, Massachusetts

Carol Pirtle
Hale Middle School
Stow, Massachusetts

Kathleen M. Poe
Kirby-Smith Middle School
Jacksonville, Florida

Cynthia B. Pope
Ruffner Middle School
Norfolk, Virginia

Anne Scammell
Geneva Middle School
Geneva, New York

Karen Riley Sievers
Callanan Middle School
Des Moines, Iowa

David M. Smith
Howard A. Eyer Middle School
Macungie, Pennsylvania

Derek Strohschneider
Plymouth Community
    Intermediate School
Plymouth, Massachusetts

Sallie Teames
Rosemont Middle School
Fort Worth, Texas

Gene Vitale
Parkland Middle School
McHenry, Illinois

Zenovia Young
Meyer Levin Junior
    High School (IS 285)
Brooklyn, New York

Contents

Earth's Waters

Prepare your students with rich, motivating content

Science Explorer is crafted for today's middle grades student, with accessible content and in-depth coverage. **Integrated Science Sections** support every chapter and the **Interdisciplinary Exploration** provides an engaging final unit.

Check your compass—regularly assess student progress.

Self-assessment tools are built right into the student text and **on-going assessment** is woven throughout the Teacher's Edition. You'll find a wealth of **assessment technology** in the Resource Pro®, Interactive Student Tutorial, and Assessment Resources CD-ROMs.

Activities

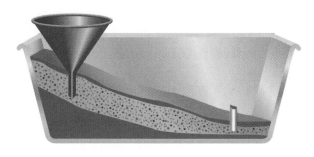

Guide your students to become science explorers.

A wide range of **student-tested** activities, from **guided to open-ended**, with options for **short- and long-term** inquiry.

Skills Lab

In-depth practice of inquiry skills

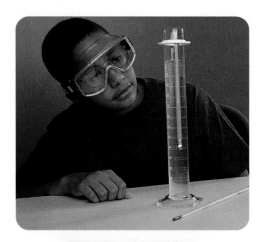

Real-World Lab

Everyday application of science concepts

EXPLORING

Visual exploration of concepts

Interdisciplinary Activities

Math Toolbox

Science and History

Science and Society

Connection

Life in a Sunless World

Focus on Oceanography

This four-page feature introduces the process of scientific inquiry by involving students in a high-interest, magazine-like article about a working scientist, oceanographer Cindy Lee Van Dover. Using Dr. Van Dover's investigation of deep-sea vents and the shrimp that cluster around them as an example, the article focuses on making observations and posing questions as key elements of scientific inquiry.

Deep-ocean exploration is presented in Chapter 5 of this book. However, students need not have any previous knowledge of that chapter's content to understand and appreciate this article.

Scientific Inquiry

◆ Before students read the article, let them read the title, examine the pictures, and read the captions on their own. Then ask: **What questions came into your mind as you looked at these pictures?** *(Students might suggest questions such as "Why is Dr. Van Dover's work important?" "What is the mini-sub doing?" "What is a black smoker vent?" and "Why are the shrimp swarming around the vent?")* Point out to students that just as they had questions about what they were seeing, scientists too have questions about what they observe.

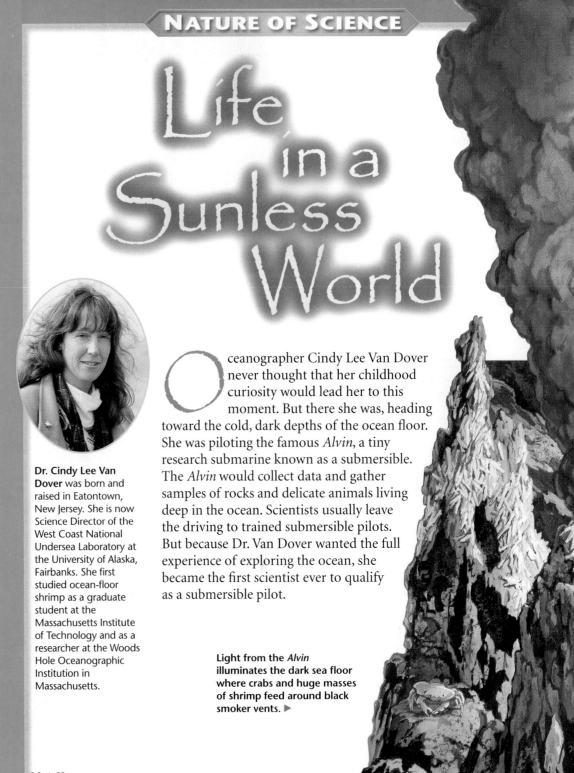

Life in a Sunless World

Dr. Cindy Lee Van Dover was born and raised in Eatontown, New Jersey. She is now Science Director of the West Coast National Undersea Laboratory at the University of Alaska, Fairbanks. She first studied ocean-floor shrimp as a graduate student at the Massachusetts Institute of Technology and as a researcher at the Woods Hole Oceanographic Institution in Massachusetts.

Oceanographer Cindy Lee Van Dover never thought that her childhood curiosity would lead her to this moment. But there she was, heading toward the cold, dark depths of the ocean floor. She was piloting the famous *Alvin*, a tiny research submarine known as a submersible. The *Alvin* would collect data and gather samples of rocks and delicate animals living deep in the ocean. Scientists usually leave the driving to trained submersible pilots. But because Dr. Van Dover wanted the full experience of exploring the ocean, she became the first scientist ever to qualify as a submersible pilot.

Light from the *Alvin* illuminates the dark sea floor where crabs and huge masses of shrimp feed around black smoker vents. ▶

Background

Defined simply, oceanography is the scientific study of Earth's oceans. In practice, however, oceanography is not a single science. That is, no oceanographer studies *everything* about the oceans. Oceanography encompasses chemistry, physics, geology, and biolollgy.

For example, an understanding of physics is needed by physical oceanographers in their study of waves, currents, and tides. Marine biologists, such as Cindy Van Dover, study ocean life and marine ecology.

Life on the Ocean Floor

Slowly, the *Alvin* entered the sunless world far beneath the surface of the Atlantic Ocean — one of the strangest and most remote places on Earth. As the *Alvin* approached an underwater mountain range, Dr. Van Dover could see colonies of animals swarming around undersea hot springs called "black smokers."

The black clouds that give these areas their name are not smoke at all. Rather they are streams of very hot water packed with minerals flowing from openings in the sea floor. Some microorganisms are able to use the minerals as their food source. Dr. Van Dover's special interest was in some very unusual shrimp that feed on these microorganisms.

▲ Black smoker vents are hot enough to glow. Water as hot as 350°C pours up from these hot springs. When the hot water mixes with the cold sea water, it quickly cools.

H ◆ 11

◆ Encourage students to tell what they already know about undersea exploration—the types of vehicles and equipment used, some discoveries that have been made, the people involved, and the animals they have seen. Specifically ask whether they have ever seen a "black smoker vent" in a film or in a magazine. Students may be most familiar with Jacques Cousteau through his television documentaries.

◆ Have a volunteer read the caption on page 11 aloud. To emphasize the extremely high temperature of the water that flows from these vents, ask: **How does this temperature compare with the boiling point of water?** *(Water's boiling point is 100°C; vent water is more than three times as hot. The intense pressure at the depth of the vents allows this superheated water to remain in the liquid state.)*

◆ If students seem particularly interested in *Alvin* and submersible technology, share the information in Background below. Also suggest that they consult library books to learn more about deep-sea exploration technology.

Background

The *Alvin*—named for Allyn Vine, an oceanographer who first proposed the idea of a deep-diving submarine in 1956—made its maiden voyage in the ocean waters off Woods Hole, Massachusetts, in 1964. Since that time, the sub has carried scientists to depths of close to 4 kilometers, enabling them to explore ocean-floor features, discover smoker vents, study deep-sea animals, and, with its tethered robot *Jason Jr.,* locate and survey the wreck of the *Titanic.* The use of twin propellers rather than a single one gives the *Alvin* great maneuverability.

◆ Ask: **What things were you curious about when you were younger? What did you want to know about these things? How did the things you were curious about change as you grew older?** *(Use students' responses to these questions to draw parallels between their own experience and Dr. Van Dover's "endless questions" when she was a child.)*

◆ After students read Could These Shrimp Have Eyes? on these two pages, ask: **How did Dr. Van Dover's investigation begin?** *(She brought one of these shrimp collected from the ocean floor to her lab. There she studied the shrimp and noticed shiny patches on its back.)* **What was the *first* question Dr. Van Dover asked herself?** *("What is the function of the patches?")* **What did her first question lead Dr. Van Dover to do?** *(Dissect the shrimp)* **When she found that within the shiny patches are organs attached to the shrimp's brain, what idea did she have?** *(These organs might be eyes.)* **What happened next?** *(Experts said the organs were eyes that detect dim light.)* **What question did this raise in Dr. Van Dover's mind?** *("What could the shrimp be looking at?")* **What reasoning did Dr. Van Dover use to try to answer this question?** *(The vents are very hot, and hot things glow.)* **What was her next question?** *("Did these vents glow?")* **Because the vents *do* glow, what did Dr. Van Dover conclude?** *(The shrimp use their eyes to find vents.)* Point out that another question was asked at this point, although the question is not stated in the article. Clue students that the question fits just before the sentence beginning "Scientists hypothesize...," and challenge them to figure out what the question is. *("**Why do the shrimp find vents?**")* Then have students answer the question. *(To feed on the microorganisms that live there)* Ask: **How do the shrimp's eyes help protect them?** *(Seeing the glow at the vent enables them to avoid the hottest water at the vent, which would kill them.)*

Endless Questions

How did Dr. Van Dover reach this moment in her life? As a child she was full of questions about everything in nature. "I had my bug period; I had my frog-and-tadpole period; I had my flower period and tree period and bird period. But I settled pretty firmly and quickly on marine invertebrates, sea animals without backbones," she explains. "That's because they were so unusual. I just loved all the odd structures they had, each with a function. Why does a crustacean have ten legs — or whatever number it might have? What does it use them all for?"

Could These Shrimp Have Eyes?

As she steered the *Alvin*, Dr. Van Dover thought about the shrimp she planned to observe. She knew that these shrimp live in the dark depths of the ocean. They lack eyestalks and the black, beady eyes of their better known relatives. She also knew that eyeless animals are common at depths too far beneath the surface for sunlight to reach.

Dr. Van Dover had made an interesting discovery about the shrimp in the lab. Her discovery

> **Other people told me I was crazy. There's no light on the sea floor. Why do they need eyes?**

came after she noticed odd, shiny patches on their backs. She asked herself what the function of the patches might be. "I dissected a shrimp in the laboratory," she recounts. "I found this pair of organs and pulled it out. It was very recognizable, and to my surprise, it was attached to what I took to be the brain of the shrimp.

▲ Each shrimp has a pair of bright spots— "eyes"— on its back.

Light-sensitive shrimp swarm around "smoker" vents deep in the Atlantic Ocean. ▶

Background

Van Dover's hypothesis that deep-ocean vents glow, much like coils in an electric stove, was an idea that could be tested. On a dive to the Juan de Fuca Ridge off the coast of California and Washington, scientists aboard the *Alvin* tried to take photographs of a vent. After turning off all the *Alvin's* lights and finding a way to hold the sub steady for 20 seconds at a time, they were able to film the vent. When the images finally appeared, the crew observed that the vent was glowing dimly. Van Dover's hypothesis was correct.

I looked at it and said, 'Looks like an eye!' Other people told me I was crazy. There's no light on the sea floor. Why do they need eyes?"

Dr. Van Dover kept an open mind and showed the structure to crustacean eye experts. They confirmed that it was not only an eye, but a very unusual one. It was able to detect very dim light. Immediately that raised another question: What could the shrimp be looking at?

"We thought about alternatives," Dr. Van Dover says. "The obvious thing is that these shrimp are only found around high-temperature black smokers. We all know that hot things glow. Did these vents glow?" The answer turned out to be yes. Those unusual eyes were just right for spotting undersea hot spots. Scientists hypothesize that the shrimp use these eyes to guide them toward the dim light in order to feed on the microorganisms. As the shrimp approach the vent, the light gets brighter. That signals the shrimp to keep a distance from the hottest water just emerging from the vent.

Looking Ahead

From time to time now, Dr. Van Dover thinks about the submersible that scientists plan to send to watery Europa, a moon of Jupiter. Scientists in a control room will pilot a robot version of *Alvin* under the oceans of Europa. "I'm delighted that I'm young enough that I'm going to see that," she says. When asked if she would like to be one of those scientists, she doesn't hesitate.

"Wouldn't that be sweet!" she says — and smiles.

▲ A surface ship lifts the *Alvin* from the ocean after a deep-sea expedition.

In Your Journal

Cindy Lee Van Dover's discoveries usually begin with her paying attention to details and then asking questions about what she finds. Think of a familiar place outdoors that you like to visit. Describe the place from memory. Jot down details. Then visit the place again to observe and record questions.

◆ After students read Looking Ahead, encourage them to suggest some questions that the scientists planning the expedition would ask about Europa's oceans.

In Your Journal Point out to students that the places they choose do not need to be large or entirely "natural." A vacant lot, a weedy embankment next to a drainage ditch, or a small wooded area at the edge of a ballfield would be suitable. Remind students to visit the area only with an adult. Provide follow-up in class by giving students an opportunity to briefly describe the places they chose and share their questions. Extend the discussion by asking: **When you observed the place carefully, what questions did you have that had never occurred to you before? What new details did you notice? How could you—or a scientist— find the answers to those questions?**

Introducing Earth's Waters

Have students look through the table of contents and the book to find the parts that relate most closely to this article. *(Chapter 5, Ocean Zones, particularly the Science & History feature; Technology and Ocean Exploration on pages 148–149; The Deep Zone on pages 166–167; and Hydrothermal Vents on pages 167–168)* Ask: **Besides the oceans, what else is this book about?** *(fresh water)* **What kinds of things do you think you'll be learning about?** *(Accept all responses without comments.)*

Earth: The Water Planet

Sections	Time	Student Edition Activities	Other Activities	
CHAPTER PROJECT 1 **Every Drop Counts** p. 15	Ongoing (2 weeks)	Check Your Progress, p. 22 Check Your Progress, p. 35 Wrap Up, p. 39		
1 How Is Water Important? pp. 16–22 ◆ Give examples of how people and other living things use water. ◆ Identify how Earth's water is distributed among saltwater and freshwater sources.	3–4 periods/ 2 blocks	**Discover** Water, Water, Everywhere?, p. 16 **Sharpen Your Skills** Calculating, p. 20	TE TE TE TE	Real-Life Learning, p. 17 Cultural Diversity, p. 18 Demonstration, p. 19 Real-Life Learning, p. 21
2 *INTEGRATING CHEMISTRY* **The Properties of Water** pp. 23–31 ◆ Describe the physical and chemical properties of water. ◆ Explain how water dissolves other polar substances. ◆ Identify the three states in which water exists on Earth.	4–5 periods/ 3–4 blocks	**Discover** What Are Some Properties of Water?, p. 23 **Try This** Follow That String, p. 25 **Try This** Comparing Solvents, p. 26 **Science at Home,** p. 29 **Skills Lab: Developing Hypotheses** Speeding Up Evaporation, pp. 30–31	TE TE TE TE TE ISLM PTA	Inquiry Challenge, p. 24 Addressing Naive Conceptions, p. 25 Building Inquiry Skills: Designing an Experiment, p. 26 Demonstration, p. 27 Language Arts Connection, p. 28 H-I, "Properties of Water" "Testing Paper Towels," pp. 1–8
3 The Water Cycle pp. 32–36 ◆ Describe how Earth's water moves through the water cycle. ◆ List ways living things depend on the water cycle.	1–2 periods/ 1 block	**Discover** Where Does the Water Come From?, p. 32 **Try This** Tabletop Water Cycle, p. 34 **Real-World Lab: You and Your Environment** Water From Trees, p. 36	TE	Including All Students, p. 33
Study Guide/Chapter Review pp. 37–39	1 period/ $\frac{1}{2}$ block		ISAB	Provides teaching and review of all inquiry skills

For Standard or Block Schedule The Resource Pro® CD-ROM gives you maximum flexibility for planning your instruction for any type of schedule. Resource Pro® contains Planning Express®, an advanced scheduling program, as well as the entire contents of the Teaching Resources and the Computer Test Bank.

CHAPTER PLANNING GUIDE

Program Resources	Assessment Strategies	Media and Technology
TR Chapter 1 Project Teacher Notes, pp. 8–9 **TR** Chapter 1 Project Student Materials, pp. 10–13 **TR** Chapter 1 Project Scoring Rubric, p. 14	**SE** Performance Assessment: Chapter 1 Project Wrap Up, p. 39 **TE** Check Your Progress, pp. 22, 35 **TR** Chapter 1 Project Scoring Rubric, p. 14	Science Explorer Internet Site
TR 1-1 Lesson Plan, p. 15 **TR** 1-1 Section Summary, p. 16 **TR** 1-1 Review and Reinforce, p. 17 **TR** 1-1 Enrich, p. 18 **SES** Book A, *From Bacteria to Plants,* Chapter 4 **SES** Book C, *Cells and Heredity,* Chapter 2	**SE** Section 1 Review, p. 22 **TE** Ongoing Assessment, pp. 17, 19, 21 **TE** Performance Assessment, p. 22 **TR** 1-1 Review and Reinforce, p. 17	Exploring Earth Science Videodisc, Unit 6 Side 2, "Ancient Farmers" Audiotapes, English-Spanish Summary 1-1 Interactive Student Tutorial CD-ROM, H-1
TR 1-2 Lesson Plan, p. 19 **TR** 1-2 Section Summary, p. 20 **TR** 1-2 Review and Reinforce, p. 21 **TR** 1-2 Enrich, p. 22 **TR** Chapter 1 Skills Lab, pp. 27–29 **SES** Book B, *Animals,* Chapter 3 **SES** Book L, *Chemical Interactions,* Chapters 2 and 3	**SE** Section 2 Review, p. 29 **SE** Analyze and Conclude, p. 31 **TE** Ongoing Assessment, pp. 25, 27 **TE** Performance Assessment, p. 29 **TR** 1-2 Review and Reinforce, p. 21	Exploring Earth Science Videodisc, Unit 2 Side 2, "Opposites Attract" Exploring Physical Science Videodisc, Unit 4 Side 2, "The Disappearing Ice Cube" Audiotapes, English-Spanish Summary 1-2 Transparency 1, "Structure of Water Molecules" Transparency 2, "Three States of Water" Interactive Student Tutorial CD-ROM, H-1
TR 1-3 Lesson Plan, p. 23 **TR** 1-3 Section Summary, p. 24 **TR** 1-3 Review and Reinforce, p. 25 **TR** 1-3 Enrich, p. 26 **TR** Chapter 1 Real-World Lab, pp. 30–31 **SES** Book A, *From Bacteria to Plants,* Chapters 4 and 5 **SES** Book I, *Weather and Climate,* Chapter 2	**SE** Section 3 Review, p. 35 **SE** Analyze and Conclude, p. 36 **TE** Ongoing Assessment, p. 33 **TE** Performance Assessment, p. 35 **TR** 1-3 Review and Reinforce, p. 25	Exploring Earth Science Videodisc, Unit 2 Side 2, "What's in Our Tap?" Audiotapes, English-Spanish Summary 1-3 Transparency 3, "Exploring the Water Cycle" Interactive Student Tutorial CD-ROM, H-1
TR Chapter 1 Performance Assessment, pp. 160–162 **TR** Chapter 1 Test, pp. 163–166	**SE** Chapter 1 Review, pp. 37–39 **TR** Chapter 1 Performance Assessment, pp. 160–162 **TR** Chapter 1 Test, pp. 163–166 **CTB** Test H–1	Interactive Student Tutorial CD-ROM, H-1 Computer Test Bank, Test H-1 Got It! Video Quizzes

Key: **SE** Student Edition   **TE** Teacher's Edition   **TR** Teaching Resources
CTB Computer Test Bank   **SES** Science Explorer Series Text   **ISLM** Integrated Science Laboratory Manual
ISAB Inquiry Skills Activity Book   **PTA** Product Testing Activities by *Consumer Reports*   **IES** Interdisciplinary Explorations Series

Meeting the National Science Education Standards and AAAS Benchmarks

National Science Education Standards	Benchmarks for Science Literacy	Unifying Themes
Science As Inquiry (Content Standard A) ◆ **Develop descriptions, explanations, predictions, and models using evidence** Students investigate factors that affect evaporation. *(Skills Lab)* ◆ **Think critically and logically to make the relationships between evidence and explanations** Students relate observations of transpiration to the role of trees in the water cycle. *(Real-World Lab)* **Physical Science** (Content Standard B) ◆ **Properties and changes of properties of matter** Water has a unique chemical structure that gives it unusual properties. *(Section 2)* ◆ **Transfer of energy** The sun is the source of energy that drives the water cycle. *(Section 3)* **Earth and Space Science** (Content Standard D) ◆ **Structure of the Earth system** Oceans cover nearly 71 percent of Earth's surface. Most fresh water is frozen in ice. Water is naturally recycled through the water cycle. *(Sections 1 and 3)* **Science in Personal and Social Perspectives** (Content Standard F) ◆ **Science and technology in society** People use water for many purposes. Irrigation is used to supply crops with water. *(Chapter Project; Section 1; Science & History)*	**1B Scientific Inquiry** Students investigate what factors increase the rate at which water evaporates. Students investigate transpiration. *(Skills Lab; Real-World Lab)* **3C Issues in Technology** People use water for household purposes, agriculture, industry, transportation, and recreation. *(Section 1; Science & History)* **4B The Earth** Oceans cover nearly 71 percent of Earth's surface. Most fresh water is frozen in ice. Water is naturally recycled through the water cycle. *(Sections 1 and 3)* **4D Structure of Matter** Water has a unique chemical structure that gives it unusual properties. *(Section 2)* **11B Models** Students use models to investigate evaporation. *(Skills Lab)* **12D Communication Skills** Students monitor water use in their homes and community and share their findings. *(Chapter Project)*	◆ **Systems and Interactions** Water is naturally recycled through the water cycle. Plants give off water through the process of transpiration. *(Section 3; Real-World Lab)* ◆ **Scale and Structure** Water has a unique structure that gives it unusual properties. *(Section 2)* ◆ **Energy** Water molecules gain or lose energy when water changes state. Compared to other substances, water has a high specific heat. The sun is the source of energy that drives the water cycle. *(Sections 2 and 3; Skills Lab)* ◆ **Patterns of Change** Water moves from bodies of water, land, and living things on Earth's surface to the atmosphere and back to Earth's surface in the water cycle. *(Section 3)*

Media and Technology

Exploring Earth Science Videodiscs
◆ **Section 1** "Ancient Farmers" illustrates irrigation methods used in ancient times.
◆ **Section 2** "Opposites Attract" describes the polar structure of the water molecule.
◆ **Section 3** "What's in Our Tap?" gives a tour of a wastewater treatment plant.

Exploring Physical Science Videodiscs
◆ **Section 2** " The Disappearing Ice Cube" shows the heating curve and phase-change diagram as ice melts.

Interactive Student Tutorial CD-ROM
◆ **Chapter Review** Interactive questions help students to self-assess their mastery of key chapter concepts.

Student Edition Connection Strategies

◆ **Section 1** Science & History, pp. 18–19
    Integrating Life Science, p. 19

◆ **Section 2** Integrating Chemistry, pp. 23–29
    Language Arts Connection, p. 28
    Integrating Life Science, p. 28

USING THE INTERNET

www.science-explorer.phschool.com

Visit the Science Explorer internet site to find an up-to-date activity for Chapter 1 of *Earth's Waters*.

ACTIVITY	Time (minutes)	Materials — Quantities for one work group	Skills
Section 1			
Discover, p. 16	20	**Consumable** large balloon **Nonconsumable** globe (about the same size as inflated balloon), permanent marker	Observing
Sharpen Your Skills, p. 20	30	**Consumable** water **Nonconsumable** 1-liter clear plastic bottle, large bowl, 5 plastic cups, permanent marker, plastic graduated cylinder, calculator, plastic dropper	Calculating
Section 2			
Discover, p. 23	15	**Consumable** water, vegetable oil, paper towels, wax paper **Nonconsumable** 2 plastic cups, scissors, meter stick, 2 plastic droppers	Observing
Try This, p. 25	20	**Consumable** string, water, tape **Nonconsumable** scissors, pitcher, plastic cup	Inferring
Try This, p. 26	20	**Consumable** water, vegetable oil, salt, baking soda, food coloring **Nonconsumable** 6 plastic cups, permanent marker, 6 plastic spoons, plastic dropper	Drawing Conclusions
Science at Home, p. 29	home	**Consumable** water, piece of paper, toothpick **Nonconsumable** penny	Predicting
Skills Lab, pp. 30–31	40	**Consumable** water, 3 index cards, paper towels **Nonconsumable** 2 plastic petri dishes, 1 petri dish cover, plastic dropper, lamp, stopwatch	Developing Hypotheses, Controlling Variables, Drawing Conclusions
Section 3			
Discover, p. 32	15	**Consumable** ice, water **Nonconsumable** pitcher, clear drinking glass	Inferring
Try This, p. 34	20; 20	**Consumable** water, plastic wrap, sand **Nonconsumable** flat-bottomed clear container, small jar, rubber band, small rock, lamp	Making a Model
Real-World Lab, p. 36	20; 20	**Consumable** 3 plastic sandwich bags, 3 twist ties **Nonconsumable** 3 small pebbles, balance	Observing, Calculating, Inferring

A list of all materials required for the Student Edition activities can be found beginning on page T14. You can order Materials Kits by calling 1-800-828-7777 or by accessing the Science Explorer Internet site at **www.science-explorer.phschool.com**

Every Drop Counts

Opening a faucet is so routine that many students are unaware of how often they run water in the home. Equally as significant, they are probably unaware of the total amount of water used, as most of it swirls down the drain.

Purpose In this project, students will measure how much water they themselves use during a week, how much water is used in their homes during the same week, and how much water is used in another type of building in a week. Gathering this information should give students a greater understanding of the importance of water and water resources.

Skills Focus After completing the Chapter 1 Project, students will be able to
- interpret data collected from a home water meter and from another building in their community;
- create data tables about home water use;
- calculate how much water is used in their home and in another building during a one-week period;
- graph the data collected about household water use;
- communicate the results of the project in a presentation to the class.

Project Timeline The entire project will require at least two weeks. See Chapter 1 Project Teacher Notes on pages 8–9 in Teaching Resources for hints and detailed directions. Also distribute to students Chapter 1 Project Student Materials and Scoring Rubric on pages 10–14 in Teaching Resources.

Early in the project, allow class time for students to discuss how to make their data tables. Although students will be making their measurements at home through the week, they will need some class time for you to check their progress.

You may want students to begin immediately looking for an appropriate nonresidential building to study. Tell students they should ask parents and other adults for suggestions. Often parents will know someone who could help students gain access to a building manager or building records. Allow the second week of the project for the gathering of this information, as well as for the preparation of student presentations.

Earth: The Water Planet

WHAT'S AHEAD

SECTION 1 How Is Water Important?

Discover Water, Water Everywhere?
Sharpen Your Skills Calculating

Integrating Chemistry
SECTION 2 The Properties of Water

Discover What Are Some Properties of Water?
Try This Follow That String
Try This Comparing Solvents
Skills Lab Speeding Up Evaporation

SECTION 3 The Water Cycle

Discover Where Does the Water Come From?
Try This Tabletop Water Cycle
Real-World Lab Water From Trees

14 ◆ H

Suggested Shortcuts If the project seems too long or involved for your students, you could have them do only the home study for one or two weeks, eliminating the monitoring of a second building. As an alternative, you could ask for a small group of student volunteers to monitor a nonresidential building and report to the class.

A further shortcut would be to simply have students monitor their own water use over several days. This would eliminate the cooperation of family members but would still fulfill the purpose of the project.

Possible Materials Students need nothing more than paper and pencil to collect the data for the project. In presenting their results at the end of the project, some students may want to use poster board to mount their graphs or other visual aids.

Every Drop Counts

With an almost deafening roar, water rushes over this waterfall and plunges into the rocky pool below. Every day, hundreds of thousands of liters of water flow over the falls. How do you think this amount compares with the amount of water that flows out of your faucets at home each day? In this chapter, you will explore the many ways that living things depend on Earth's water. To learn how water is used in your own home and community, you will design a method for tracking water use over a one-week period.

Your Goal To monitor water use in your home and in another building in your community for one week.

To complete the project you will
◆ track your personal water use at home
◆ determine the total amount of water used in your home
◆ find out how much water is used by a business, school, hospital, or other building in your community

Get Started Begin now by brainstorming the ways you use water at home. Use this list to create a data table in which you will record each time you perform these activities during the week.

Check Your Progress You'll be working on this project as you study this chapter. To keep your project on track, look for Check Your Progress boxes at the following points.
Section 1 Review, page 22: Calculate your total water use.
Section 3 Review, page 35: Investigate water use at another building in your community.

Wrap Up At the end of the chapter (page 39), you will graph your household water-use data and share the information with your classmates.

Hikers in California's Yosemite National Park are awed by its thundering waterfalls.

Launching the Project To introduce this project to students, ask: **What are some of the ways you and your family use water daily in and around the home?** *(Flushing toilets, taking baths and showers, brushing teeth, cleaning dishes, washing clothes, watering the lawn, washing the car, and so on)* Write students' suggestions on the board. Then challenge students to estimate how many liters of water each of them uses in a day. After students have shared their estimates, tell them that in this country residential water use averages about 300 L per person per day. Encourage students to compare this average with their own water use to estimate if they use more or less than the average.

Finally, have students read the description of the project in their text and in the Chapter 1 Project Overview on pages 10–11 in Teaching Resources. Encourage students to come up with their own ideas of how they could accomplish the tasks involved.

Program Resources

◆ **Teaching Resources** Chapter 1 Project Teacher Notes, pp. 8–9; Chapter 1 Project Student Materials, pp. 10–13; Chapter 1 Project Scoring Rubric, p. 14

Performance Assessment

The Chapter 1 Project Scoring Rubric on page 14 of Teaching Resources will help you evaluate how well students complete the Chapter 1 Project. Students will be assessed on
◆ how completely and accurately they collect data from their homes and a second building,
◆ how thorough and interesting their class presentations are,
◆ their participation in their groups.
By sharing the Chapter 1 Project Scoring Rubric with students at the beginning of the project, you will make it clear to them what they are expected to do.

Objectives

After completing the lesson, students will be able to
- give examples of how people and other living things use water;
- identify how Earth's water is distributed among saltwater and freshwater sources.

Key Terms irrigation, photosynthesis, habitat, water vapor, groundwater

1 Engage/Explore

Activating Prior Knowledge

Challenge students to think of ways that they directly or indirectly use water each day. Ask: **Who can give two examples of how you have used water today?** *(Examples might include showering, brushing teeth, and drinking.)* Then hold up a piece of paper. Ask: **Is water connected to this object in any way?** *(Paper is made from wood, which contains water, and water is used in the production of paper.)* Again challenge students to think of ways they directly or indirectly use water.

DISCOVER

Skills Focus observing
Materials *large balloon (round when inflated), permanent marker, globe (about the same size as inflated balloon)*
Time 20 minutes
Tips Make sure the markers are permanent markers so they will mark on the balloons. Caution students not to press too hard with the permanent marker, so that the balloon does not burst. Assure students that their drawings of the continents may be very simple. Be sure to keep the globe out of sight until all students have prepared their balloons.
Think It Over Students' drawings will vary, though most will have drawn more land area than there actually is. After examining the globe, students should recognize that areas of ocean cover much more of Earth than areas of land.

SECTION 1 How Is Water Important?

DISCOVER ·········· ACTIVITY

Water, Water Everywhere?

1. Blow up a large, round balloon. Tie a knot at the end.

2. Pretend that your balloon is a globe. Using a permanent marker, draw the basic shapes of the continents at the size they would be if Earth were the size of your balloon. Shade the continents with the marker.

3. Now compare your balloon to an actual globe. Look at the amount of land compared to the amount of ocean on each.

North America, Eurasia, Africa, South America, Australia, Antarctica

Think It Over

Observing Does your balloon show more land area or ocean area? How do the areas of land and ocean actually compare on Earth?

GUIDE FOR READING

- How do people and other living things use water?
- How is Earth's water distributed among saltwater and freshwater sources?

Reading Tip As you read, use the headings to make an outline showing how water is important and where it is found.

Imagine a world without water. The planet is a barren desert. There are no cool green forests or deep oceans. The world is silent — no rain falls on rooftops; no birds or other animals stir. No clouds shield the planet from the hot sun. Even the shape of the land is different. Without water to wear them down, the mountains are jagged and rough. There are no Great Lakes, no Niagara Falls, and no Grand Canyon.

Can you imagine living in such a world? In fact, you could not survive there. The presence of water is essential for life to exist on the planet Earth. In this section, you will explore the ways that all living things depend on water.

How Do People Use Water?

Take a minute to list all of the ways you used water this morning. You probably washed your face, brushed your teeth, and flushed the toilet. Perhaps you drank a glass of water or used water to make oatmeal. These are some common uses of water in the home. But the water people use at home is just a small percentage of all the water used in the United States. **In addition to household purposes, people use water for agriculture, industry, transportation, and recreation.**

Agriculture Has your family ever had a garden? If so, you know that growing fruits and vegetables requires water. On a large farm, a constant supply of fresh water is essential.

16 ◆ H

READING STRATEGIES

Reading Tip If necessary, review with students how to make an outline. Encourage students to read the section once before starting their outlines. Students should use the main heads in the section as the main topics of their outlines. The section subheads should provide the outline subtopics. Students should use information from the text for supporting details in their outlines. Each outline should have a title, such as "How water is important and where it is found." Suggest that students use their outlines as a study aid.

Vocabulary Call students' attention to the boldfaced term *photosynthesis* on page 19. Explain that *photo* means "light" and *synthesis* means "to put together." Ask how these two meanings relate to the process of photosynthesis. Help students understand that photosynthesis is the process of putting together water and carbon dioxide in the presence of sunlight to make food.

Figure 1 The food processing industry requires large amounts of water. Before these juicy red tomatoes can be made into ketchup or spaghetti sauce, they must be washed.

Growing the wheat to make a single loaf of bread takes 435 liters of water, enough to fill 1,200 soft drink cans!

However, some parts of the United States don't receive enough regular rainfall for agriculture. For example, parts of California's Central Valley receive less than 26 centimeters of rain a year. Yet this area is one of the most productive farming regions in the country. How is it possible to farm in this dry place? The solution is irrigation. **Irrigation** is the process of supplying water to areas of land to make them suitable for growing crops. In the United States, more water is used for irrigating farmland than for any other single purpose.

Industry Think about the objects in a typical school locker. There's a jacket, some textbooks, a few pens without caps, and maybe a basketball or a flute for band practice. Did you know that water is needed to produce all these objects? Even though water is not part of the final products, it plays a role in the industrial processes that created them. For example, water is needed to make the paper in the textbooks. Wood chips are washed and then soaked in vats of water and chemicals to form pulp. The pulp is rinsed again, squeezed dry, and pressed into paper.

Industries use water in many other ways. For example, power plants and steel mills both need huge volumes of water to cool down hot machinery. Water that is used for cooling can often be recycled, or used again for another purpose.

Transportation If you live near a large waterway, you have probably seen barges carrying heavy loads of coal or iron. Oceans and rivers have been used for transporting people and goods since ancient times. If you look at a map of the United States, you will notice that many large cities are located on the coasts.

Water Used in the Home	
Task	**Water Used (liters)**
Showering for 5 minutes	95
Brushing teeth	10
Washing hands	7.5
Flushing standard toilet	23
Flushing "low-flow" toilet	6
Washing one load of laundry	151
Running dishwasher	19
Washing dishes by hand	114

Figure 2 Many common household activities involve water. *Interpreting Data How much water would a person save per flush by replacing a standard toilet with a "low-flow" toilet?*

How Do People Use Water?

Using the Visuals: Figure 2

To give students a sense of how much water is in a liter, pour a liter of water from one container into another. Ask: **Are you surprised at any of the figures listed in the table?** (*Students may be surprised, for example, by the number of liters used in washing dishes.*) Emphasize that the figures in the table are only averages. Ask: **What factors might make individual water-use figures vary from these averages?** (*Length of time, type of equipment*) **learning modality: logical/mathematical**

Real-Life Learning

Use magazine pictures of examples of water used in agriculture, household purposes, industry, transportation, and recreation as a starting point for students to brainstorm a list of uses under each category. Then divide the class into five groups, assigning each to one of the five categories. Group members can then work together to make a list of uses in their category and find pictures of those uses in old magazines. Volunteers from each group can then collaborate to prepare a bulletin board that illustrates the five categories of water use. **cooperative learning**

Media and Technology

Audiotapes English-Spanish Summary 1-1

Exploring Earth Science Videodisc Unit 6, Side 2, "Ancient Farmers"

Chapter 4

Answers to Self-Assessment

Caption Question

Figure 2 A person would save the difference between 23 L and 6 L, or 17 L per flush.

Program Resources

◆ **Teaching Resources** 1-1 Lesson Plan, p. 15; 1-1 Section Summary, p. 16

Ongoing Assessment

Writing Have students write a description of how they used water the day before, classifying each use according to one of the five categories.

SCIENCE & History

Invite student volunteers to read aloud to the class the annotations to the time line. Have a world map available for students to use to locate the various sites. For each method of irrigation, encourage students to draw conclusions about the environment in which it was used and how well the technology worked. Ask: **Do you think all these methods are used somewhere in the world today?** (*Students' responses will vary. Each method is still used today at some place.*)

In Your Journal Give students time to research one of the irrigation techniques discussed in the feature. Students can find out more about the techniques by looking under *irrigation* in an encyclopedia or by doing a library computer search for *irrigation* or *agriculture* and for the various countries listed in the feature. Once students have written their letters, encourage volunteers to read theirs aloud to the class. **learning modality: verbal**

Portfolio Students can save their letters in their portfolios.

Cultural Diversity

Note for students that *paddy* is the Malay word for wet rice. The growing of wet rice, or paddy farming, provides the staple food in much of China and Southeast Asia. Ask some students to prepare a report to the class on this agricultural method, complete with pictures and a flow chart showing the process. **cooperative learning**

ACTIVITY

Ocean travel led to the growth of port cities such as Boston, New York, and San Francisco. In early America, rivers also served as natural highways. St. Louis, Memphis, and Baton Rouge are some cities that began as trading posts along the Mississippi River.

Recreation Do you like to swim in a neighborhood pool? Catch fish from a rowboat in the middle of a lake? Walk along a beach collecting seashells? Or maybe just sit on the edge of a dock and dangle your feet in the water? Then you know some ways water is used for recreation. And if you brave the winter cold to ski or skate, you are enjoying water in its frozen form.

✓ *Checkpoint* List an agricultural use, an industrial use, and a household use of water that you relied on today.

SCIENCE & History

Water and Agriculture

Plants require a steady supply of water to grow. How have farmers throughout history provided their crops with water? This time line shows some methods developed in different parts of the world.

2000 B.C. Egypt

Egyptian farmers invented a way to raise water from the Nile River. The device, called a *shaduf*, acted as a lever to make lifting a bucket of water easier. The farmers then emptied the water into a network of canals to irrigate their fields. The *shaduf* is still in use in Egypt, India, and other countries.

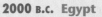

3000 B.C.	2000 B.C.	1000 B.C.

3000 B.C. China

One of the oldest known methods of irrigation was developed for growing rice. Farmers built paddies, or artificial ponds with raised edges. The farmers flooded the paddies with water from a nearby stream. This ancient technique is still widely used throughout Southeast Asia.

700 B.C. Assyria

Sennacherib, king of the ancient nation Assyria, surrounded the capital city of Nineveh with fruit trees, cotton, and exotic plants. To help irrigate the plantations, he built a 10-kilometer canal and a stone aqueduct to transport water from the nearby hills.

18 ◆ H

Background

Facts and Figures In the early twentieth century, the settlers of the Great Plains used windmills to provide the water to irrigate their crops. But most of those windmills could raise water less than 10 m. With the advent of deep-well drilling and modern pumps, farmers of the 1930s began to reach groundwater much deeper underground. Modern farmers on the Great Plains no longer use ditches in irrigating their fields.

That method loses too much water to evaporation, seepage, and runoff—50–60 percent of the total. Instead, many farmers use center-pivot sprinkler systems. The water is pumped underground in pipes to a central pivot and then out through a long, turning "boom" with sprinklers along its length. The result is a circular field of crops. The center-pivot method wastes only 20–30 percent of the water.

Water and Living Things

INTEGRATING LIFE SCIENCE Here's a riddle for you: What do you and an apple have in common? You both consist mostly of water! In fact, water is a large part of every living thing. Water makes up nearly two thirds of your body. That water is necessary to keep your body functioning.

Water is essential for living things to grow, reproduce, and carry out other important processes. For example, plants use water, plus carbon dioxide and energy from the sun, to make food in a process called **photosynthesis** (foh toh SIN thuh sis). Animals and many other living things depend on the food made by plants. They may eat the plants directly or eat other organisms that eat plants.

In Your Journal

Find out more about one of these agricultural techniques. Imagine that you are a farmer seeing the method in action for the first time. Write a letter to a friend describing the new technique. What problem will it solve? How will it improve your farming?

A.D. 1870 United States

When homesteaders arrived on the dry Great Plains of the central United States, they had to rely on water stored underground. Windmills provided the energy to pump the groundwater to the surface. The farmers dug ditches to carry the water to irrigate their fields.

A.D. 1   **A.D. 1000**   **A.D. 2000**

A.D. 500 Mexico

To grow crops in areas covered by swampy lakes, the Aztecs built raised plots of farmland called *chinampas*. They grew maize on fertile soil scooped from the lake bottom. A grid of canals kept the crops wet and allowed the farmers to navigate boats between the *chinampas*.

Present Israel

Irrigation is the key to survival in desert regions. Today, methods such as drip irrigation ensure that very little water is wasted when crops are watered. Holes in the pipe allow water to drip directly onto the soil around the roots of each plant.

Answers to Self-Assessment

✓ Checkpoint

Students' responses will vary. A typical response might mention irrigation or watering for an agricultural use, the making of paper for an industrial use, and taking a shower for a household use.

Water and Living Things

Integrating Life Science

To help students better understand water's importance to living things, write these words on the board: *carbon dioxide, food, oxygen, water*. Explain that oxygen is another product of photosynthesis. Then challenge students to write an equation in words that expresses what occurs in photosynthesis. (*carbon dioxide + water = food + oxygen*) Help students understand that the "food" created is in the form of certain molecules (sugars and starches) that plants and other organisms can break down to obtain energy. Ask: **What is one reason a plant dies if it cannot get enough water?** (*It cannot carry out photosynthesis without water, and therefore cannot make food for itself.*) **learning modality: visual**

Demonstration

Materials *2 apples, paring knife or peeler*
Time 10 minutes for setup; periodic observation over 2 weeks

After students have learned about the importance of water to living things, use a paring knife or peeler to peel most of the skin off an apple. Place that apple next to an unpeeled apple on a windowsill that receives direct sunlight much of the day. Over the next two weeks, students can observe how the unpeeled apple remains essentially unchanged while the peeled apple shrinks. In connection with this shrinking apple, discuss evaporation and the role outer coverings play in keeping living things from drying out.
learning modality: visual

Ongoing Assessment

Oral Presentation Call on students at random to assess whether they understand the six types of irrigation shown in the Science & History feature. Ask them to explain each method in their own words.

Water on Earth

Using the Visuals: Figure 3

Students may have difficulty interpreting these circle graphs. Focus their attention first on the upper graph. Ask: **What significant fact does this circle graph tell you at a glance?** *(Salt water makes up almost all of the water on Earth.)* **How is the lower graph related to the upper graph?** *(The lower graph represents all the water in the smaller wedge of the upper graph.)* Help students understand that ice, for instance, represents 76% of the 3% of the total water on Earth; that is, ice accounts for about 2.28% of Earth's total water. **learning modality: logical/mathematical**

Sharpen your *Skills*

Calculating

Materials *water, 1-liter clear plastic bottle, large bowl, 5 plastic cups, plastic graduated cylinder, calculator, plastic dropper*

Time 30 minutes

Tips Students should pour 97% of 1000 mL, or 970 mL, into the bowl. Point out that the water remaining in the bottle represents only 3% of the total *(30 mL)*. As students proceed, ask them to examine the lower circle graph in Figure 3. Explain that the 3%, or 30 mL, remaining in the bottle represents 100% of the fresh water on Earth. Then have them use the circle graph and a calculator to calculate the amount of water to be placed in each of the five cups. *(Ice: 76% of 30 mL, or about 22 mL; Shallow Groundwater: 12% of 30 mL, or 3.6 mL; Deep Groundwater: 11% of 30 mL, or 3.3 mL; Lakes and Rivers: 0.34% of 30 mL, or about 0.1 mL; and Water Vapor: 0.037% of 30 mL, or about 0.01 mL.)*

Expected Outcome Students should conclude that only the water in the two cups labeled Lakes and Rivers and Shallow Groundwater is available for human use, or a little more than 3.6 mL. That figure is less than 1% of the original one liter.

Extend Ask students to repeat steps 3 and 4, but this time starting with a full bottle of water that represents Earth's total fresh water. **learning modality: kinesthetic**

Sharpen your Skills

Calculating

This activity shows how Earth's water is distributed.

1. Fill a one-liter plastic bottle with water. This represents the total water on Earth.

2. First, measure 97 percent, or 970 milliliters (mL), of the water and pour it into a large bowl. This represents the salt water in Earth's oceans and salt lakes.

3. Next, you will demonstrate how the remaining fresh water is divided. Label five cups to match the fresh-water sources in Figure 3. Calculate how much of the remaining 30 mL of water you should pour into each cup to represent the percentage of Earth's fresh water found there.

4. Use a plastic graduated cylinder to measure out the amount of water for each cup. Use a plastic dropper to approximate amounts that are too small to measure accurately.

Which cups contain water that is available for humans to use? How does the amount of water in these cups compare to the original one liter?

Another way that living things use water is as a home. An organism's **habitat** is the place where it lives and that provides the things it needs to survive. Both fresh water and salt water provide habitats for many living things.

Water on Earth

Why do you think Earth is often called the "water planet"? Perhaps an astronaut suggested this name. From space, an astronaut can see that there is much more water than land on planet Earth. Oceans cover nearly 71 percent of Earth's surface.

Figure 3 shows how Earth's water is distributed. **Most of Earth's water — more than 97 percent — is salt water that is found in the oceans. Only 3 percent is fresh water.** Of that 3 percent, about three quarters is found in the huge masses of ice near the North and South Poles. A fraction more is found in the atmosphere. Most water in the atmosphere is invisible **water vapor,** the gaseous form of water. Less than 1 percent of the water on Earth is fresh water that is available for humans to use.

To explore where Earth's water is found, you can take an imaginary boat trip around the world. As you read, follow your route on the map in Figure 4.

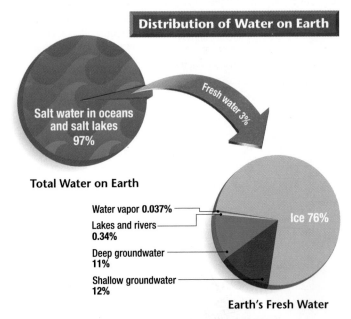

Figure 3 Most of Earth's water is salt water. Of the freshwater sources shown in the bottom circle graph, only the water in lakes, rivers, and shallow groundwater is available for human use.

Background

Facts and Figures Most of the ice that makes up about three quarters of Earth's fresh water can be found at the poles. Ice around the North Pole includes sea ice covering much of the Arctic Ocean, as well as the continental glaciers covering Greenland. But the continental glaciers on Antarctica contain most of the world's ice—in fact, 90 percent of it.

Not all of Earth's groundwater is available for human use either. Below a certain depth it is not practical to raise groundwater to the surface. Therefore, only shallow groundwater is considered available.

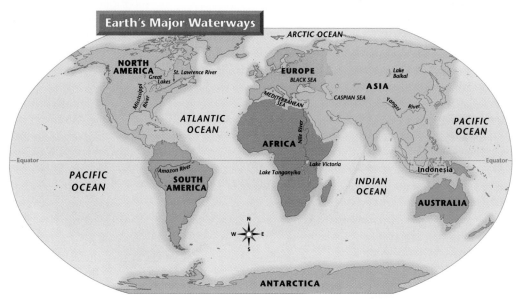

Earth's Major Waterways

ARCTIC OCEAN

NORTH AMERICA

St. Lawrence River

Great Lakes

Mississippi River

EUROPE

BLACK SEA

ASIA

Lake Baikal

MEDITERRANEAN SEA

CASPIAN SEA

Yangzi River

ATLANTIC OCEAN

AFRICA

Nile River

PACIFIC OCEAN

PACIFIC OCEAN

Amazon River

SOUTH AMERICA

Lake Tanganyika

Lake Victoria

INDIAN OCEAN

Indonesia

AUSTRALIA

Equator

ANTARCTICA

Oceans Your journey starts in Miami, Florida. From here, you can sail completely around the world without ever going ashore. Although people have given names to regions of the ocean, these regions are all connected, forming a single world ocean.

First you sail southeast across the Atlantic Ocean toward Africa. Swinging around the continent's southern tip, you enter the smaller but deeper Indian Ocean. After zigzagging among the islands of Indonesia, you head east across the Pacific Ocean, the longest part of your trip. This vast ocean, dotted with islands, covers an area greater than all the land on Earth put together.

Ice How can you get back to Miami? If you're not in a hurry, you could sail all the way around South America. But watch out for icebergs! These floating chunks of ice are your first encounter with fresh water on your journey. Icebergs in the southern Pacific and Atlantic oceans have broken off the massive sheets of ice that cover most of Antarctica. You would also find icebergs in the Arctic Ocean around the North Pole.

Rivers and Lakes To see examples of fresh water in rivers and lakes, you'll have to make a side trip inland. Sail north past Nova Scotia, Canada, to the beginning of the St. Lawrence Seaway. Navigate through the series of locks along the St. Lawrence River. Suddenly the river widens and you enter Lake Ontario, one of North America's five Great Lakes. Together, the Great Lakes cover an area nearly twice the size of New York state. They contain nearly 20 percent of all the water in the world's freshwater lakes.

Figure 4 Earth's oceans are all connected, enabling a ship to sail all the way around the world. This map also shows some of the world's major rivers and lakes. *Interpreting Maps Which continents touch the Pacific Ocean? The Atlantic Ocean?*

Including All Students

For students who have difficulty understanding why only some water on Earth is available for human use, encourage them to re-examine each of the various categories listed in Figure 3 and discussed in the text. Ask: **Why do you think salt water isn't available for human use?** (*The human body can't utilize salt water because the salt causes the body's cells to dry out. A person who drinks only salt water will die.*) **Why isn't deep groundwater available for human use?** (*It would be too difficult or too expensive to bring that water to the surface to be used by people.*) **learning modality: verbal**

Real-Life Learning

ACTIVITY

To make students aware of where water is found in your local area, give each student an outline map of your state. Then ask students to draw and label any ocean and the major rivers and lakes that are found there. Provide access to almanacs and atlases, and give students one or two days to complete their maps. **learning modality: kinesthetic**

 Students can save their maps in their portfolios.

Answers to Self-Assessment

Caption Question

Figure 4 North America, South America, Antarctica, Australia and Asia touch the Pacific Ocean; Africa, Antarctica, Europe, North America, and South America touch the Atlantic Ocean.

Ongoing Assessment

Skills Check Have students make a circle graph of the water available for human use, using Figure 3 as a reference. Students may estimate the relative sizes of the wedges. (*Graphs should have two wedges, one thin one for lakes and rivers and the rest for shallow groundwater.*)

3 Assess

Section 1 Review Answers

1. The major uses are for household purposes, agriculture, industry, transportation, and recreation.

2. Answers may vary. A typical answer will mention water used by plants in making food and water used to provide a habitat.

3. About 97 percent of Earth's water is salt water and about 3 percent is fresh water.

4. Most fresh water is found in the huge masses of ice near the poles.

5. Groundwater, iceberg, and river should be classified as fresh water; ocean should be classified as salt water.

CHAPTER PROJECT 1

Check Your Progress

As you review students' data tables at this point, make sure each has kept a daily record of water use. Also, check that students have listed most or all of the uses shown in Figure 2. To calculate the total amount of water used in the home over the week, most students should have recorded readings of a water meter. Students without access to a water meter should have made estimates based on their daily records. At this stage, encourage students to identify another type of building to monitor.

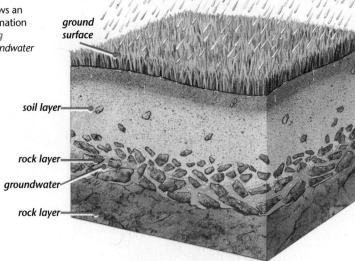

Figure 5 This diagram shows an earthworm's view of the formation of groundwater. *Interpreting Diagrams* Why does the groundwater collect where you see it in this diagram?

ground surface

soil layer

rock layer

groundwater

rock layer

Below Earth's Surface On your journey around the world, you would not see most of Earth's liquid fresh water. Far more fresh water is located underground than in all Earth's rivers and lakes. How did this water get underground?

As Figure 5 shows, when rain or snow falls some of the water soaks into the ground. The water trickles downward through spaces between the particles of soil and rock. Eventually the water reaches a layer that it cannot move through. Then the water begins to fill up the spaces above that layer. Water that fills the cracks and spaces in underground soil and rock layers is called **groundwater.** Chapter 2 explains more about groundwater, the source of much of the water used by humans.

Section 1 Review

1. What are five major ways that people in the United States use water?

2. Describe two ways that plants and other living things depend on water.

3. What percent of Earth's water is salt water? What percent is fresh water?

4. Where is most of the fresh water on Earth found?

5. **Thinking Critically** *Classifying* Classify the following as fresh water or salt water: groundwater, iceberg, ocean, and river.

CHAPTER PROJECT 1

Check Your Progress

Complete your water-use data table by calculating the total amount of water you used during the week. Use Figure 2 to estimate the water used for some common activities. Then determine how much water your family used during the week. You can do this by reading your water meter, estimating based on your personal water use, or having your family members record their usage. (*Hint:* Convert all amounts to liters.)

Performance Assessment

Oral Presentation Divide the class into small groups and challenge each group to list ways people use water locally for one of the water-use categories in the text and report to the class.

Background

Facts and Figures Scientists estimate that between Earth's surface and 4 km below the surface there are more than 8 million cubic kilometers of fresh water. About half of the United States population gets at least some of its fresh water from groundwater sources.

Answers to Self-Assessment

Caption Question

Figure 5 The rock layer does not allow water to pass through, so the water collects.

Program Resources

◆ **Teaching Resources** 1-1 Review and Reinforce, p. 17; 1-1 Enrich, p. 18

SECTION 2 The Properties of Water

DISCOVER .... ACTIVITY

What Are Some Properties of Water?

1. Pour a small amount of water into a plastic cup. Pour an equal amount of vegetable oil into a second cup.

2. Cut two strips of paper towel. Hold the strips so that the bottom of one strip is in the water and the other is in the oil.

3. After one minute, measure how high each substance climbed up the paper towel.

4. Using a plastic dropper, place a big drop of water onto a piece of wax paper.

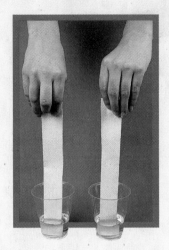

5. Using another dropper, place a drop of oil the same size as the water drop beside it on the wax paper.

6. Observe the shape of the two drops from the side.

7. Follow your teacher's instructions for disposing of the oil when you clean up after this activity.

Think It Over
Observing What differences do you notice between the water and the oil in each experiment?

H ow would you describe water to someone who had never seen it before? You might say that pure water has no color, no taste, and no odor. You might even say that water is a rather plain, ordinary substance. But if you asked a chemist to describe water, the response would be different. The chemist would say that water is very unusual. Its properties differ from those of most other familiar substances.

Are you and the chemist talking about the same substance? To understand the chemist's description of water, you need to know something about the chemical structure of water.

Water's Unique Structure

Like all matter, water is made up of atoms. Just as the 26 letters of the alphabet combine in different ways to form all the words in the English language, about 100 types of atoms combine in different ways to form all types of matter. Atoms attach together, or bond, to form molecules. Two hydrogen atoms bonded to an oxygen atom form a water molecule. A short way of writing this is to use the chemical formula for water, H_2O.

GUIDE FOR READING

◆ How does the chemical structure of water molecules cause them to stick together?

◆ How does water dissolve other polar substances?

◆ What are the three states in which water exists on Earth?

Reading Tip As you read, make a list of water's properties. Write a sentence describing each property.

SECTION 2 The Properties of Water

Objectives
After completing the lesson, students will be able to
◆ describe the physical and chemical properties of water;
◆ explain how water dissolves other polar substances;
◆ identify the three states in which water exists on Earth.

Key Terms polar molecule, surface tension, capillary action, solution, solvent, state, evaporation, condensation, specific heat

1 Engage/Explore

Activating Prior Knowledge

Hold a clear glass full of water in your hand and, as students watch, place two large ice cubes in the water. Ask: **How is the ice in the glass related to the liquid?** *(Ice is the solid state of liquid water.)* **Why do you think the ice floats?** *(Some students may know that ice is less dense than liquid water.)* Challenge students to describe other properties of water. Note their misconceptions. Tell them that they will learn about the properties of water in this section.

.... DISCOVER ....

Skills Focus observing
Materials *water, 2 plastic cups, vegetable oil, paper towel, scissors, meter stick, 2 pieces of wax paper, 2 plastic droppers*
Time 15 minutes
Tips Students need only a small amount of water and oil in the cups. You may want to cut the strips of paper towel yourself, before class begins.
Think It Over The water climbs up the paper towel faster than the oil, and the water forms a taller, rounder drop on the wax paper than the oil.

Water's Unique Structure

Using the Visuals: Figure 6

First, point out that there is a scale difference between each part of this figure. Then call students' attention to the middle illustration in the figure. Ask: **What accounts for the attraction between water molecules?** *(The positive charges of the hydrogen atoms are attracted to the negative charges of the oxygen atoms on different molecules.)* **Why do you think beads of water stick to other substances?** *(The charged ends of water molecules are attracted to the charged parts of molecules of the other substances.)* **learning modality: visual**

Surface Tension

Inquiry Challenge

Materials *water, bowl, pepper, liquid detergent*
Time 20 minutes
Pose this question to students: **What effect does detergent have on the surface tension of water?** Provide each group with the materials, and challenge them to investigate this question. Students should find that the pepper easily floats on the surface of the water until they add the detergent. Then some of the pepper will sink and much of it will move to the side of the bowl, away from the detergent, where surface tension remains strong. Students should conclude that detergent lowers water's surface tension. This characteristic of detergents helps water to penetrate soiled materials more completely. **learning modality: kinesthetic**

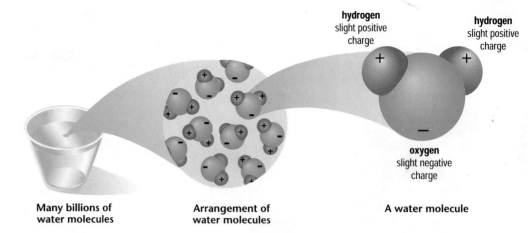

hydrogen
slight positive charge

hydrogen
slight positive charge

oxygen
slight negative charge

Many billions of water molecules

Arrangement of water molecules

A water molecule

Figure 6 A glass of water contains many billions of water molecules. Notice how the water molecules are arranged in the center image. The positive ends of one molecule are attracted to the negative end of another molecule.

Figure 6 shows how the hydrogen and oxygen atoms are arranged in a water molecule. Each end of the molecule has a slight electric charge. The oxygen end has a slight negative charge. The hydrogen ends have a slight positive charge. A molecule that has electrically charged areas is called a **polar molecule**. Because water consists of polar molecules, it is called a polar substance.

Have you ever played with bar magnets? If so, you know that the opposite poles of two magnets attract each other. The same is true with polar molecules, except that an electric force rather than a magnetic force causes the attraction. **The positive hydrogen ends of one water molecule attract the negative oxygen ends of nearby water molecules. As a result, the water molecules tend to stick together.** Many of water's unusual properties occur because of this attraction among the polar water molecules.

✓ *Checkpoint* *Describe the arrangement of the atoms in a water molecule. What makes it a polar molecule?*

Surface Tension

Have you ever watched a water strider like the one at the left? These insects can skate across the surface of a pond without sinking. They are supported by the surface tension of the water. **Surface tension** is the tightness across the surface of water that is caused by the polar molecules pulling on each other. The molecules at the surface are being pulled by the molecules next to them and below them. The pulling forces the surface of the water into a curved shape. Surface tension also causes raindrops to form round beads when they fall onto a car windshield.

Figure 7 A water strider skips lightly across the surface of a pond. *Applying Concepts How do water's polar molecules keep the insect from falling into the water?*

Background

Facts and Figures A hydrogen atom consists of a proton and an electron. In a water molecule, the electrons of the two hydrogen atoms are usually found close to the oxygen atom. The result is that each hydrogen atom tends to behave like a free proton, with a positive charge. This positive charge, in turn, causes a strong attraction to the negative oxygen atoms of nearby water molecules.

Program Resources

Science Explorer Series *Chemical Interactions*, Chapters 2 and 3, has more information on chemical bonding and solutions.

Capillary Action

The next time you have a drink with a straw in it, look closely at the level of the liquid outside and inside the straw. You will see that the liquid rises higher inside the straw. Similarly, water will climb up into the pores of a brick or piece of wood. How does water move up against the force of gravity? Just as water molecules stick to each other, they also stick to the sides of a tube. As water molecules are attracted to the tube, they pull other water molecules up with them. The combined force of attraction among water molecules and with the molecules of surrounding materials is called **capillary action.** Capillary action allows water to move through materials with pores or narrow spaces inside.

Capillary action causes water molecules to cling to the fibers of materials like paper and cloth. You may have seen outdoor or athletic clothing that claims to "wick moisture away from the skin." The capillary action that occurs along the cloth's fibers pulls water away from your skin. By pulling the water away from your skin, the fibers keep you dry.

Water, the Universal Solvent

What happens when you make lemonade from a powdered mix? As you stir the powder into a pitcher of water, the powder seems to disappear. When you make lemonade, you are making a solution. A **solution** is a mixture that forms when one substance dissolves another. The substance that does the dissolving is called the **solvent.** In this example, the water is the solvent.

One reason that water is able to dissolve many substances is that it is polar. The charged ends of the water molecule attract the molecules of other polar substances. Sugar is a familiar polar substance. When you add a sugar cube to a cup of hot tea, the polar water molecules in the tea pull on the polar sugar molecules on the surfaces of the cube. As those sugar molecules

Follow That String

You can use a  string to pour water sideways! Try this activity over a sink or outdoors.

1. Cut a piece of string as long as your arm. Wet the string.
2. Fill a pitcher with water. Tie the string to the handle.
3. Drape the string across the spout and let the other end dangle into a plastic cup. Tape the end of the string to the inside of the cup.

4. Hold the cup below the pitcher so that the string is pulled tight. As your partner gently pours the water into the cup, slowly move the cup to the right of the spout, keeping the string tight.

Inferring How do water's polar molecules cause it to follow the string?

Figure 8 Water's ability to dissolve limestone created the spiky stalactites and stalagmites in this cave in Arkansas' Ozark Mountains. As the water evaporated, the rock formations were left behind.

Answers to Self-Assessment

Caption Question

Figure 7 Water's molecules pull on each other, which causes surface tension. This surface tension supports the water strider.

☑ *Checkpoint*

Two hydrogen atoms bonded to an oxygen atom form a water molecule. A water molecule is polar because it has electrically charged areas.

Capillary Action

TRY THIS

Skills Focus inferring   **ACTIVITY**
Materials *string, scissors, water, pitcher, plastic cup, tape*
Time 20 minutes
Tips Make sure students keep tension on the string and pour the water from the pitcher slowly. Do this activity outside or over a big sink.
Expected Outcome As the student slowly moves the cup away from the pitcher, the water should flow down the string into the cup. Students may infer that water molecules on the wet string cling to the string and the water molecules flowing from the pitcher are attracted to the water molecules on the string.
Extend Students can explore whether the pitcher height affects how the water flows down the string. **learning modality: kinesthetic**

Water, the Universal Solvent

Addressing Naive Conceptions

Materials *sugar, water, spoon, plastic cup, plastic saucer*
Time 5 minutes × 2 days
Many students assume that when a solute "disappears" into a solvent, the original components can never be separated, as in a chemical reaction. Invite students to stir several spoonfuls of sugar into a cup of water. Students will observe that the sugar is "gone" and that the water remains clear. Then have students pour some of the solution into a small saucer and place the saucer in a warm spot. After the water evaporates, students can observe the residue of sugar that remains. **learning modality: visual**

Ongoing Assessment

Drawing Challenge students to draw and cut out three water molecules and use them to show how the charged ends of one molecule attract the ends of other water molecules.

Water, The Universal Solvent, continued

TRY THIS

Skills Focus drawing conclusions

Materials *6 small plastic cups, permanent marker, water, vegetable oil, 6 plastic spoons, salt, baking soda, food coloring, plastic dropper*

Time 20 minutes

Tips Students should use a clean spoon to add the substance to each cup.

Expected Outcome Each of the three substances dissolves better in water than in oil. The substances must have had charged particles that were attracted to water's polar molecules, but not to the nonpolar oil molecules.

Extend Have students test whether a variety of other substances will dissolve in water. **learning modality: kinesthetic**

Changing State

Including All Students

Ask a volunteer to read a definition of the word *state*. Most definitions will focus on the "condition" of a person, an organism, or an object. Emphasize that when a substance changes state, it changes its condition while still remaining the same substance. Challenge students to identify the state of some familiar substances. **limited English proficiency**

Building Inquiry Skills: Designing an Experiment

After students have learned about melting and freezing, ask: **Are the melting point and the freezing point of water the same temperature?** Have students meet in groups to design an experiment to investigate this question. Explain that their designs should use materials that could be found in a school or home. Ask that they write a hypothesis, a list of materials, and a step-by-step procedure. *(A typical experiment might use a thermometer to measure the temperature at which ice cubes melt in a glass of water and the temperature at which water freezes in a freezer.)* **cooperative learning**

Comparing Solvents

In this activity you will compare how well water and oil dissolve several substances.

1. Label six small plastic cups A, B, C, D, E, and F.
2. Add water to cups A, B, and C until they are half full. Add the same amount of vegetable oil to cups D, E, and F.
3. Make a table like the one shown below to help organize your observations.

Cup	Contents	Result
A	Water	
	Salt	

4. Now stir a spoonful of salt into cups A and D. Record your observations.
5. Stir a spoonful of baking soda into cups B and E. Record your observations.
6. Add two drops of food coloring to cups C and F. Do not stir. Record your observations.

Drawing Conclusions In which solvent did each substance dissolve better? Propose an explanation for your results. (*Hint:* Think about the difference between polar and nonpolar molecules.)

---

dissolve, other sugar molecules are exposed to the water. Eventually the sugar cube dissolves into many individual molecules too small to see. The result is a solution of sweetened tea.

Water dissolves so many substances that it is often called the "universal solvent." It can dissolve solids, such as salt and soap, and liquids, such as bleach and rubbing alcohol. Water also dissolves many gases, including oxygen and carbon dioxide. These dissolved gases are important for organisms that live in the water.

However, some substances, such as oils and wax, do not dissolve in water. You have observed this if you have ever seen the oil separate from the vinegar and water in salad dressing. The molecules of oil are nonpolar molecules — they have no charged regions. Nonpolar molecules do not dissolve well in water.

☑ *Checkpoint* List a solid, a liquid, and a gas that dissolve in water.

Changing State

It's a hot, humid summer day. To cool down, you put some ice cubes in a glass and add cold water. Is there anything unusual about this scene? Surprisingly, yes! You are interacting with water in three different **states,** or forms: solid, liquid, and gas. **The ice is a solid, the water is a liquid, and the water vapor in the air is a gas.** In terms of chemistry, this is a remarkable situation. Water is the only substance on Earth that commonly exists in all of its different states.

As you know if you have ever boiled water or made ice cubes, water can change from one state to another. Most other substances require extremes of hot or cold to change state. A steel car door doesn't melt in a July heat wave. In fact, steel would remain a solid even inside your kitchen oven. The air you breathe remains a gas whether the weather is hot or cold. Water, however, can change states within the range of Earth's normal temperatures.

Melting To understand how temperature is related to change of state, start by thinking about an ice cube. The ice is a solid. It has a regular shape because its molecules are arranged in a rigid structure. Suppose that the temperature of the ice is −10°C. What does the temperature tell you? Temperature is a measurement of the average speed of the molecules. Although you can't see them, all the molecules in a substance are constantly moving. At −10°C, the molecules in the ice cube are vibrating back and forth, but they are not moving fast enough to break free of their structure.

Now suppose that you put the ice cube in a pan on the stove. As heat energy is added, the molecules in the ice start moving faster. The temperature rises. When the temperature reaches 0°C, the solid ice melts and becomes liquid water.

Background

Facts and Figures In liquid water, the water molecules are constantly moving at a variety of speeds and in all directions. Thus, some molecules are moving upward. The fastest of these can escape the attraction of the other water molecules. These fast-moving molecules escape into the air through the surface of the liquid—that is, they evaporate. Evaporation occurs at all temperatures. If enough heat is added to raise the temperature of liquid water to 100°C, the water boils. Now even molecules moving at an average speed can escape the attraction of other water molecules, and a change of state occurs throughout the liquid. Thus, boiling is different from evaporation in two ways: (1) boiling occurs only at the boiling point, while evaporation occurs at all temperatures; and (2) boiling occurs throughout the liquid, while evaporation occurs only at the surface.

Boiling and Evaporation As you know, liquid water looks very different from solid ice. The liquid flows and takes the shape of the pan. This is true because the molecules in liquid water have more energy than the molecules in ice. The molecules move more freely, bouncing off each other.

What happens if you continue to heat the water on the stove? As more energy is added to the liquid water, the speed of the molecules increases and the temperature rises. At 100°C, the water boils and another change of state occurs. The molecules have enough energy to escape the liquid and become invisible water vapor. The molecules in a gas move even more freely than those in a liquid. They spread out to fill their container — in this example, your whole kitchen!

Another way that liquid water can become a gas is through evaporation. **Evaporation** is the process by which molecules at the surface of a liquid absorb enough energy to change to the gaseous state. If you let your hair air-dry after going swimming, you are taking advantage of evaporation.

Condensation As water vapor cools down, it releases some of its energy to its surroundings. The molecules slow down and the temperature decreases. As the temperature of the gas reaches the boiling point, the water vapor begins to change back to the liquid state. The process by which a gas changes to a liquid is called **condensation.** When you fog up a window by breathing on it, you are seeing the effects of condensation. The invisible water vapor in your breath is cooled by the window and forms visible drops of liquid water.

Figure 9 Water exists on Earth in all three states: solid, liquid, and gas. **A.** The molecules in solid ice are close together and form a rigid structure. **B.** In liquid water, the molecules move more freely and the water takes the shape of its container. **C.** The molecules in gaseous water vapor move very freely and spread out to fill a space. *Comparing and Contrasting In which state do the molecules move the slowest? The fastest?*

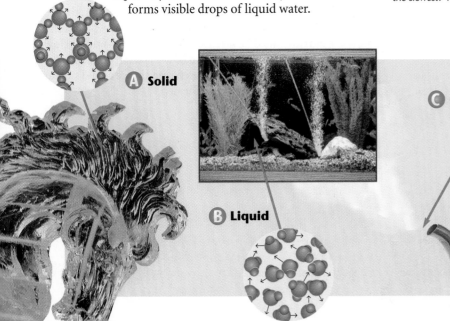

Ⓐ **Solid**

Ⓑ **Liquid**

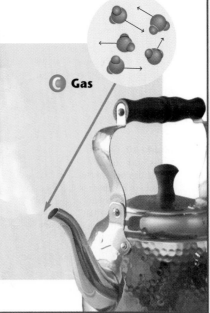

Ⓒ **Gas**

Media and Technology

 Transparencies "Three States of Water," Transparency 2

 Exploring Physical Science Videodisc Unit 4, Side 2, "The Disappearing Ice Cube"

Chapter 6

Answers to Self-Assessment

Caption Question

Figure 9 Slowest in the solid state; fastest in the gas state

☑ *Checkpoint*

Answers may vary. Sample answer: Sugar is a solid that dissolves in water, bleach is a liquid that dissolves in water, and carbon dioxide is a gas that dissolves in water.

Using the Visuals: Figure 9

Use the illustrations of molecules in the figure to emphasize the differences at the molecular level among the three states. Ask: **Why can't a solid flow like a gas or a liquid?** *(A solid's molecules are rigidly held in place, unlike the molecules of a liquid or a gas.)* **How is the arrangement of molecules of liquid water different from the arrangement of molecules of water vapor?** *(The molecules of liquid water are arranged much closer together than the molecules of water vapor).* **learning modality: visual**

Demonstration

Materials *goggles, lab apron, water, beaker, hot plate*
Time 15 minutes

Wear goggles and a lab apron. Add a little water to a beaker and place the beaker on a hot plate. Shortly, the water will begin to boil. Ask: **What caused the water to boil?** *(The heat from the hot plate added energy to the water molecules.)* **What happened to the water molecules after they boiled?** *(They changed from liquid water to water vapor.)* **Why didn't the glass in the beaker change state as well?** *(It requires a higher temperature to change state.)* **learning modality: visual**

Including All Students

To help students understand differences among the three states of water, display pictures of (1) a military formation, (2) a milling crowd of people, and (3) soccer players dispersed on a field. Ask students to make analogies between each picture and a state of matter. *(The pictures represent the molecular arrangements of a solid, a liquid, and a gas, respectively.)* **learning modality: visual**

Ongoing Assessment

Skills Check Have students make a compare/contrast table of the three states of water. They should include information about movement of particles and temperatures.

Integrating Life Science

Encourage students to imagine a frozen-over lake in winter. Ask: **Is there anything living in this lake during wintertime?** *(A variety of living things, including fish, turtles, and many different protists.)* **What would happen to these organisms if ice were more dense than liquid water?** *(The ice would sink as it formed instead of forming a protective shield for the organisms in the water below.)* **learning modality: verbal**

Language Arts
CONNECTION

Show students several examples of magazine ads. Ask: **What are some characteristics that all these ads have in common?** *(Students might mention large type for key words, attractive pictures, and persuasive language.)* **What strategies did the ad writers use to capture the reader's attention?** *(Students might suggest that writers tried to appeal to a need of the consumer.)* Encourage students to use these techniques in their ads. **learning modality: verbal**

Specific Heat

Including All Students

To help students better understand the effect of water's high specific heat, show them a map of North America. Point to Bismarck, North Dakota, and to Juneau, Alaska, and have students predict which place is colder in winter. Then explain that the average January temperature in Bismarck is –12°C, while the average January temperature in Juneau is –4°C. Ask: **Why is Bismarck colder than Juneau when Juneau is farther north?** *(Juneau is on the coast while Bismarck is not near any large body of water. Because of water's high specific heat, the air over water is warmer than the air over land in the winter, and this helps to moderate Juneau's winter temperatures.)* **learning modality: logical/mathematical**

Language Arts
CONNECTION

Imagine that you work at an advertising agency. Your agency has just been hired to design an advertising campaign for water. You know that water has many properties that make it unique. Your plan is to highlight one or more of these properties in an ad to show people what an unusual substance water is.

In Your Journal

Before you begin to write, decide which properties you will highlight in your ad. Write down some facts about each property that you think will interest people. Now you are ready to create the ad. Use humor, pictures, and everyday examples to make your point in an appealing way. Will your ad convince people that water is a unique substance?

Freezing If the liquid water continues to be cooled, the molecules continue to lose energy. They move more and more slowly. At 0°C, the liquid water freezes, changing back into solid ice. If you have ever observed an icicle forming from water dripping off a roof, you have seen this change of state in progress.

☑ *Checkpoint* **In which state do water molecules have the most energy?**

Why Ice Floats

You know from experience that ice cubes in a glass float at the top of the water. If you combine the solid and liquid forms of most other substances, the solid sinks to the bottom. You have observed this if you have ever melted wax to make candles. The solid wax pieces sink to the bottom of the hot liquid wax.

As most liquids cool, their molecules slow down and move closer together until they reach their compact solid form. But surprisingly, something different happens to water. When water cools below about 4°C, the molecules begin to line up in a gridlike crystal structure. The molecules take up more space in this crystal structure than as a liquid. Frozen water in an ice cube tray contains the same amount of matter as when it was a liquid. However, the water takes up more space as ice than it did as a liquid. This means that ice is less dense than liquid water. Less dense substances, like the ice, float on more dense substances, like the liquid water.

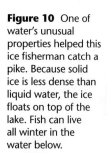 **INTEGRATING LIFE SCIENCE** The fact that ice floats has important consequences for fish and other organisms that live in water. When lakes and ponds freeze in the winter, the ice stays at the top. The ice layer shelters the water below from the coldest winds and air. The fish are able to live in the water below the ice and find food on the bottom of the lake. If water acted as most substances do when they freeze, the ice would sink to the bottom of the lake as it formed.

Figure 10 One of water's unusual properties helped this ice fisherman catch a pike. Because solid ice is less dense than liquid water, the ice floats on top of the lake. Fish can live all winter in the water below.

Background

Integrating Science When water freezes, it expands. This phenomenon is responsible for much of the change that occurs on Earth's surface through the process called weathering. Water seeps into the cracks in rocks, and then freezes and thaws with changes in temperature. Over time, this process widens the cracks, breaking off pieces of the rock.

Media and Technology

Interactive Student Tutorial CD-ROM H-1

Boiling and Evaporation As you know, liquid water looks very different from solid ice. The liquid flows and takes the shape of the pan. This is true because the molecules in liquid water have more energy than the molecules in ice. The molecules move more freely, bouncing off each other.

What happens if you continue to heat the water on the stove? As more energy is added to the liquid water, the speed of the molecules increases and the temperature rises. At 100°C, the water boils and another change of state occurs. The molecules have enough energy to escape the liquid and become invisible water vapor. The molecules in a gas move even more freely than those in a liquid. They spread out to fill their container — in this example, your whole kitchen!

Another way that liquid water can become a gas is through evaporation. **Evaporation** is the process by which molecules at the surface of a liquid absorb enough energy to change to the gaseous state. If you let your hair air-dry after going swimming, you are taking advantage of evaporation.

Condensation As water vapor cools down, it releases some of its energy to its surroundings. The molecules slow down and the temperature decreases. As the temperature of the gas reaches the boiling point, the water vapor begins to change back to the liquid state. The process by which a gas changes to a liquid is called **condensation.** When you fog up a window by breathing on it, you are seeing the effects of condensation. The invisible water vapor in your breath is cooled by the window and forms visible drops of liquid water.

Figure 9 Water exists on Earth in all three states: solid, liquid, and gas. **A.** The molecules in solid ice are close together and form a rigid structure. **B.** In liquid water, the molecules move more freely and the water takes the shape of its container. **C.** The molecules in gaseous water vapor move very freely and spread out to fill a space. *Comparing and Contrasting In which state do the molecules move the slowest? The fastest?*

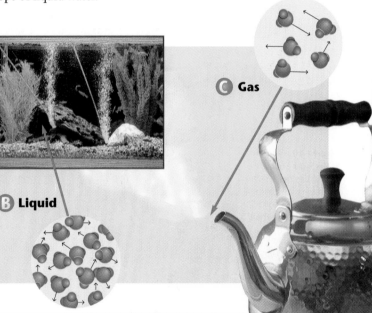

A Solid

B Liquid

C Gas

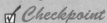

Why Ice Floats

Integrating Life Science

Encourage students to imagine a frozen-over lake in winter. Ask: **Is there anything living in this lake during wintertime?** *(A variety of living things, including fish, turtles, and many different protists.)* **What would happen to these organisms if ice were more dense than liquid water?** *(The ice would sink as it formed instead of forming a protective shield for the organisms in the water below.)* **learning modality: verbal**

Language Arts
CONNECTION

Show students several examples of magazine ads. Ask: **What are some characteristics that all these ads have in common?** *(Students might mention large type for key words, attractive pictures, and persuasive language.)* **What strategies did the ad writers use to capture the reader's attention?** *(Students might suggest that writers tried to appeal to a need of the consumer.)* Encourage students to use these techniques in their ads. **learning modality: verbal**

ACTIVITY

Specific Heat

Including All Students

To help students better understand the effect of water's high specific heat, show them a map of North America. Point to Bismarck, North Dakota, and to Juneau, Alaska, and have students predict which place is colder in winter. Then explain that the average January temperature in Bismarck is −12°C, while the average January temperature in Juneau is −4°C. Ask: **Why is Bismarck colder than Juneau when Juneau is farther north?** *(Juneau is on the coast while Bismarck is not near any large body of water. Because of water's high specific heat, the air over water is warmer than the air over land in the winter, and this helps to moderate Juneau's winter temperatures.)* **learning modality: logical/mathematical**

Language Arts
CONNECTION

Imagine that you work at an advertising agency. Your agency has just been hired to design an advertising campaign for water. You know that water has many properties that make it unique. Your plan is to highlight one or more of these properties in an ad to show people what an unusual substance water is.

In Your Journal

Before you begin to write, decide which properties you will highlight in your ad. Write down some facts about each property that you think will interest people. Now you are ready to create the ad. Use humor, pictures, and everyday examples to make your point in an appealing way. Will your ad convince people that water is a unique substance?

Freezing If the liquid water continues to be cooled, the molecules continue to lose energy. They move more and more slowly. At 0°C, the liquid water freezes, changing back into solid ice. If you have ever observed an icicle forming from water dripping off a roof, you have seen this change of state in progress.

✓ *Checkpoint* In which state do water molecules have the most energy?

Why Ice Floats

You know from experience that ice cubes in a glass float at the top of the water. If you combine the solid and liquid forms of most other substances, the solid sinks to the bottom. You have observed this if you have ever melted wax to make candles. The solid wax pieces sink to the bottom of the hot liquid wax.

As most liquids cool, their molecules slow down and move closer together until they reach their compact solid form. But surprisingly, something different happens to water. When water cools below about 4°C, the molecules begin to line up in a gridlike crystal structure. The molecules take up more space in this crystal structure than as a liquid. Frozen water in an ice cube tray contains the same amount of matter as when it was a liquid. However, the water takes up more space as ice than it did as a liquid. This means that ice is less dense than liquid water. Less dense substances, like the ice, float on more dense substances, like the liquid water.

INTEGRATING LIFE SCIENCE The fact that ice floats has important consequences for fish and other organisms that live in water. When lakes and ponds freeze in the winter, the ice stays at the top. The ice layer shelters the water below from the coldest winds and air. The fish are able to live in the water below the ice and find food on the bottom of the lake. If water acted as most substances do when they freeze, the ice would sink to the bottom of the lake as it formed.

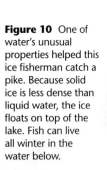

Figure 10 One of water's unusual properties helped this ice fisherman catch a pike. Because solid ice is less dense than liquid water, the ice floats on top of the lake. Fish can live all winter in the water below.

Background

Integrating Science When water freezes, it expands. This phenomenon is responsible for much of the change that occurs on Earth's surface through the process called weathering. Water seeps into the cracks in rocks, and then freezes and thaws with changes in temperature. Over time, this process widens the cracks, breaking off pieces of the rock.

Media and Technology

Interactive Student Tutorial CD-ROM H-1

Specific Heat

Imagine a steamy July day. The air is hot, the sidewalk is hot, and the sandy beach is hot. You jump into a pool or the ocean, and the water is surprisingly cool! But if you go for an evening swim, the water is warm compared to the cool air.

You feel this difference in temperature because of water's unusually high specific heat. **Specific heat** is the amount of heat needed to increase the temperature of a certain mass of a substance by 1°C. Compared to other substances, water requires a lot of heat to increase its temperature.

Water's high specific heat is due to the many attractions among water molecules. Other substances, such as air and rocks, have fewer attractions between their molecules. Their temperature increases more quickly as they are heated than water that is heated the same amount.

One effect of water's high specific heat is that land areas located near large bodies of water experience less dramatic temperature changes than areas far inland. In the summer, the sun's heat warms the land more quickly than the water. The warm land heats the air above it to a higher temperature than the air over the ocean. As a result, the air is warmer inland than on the coast. Just the opposite effect occurs in the winter. The land loses heat to the air more quickly than the water. The water remains warm and keeps the air above it warmer than the air over the cold land.

Figure 11 What could be more refreshing than a swim on a hot summer day? This swimmer is taking advantage of water's high specific heat. *Applying Concepts How does this property of water help the swimmer cool off?*

Section 2 Review

1. What causes water molecules to be attracted to each other?
2. Why does sugar dissolve well in water?
3. Describe what is happening to the water molecules as ice melts.
4. What unusual fact about ice causes it to float in liquid water?
5. **Thinking Critically** *Predicting* If you place a cup of sand and a cup of water in the sun, which one will heat up faster? Explain your prediction in terms of a property of water.

Science at Home

COINS

Put a penny on a piece of paper. With a plastic dropper or a toothpick, have a family member place a single drop of water on the penny. Ask the person to predict how many more drops he or she can add before the water spills off the penny onto the paper. Have the person add drops one at a time until the water overflows. How does the result differ from the prediction? Explain to your family member which property of water might account for this result.

Chapter 1 **H ◆ 29**

Program Resources

◆ **Teaching Resources** 1-2 Review and Reinforce, p. 21; 1-2 Enrich, p. 22
  Science Explorer Series *Animals*, Chapter 3, has more information on fish and their environments.
◆ **Integrated Science Laboratory Manual** H-1, "Properties of Water"
◆ **Product Testing Activities by** *Consumer Reports* "Testing Paper Towels," pp. 1–8

Answers to Self-Assessment

Caption Question

Figure 11 Because of water's high specific heat, it does not heat up as fast as the air and land around it. Therefore, on a hot summer day, the water is cooler than the surrounding air and land.

☑ *Checkpoint*

In the gas state.

---

3 Assess

Section 2 Review Answers

1. The positive hydrogen ends of one water molecule attract the negative oxygen ends of nearby water molecules.
2. Sugar dissolves well in water because sugar is a polar substance. The charged ends of the water molecule attract the molecules of other polar substances.
3. As ice melts, the water molecules absorb energy and move faster and faster.
4. Ice floats in liquid water because ice is less dense than liquid water.
5. The sand will heat up faster than the water because of water's unusually high specific heat. As a result, the temperature of water does not increase as quickly as the temperature of sand that is heated the same amount.

Science at Home

Materials *penny, piece of paper, toothpick or plastic dropper* **ACTIVITY**

Tips Have a volunteer read aloud the Science at Home instructions. Encourage students to challenge family members to predict how many drops can be added to the penny, perhaps by making it a game between family members to see who can predict most accurately. Most people will predict too few drops. Ask: **What property of water accounts for this result?** *(surface tension)* Have students rehearse aloud their explanations to family members about why the penny held so many drops.

Performance Assessment

Drawing Have students make a series of drawings showing the various ways that water changes from one state to another. Tell students that they should prepare these drawings as if they were preparing an instruction sheet. Their drawings should include illustrations of melting, freezing, evaporation, and condensation. With captions, labels, and arrows, they should include as much information as they can about change of state in water.

29 ◆ H

Speeding Up Evaporation

Preparing for Inquiry

Key Concept Various factors influence the rate at which water evaporates, including exposure to a heat source, the use of a cover, and the presence of wind.

Skills Objectives Students will be able to

◆ develop hypotheses about factors affecting the evaporation of water;

◆ control variables to determine the effect of different factors;

◆ draw conclusions about how various factors affect evaporation.

Time 40 minutes

Advance Planning Have locations picked out for each group's dishes for all three parts. The locations for the dishes in Part 1 are especially important because of the need for an electrical outlet.

Alternative Materials In Part 1, you may want to shorten the time of evaporation by having students place the dish in direct sunlight on a dark surface. You could also have students use a heat source in Part 2, as long as both dishes are exposed to the same amount of heat. In Part 3, you could shorten the time by having students use small fans set on low.

Guiding Inquiry

Invitation To help students think of prior experiences with evaporation, ask: **Do you think evaporation occurs faster in a desert or a forest?** *(in a desert)* **Does it occur faster on a windy day or a calm day?** *(on a windy day)* Then challenge students to explain why evaporation would be faster in each situation.

Introducing the Procedure

◆ Call on students to describe the process of evaporation at the molecular level. If students have difficulty, have them read again the explanation of evaporation in Section 2.

◆ Have students read through the complete procedure. Then ask: **What variable is being tested in each part?** *(In Part 1, exposure to a heat source; in Part 2, the use of a cover; in Part 3, the presence of wind)*

Skills Lab

Speeding Up Evaporation

You have just learned that water changes from a liquid to a gas through evaporation. In this lab, you will develop hypotheses as you investigate this process.

Problem

What factors increase the rate at which water evaporates?

Materials

water	3 index cards
plastic dropper	paper towels
2 plastic petri dishes	stopwatch
1 petri dish cover	lamp

Procedure

Part 1 Effect of Heat

1. Copy the data table into your notebook.
2. How do you think heating a water sample will affect how fast it evaporates? Record your hypothesis in the data table.
3. Place each petri dish on an index card.
4. Add a single drop of water to each of the petri dishes. Try to make the two drops the same size.
5. Position the lamp over one of the dishes as a heat source. Turn on the light. Make sure the light does not shine on the other dish. **CAUTION:** *The light bulb will become very hot. Avoid touching the bulb or getting water on it.*
6. Observe the dishes every 3 minutes to see which sample evaporates faster. Record your result in the data table.

Part 2 Effect of a Cover

7. How do you think placing a cover over the water sample will affect how fast it evaporates? Record your hypothesis in the data table.
8. Dry both petri dishes and place them side by side over the index cards. Add a drop of water to each dish as you did in Step 4.
9. Place a cover over one dish. Leave the other dish uncovered.
10. Observe the dishes after 10 minutes to see which sample evaporates faster. Record your result in the data table.

Part 3 Effect of Wind

11. How do you think fanning the water sample will affect how fast it evaporates? Record your hypothesis in the data table.
12. Dry both petri dishes and place them over the index cards. Add a drop of water to each dish as you did in Step 4.

DATA TABLE	
Part I Effect of Heat	
Hypothesis	
Result	
Part 2 Effect of a Cover	
Hypothesis	
Result	
Part 3 Effect of Wind	
Hypothesis	
Result	

Troubleshooting the Experiment

◆ Emphasize that in each part, both dishes should contain the same amount of water. Thus, the single drops of water must be the same size. You may want to demonstrate the use of the plastic dropper, modeling how to make two small drops the same size.

◆ You may want to have students set up Part 1 and Part 2 and then proceed to Part 3 without waiting for results of the first two parts. Part 3 requires students to fan the water sample continuously until it evaporates.

Once results in that part are obtained, students can turn their attention back to the first two parts.

Expected Outcome

In Part 1, the water exposed to a lamp's heat will evaporate faster. In Part 2, the water in the uncovered dish will evaporate faster. In Part 3, the water fanned by the index card will evaporate faster.

13. Use an index card to fan one of the dishes for 5 minutes. Be careful not to fan the other dish as well.

14. Observe the dishes to see which sample evaporates faster. Record your result in the data table.

Analyze and Conclude

1. In which cases were your hypotheses correct? In which cases were they incorrect?

2. For each part of the experiment, explain why the water evaporated faster in one dish than the other. (*Hint:* Think about what happened to the water molecules in each dish.)

3. Make a general statement about factors that increase the rate at which water evaporates.

4. Based on this experiment, predict what would happen in each of the following situations.
   a. Would a wet swimsuit dry faster in a plastic bag or out in the open? Explain.
   b. Would wet clothes on a clothesline dry faster on a windy day or on a calm day? Explain.
   c. Would wet clothes dry faster if they were hung on a clothesline located on the sunny side of a house or on the shady side? Explain.

5. **Think About It** What knowledge or everyday experiences helped you make your hypotheses at the beginning of the experiment? Explain how hypotheses differ from guesses.

More to Explore

How do you think increasing the surface area of a water sample will affect how fast it evaporates? Write your hypothesis and then design an experiment to test it. Be sure to check your plan with your teacher before carrying out your experiment.

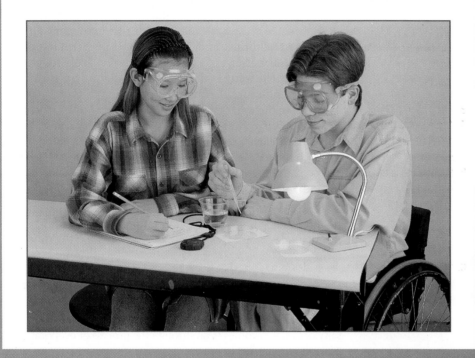

Sample Data Table

	Hypothesis	Result
Effect of Heat	Water exposed to heat will evaporate faster.	The water in the dish under the light evaporated faster.
Effect of a Cover	Water in an uncovered container will evaporate faster than water in a covered container.	The water in the uncovered dish evaporated faster.
Effect of Wind	Water exposed to wind will evaporate faster than water not exposed to wind.	The water that was fanned evaporated faster.

Program Resources

◆ **Teaching Resources** Skills Lab blackline masters, pp. 27–29

Safety

Caution students to be careful when handling the lamp, because the bulb gets hot and can explode if splashed with water. Review the safety guidelines in Appendix A.

Analyze and Conclude

1. Answers will vary. Some students may have foreseen the results correctly in each case and confirmed their hypotheses through the experiment.

2. In Part 1, the water in the dish exposed to the heat source evaporated faster because the heat energy caused the water molecules in that dish to move faster. In Part 2, the water in the uncovered dish evaporated faster because a cover limits the movement of the water vapor. In Part 3, the water exposed to the wind evaporated faster because the wind increases the energy of the molecules at the surface.

3. Factors that increase the rate of evaporation of water include exposure to a heat source, the absence of a cover over a container, and exposure to wind.

4 a. A swimsuit would dry faster out in the open because the movement of water vapor is not limited as it would be in a plastic bag.

b. Clothes would dry faster on a windy day because water molecules would absorb energy from the wind.

c. Clothes would dry faster on the sunny side because the water molecules could absorb energy from sunlight.

5. Think About It A typical response might mention how quickly wet clothes or a car or puddle dries when in the sun or exposed to wind and how covers usually keep foods from drying out. Hypotheses are based on information gathered through study or experience, whereas guesses are based only on feelings or intuition.

Extending the Inquiry

More to Explore A typical hypothesis might suggest that increasing the surface area of a water sample will increase the rate of evaporation. A typical design might suggest pouring equal amounts of water into a deep bowl and a shallow pan and then exposing both to the same amount of heat or wind. As you review students' hypotheses and plans, challenge them to explain why they think increasing the surface area would increase the rate.

SECTION 3 The Water Cycle

Objectives

After completing the lesson, students will be able to

◆ describe how Earth's water moves through the water cycle;

◆ list ways that living things depend on the water cycle.

Key Terms water cycle, transpiration, precipitation

1 Engage/Explore

Activating Prior Knowledge

Invite a student volunteer to describe a rainstorm. Ask: **Where does the water come from that falls as rain?** *(from clouds)* **How does the water get into the clouds?** *(Some students may know that water vapor in the atmosphere condenses to form clouds.)* Continue this line of questioning, guiding students through the water cycle to put the parts together to form a cycle.

DISCOVER

Skills Focus inferring
Materials *ice, water, pitcher, clear drinking glass*

ACTIVITY

Time 15 minutes
Tips Add enough ice to a pitcher of water to make the water very cold, thus ensuring that droplets will quickly form on the outer surface of the glass. Advise students to be careful not to spill the water onto the outside of the glass when pouring from the pitcher. Once students have completed the activity, you may want to spend time exploring their misconceptions about this phenomenon.

Think It Over Some students may correctly infer that the water droplets come from water vapor in the air condensing on the cold surface of the glass. Some students, however, will propose that the water somehow came from inside the glass.

DISCOVER ·········· ACTIVITY

Where Does the Water Come From?

1. Fill a glass with ice cubes and water, being careful not to spill any water. Set the glass aside for 5 minutes.

2. Observe the outside of the glass and the surface it was sitting on.

Think It Over

Inferring Where did the water on the outside of the glass come from? How do you think it got there?

GUIDE FOR READING

◆ How does Earth's water move through the water cycle?

◆ In what ways do living things depend on the water cycle?

Reading Tip Before you read, preview *Exploring the Water Cycle* on the facing page. Make a list of any unfamiliar words in the diagram.

The next time it rains, cup your hand and catch some raindrops. Think about where a single water molecule in one of those raindrops may have traveled. Most recently, it was part of the gray cloud overhead. Last year, it may have tumbled over a waterfall or floated down the Nile River. Perhaps it spent years as part of the Pacific Ocean. The same water molecule may even have fallen as rain on a dinosaur millions of years ago.

How could one water molecule reappear in so many different places and forms? In fact, all the water on Earth has been through similar changes. Water is naturally recycled through the water cycle. The **water cycle** is the continuous process by which water moves through the living and nonliving parts of the environment. **In the water cycle, water moves from bodies of water, land, and living things on Earth's surface to the atmosphere and back to Earth's surface.** The sun is the source of energy that drives the water cycle.

Water Evaporates

Water moves continuously through the water cycle. The cycle has no real beginning or end. You can follow a water molecule through one complete cycle in *Exploring the Water Cycle* on the facing page.

Think about a molecule of water floating near the surface of an ocean. The sun is shining and the air is warm. Soon, the molecule has absorbed enough heat energy to change state. It evaporates and becomes water vapor. Although the water comes from the salty ocean, it becomes fresh through the process of evaporation. The salt remains in the ocean.

READING STRATEGIES

Reading Tip On the board, make a list of words from *Exploring the Water Cycle* that might be unfamiliar to students, including *water cycle, continuous, environment, evaporation, transpiration, condensation,* and *precipitation.* Call on one student to give the meaning of a word, and then call on another student to use that word in a sentence. Have students who are not yet familiar with the term *water cycle* consider a bicycle, tricycle, and unicycle. Lead students to conclude that they all have a round wheel in common. Help students understand that in the water cycle, water moves through a continuous series of steps with no beginning or end, like a wheel. If students do not know the term *transpiration,* have a volunteer read the definition from the text.

Large amounts of water evaporate constantly from the surfaces of oceans and large lakes. In addition, small amounts evaporate from the soil, puddles, and even from your skin.

A significant amount of water is given off by plants. Plants draw in water from the soil through their roots. Eventually the water is given off through the leaves as water vapor in a process called **transpiration.** You may be surprised to learn how much water plants release to the atmosphere through transpiration.

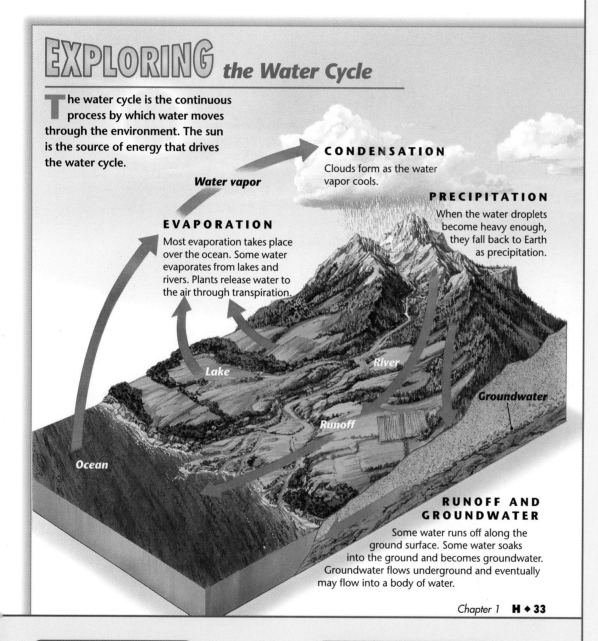

EXPLORING the Water Cycle

The water cycle is the continuous process by which water moves through the environment. The sun is the source of energy that drives the water cycle.

Water vapor

CONDENSATION
Clouds form as the water vapor cools.

EVAPORATION
Most evaporation takes place over the ocean. Some water evaporates from lakes and rivers. Plants release water to the air through transpiration.

PRECIPITATION
When the water droplets become heavy enough, they fall back to Earth as precipitation.

Lake

River

Groundwater

Runoff

Ocean

RUNOFF AND GROUNDWATER
Some water runs off along the ground surface. Some water soaks into the ground and becomes groundwater. Groundwater flows underground and eventually may flow into a body of water.

Chapter 1 **H ◆ 33**

Program Resources

Science Explorer Series *From Bacteria to Plants*, Chapters 4 and 5, has more information about plants.
◆ **Teaching Resources** 1-3 Lesson Plan, p. 23; 1-3 Section Summary, p. 24

Media and Technology

Audiotapes English-Spanish Summary 1-3

Transparencies "Exploring the Water Cycle," Transparency 3

2 Facilitate

Water Evaporates

Including All Students

To reinforce students' understanding of transpiration, invite students to examine a small plant, such as a geranium, out of soil. Ask: **Through which part does a plant take in water?** *(through its roots)* **What is one way a plant uses water?** *(Plants use water to make food through the process of photosynthesis.)* Help students trace the path that water takes through a plant: from the roots up through the stem and branches to the leaves, where photosynthesis occurs. Transpiration takes place on the underside of leaves, through openings called stomata. **learning modality: kinesthetic**

EXPLORING the Water Cycle

After students have examined the illustration, ask: **What are the three processes in the water cycle?** *(Evaporation, condensation, and precipitation)* **Which process begins the cycle?** *(Students might mention evaporation, because that is the first shown on the illustration).* Help students understand that a cycle has no beginning or no end, and that one process is no more important than the others. Point out that the water cycle is continuous and has been continuous for billions of years. **learning modality: visual**

Ongoing Assessment

Skills Check Have each student make a cycle diagram that shows the steps in the water cycle.

Clouds Form

Water Falls as Precipitation

Figure 12 Clouds and mist blanket this lush rain forest in Costa Rica. *Relating Cause and Effect Describe how the processes of evaporation and condensation can cause clouds to form.*

TRY THIS

Tabletop Water Cycle

In this activity you will build a model of the water cycle. **ACTIVITY**

1. Put on your goggles. Pour enough water into a flat-bottomed bowl to cover the bottom. Fill a small jar with sand and place it in the bowl.

2. Loosely cover the top of the bowl with plastic wrap. Secure with a rubber band.

3. Place a rock on top of the plastic, directly over the jar.

4. Place the bowl in direct sunlight or under a lamp. After one hour, observe the bowl and plastic wrap.

Making a Model What features of the water cycle are represented in your model?

The thousands of leaves on a single birch tree, for example, may give off 260 liters of water in one day — enough to fill nine kitchen sinks!

Have you ever seen your breath on a cold day? If so, you have observed another way that water vapor enters the atmosphere. Small amounts of water vapor are released by animals when they exhale. Tiny amounts of water vapor also enter the air from ice, when water passes directly from the solid state to the gaseous state.

☑ *Checkpoint* List three places from which water evaporates.

Clouds Form

Once a water molecule has found its way into the atmosphere, what happens next? Warm air carries the water molecule higher into the atmosphere. Higher up, the air tends to become much colder. Cold air holds less water vapor than warm air. Some of the water vapor cools and condenses into liquid water. Condensed droplets of water clump together around tiny dust particles in the air, forming clouds. In even colder parts of the upper atmosphere, the water vapor sometimes forms ice crystals rather than water droplets.

Water Falls As Precipitation

As more water vapor condenses, the water droplets in a cloud grow larger and larger. Eventually, the drops become so heavy that they fall back to Earth. Water that falls to Earth as rain, snow, hail, or sleet is called **precipitation.** Most water molecules probably spend only about 10 days in the atmosphere before falling back to Earth. Most precipitation falls directly into the oceans. Water in the ocean may stay there for many years before evaporating, thus continuing the cycle.

When precipitation falls on land, some of the water evaporates again immediately. Some runs off the surface of the land into rivers and lakes. From there, it may eventually evaporate or flow back into the ocean. Some water trickles down into the ground and forms groundwater. Groundwater may move underground until it reaches a river, lake, or ocean. Once groundwater reaches the surface, it can continue through the cycle by evaporating again.

Before returning to the atmosphere, some water passes through living things. Animals drink the water and eventually release it back to the environment as a waste product. Plants use the water to grow and to produce food. When these living things die, their bodies are broken down slowly, and the water returns to the environment.

A Global Process

Precipitation is the source of all fresh water on and below Earth's surface. The water cycle renews the usable supply of fresh water on Earth. For millions of years, the total amount of water on Earth has remained fairly constant. The worldwide amounts of evaporation and precipitation balance each other. This may not seem believable if you live in an area where there is either a lot of precipitation or very little. It is possible for parts of India to receive as much as 1,000 centimeters of precipitation in a year, while the Sahara, a desert in Africa, may get only 5 centimeters. But in the world as a whole, the rates of evaporation and precipitation are balanced.

Figure 13 These thirsty zebras are a part of the water cycle. The water they drink passes through their bodies and is released in their wastes.

Section 3 Review

1. Describe the general path of water as it moves through the water cycle.
2. How does the water cycle renew Earth's supply of fresh water?
3. What is the source of the energy that drives the water cycle?
4. **Thinking Critically Relating Cause and Effect** How might cutting down trees affect the amount of evaporation in an area?

Check Your Progress

CHAPTER PROJECT 1

By now you should have chosen a building in your community to monitor. How will you determine the amount and type of water usage there? Be sure to check with your teacher before contacting anyone at the site. (*Hint:* A building manager or facilities manager often has information about water use. You may find it helpful to write down your questions before you interview the person.)

Program Resources

◆ **Teaching Resources** 1-3 Review and Reinforce, p. 25; 1-3 Enrich, p. 26
◆ **Science Explorer Series** *Weather and Climate*, Chapter 2, discusses cloud formation.

Answers to Self-Assessment

Caption Question

Figure 12 Water evaporates from bodies of water. When water vapor rises in the atmosphere, it cools and condenses into liquid water. Condensed droplets then clump together with dust particles in the air, forming clouds.

☑ *Checkpoint*

Sample answer: oceans, lakes, puddles

A Global Process

Building Inquiry Skills: Communicating

Challenge students to apply the concept of a global water cycle by writing a creative story about a water molecule that begins the year in one part of the world and ends the year in another part. Students should take the molecule through the water cycle as well as through each of the three states of matter. **learning modality: verbal**

3 Assess

Section 3 Review Answers

1. Liquid water evaporates from Earth's surface to become water vapor. Clouds form as water vapor rises and cools. Water droplets condense, and then fall back to Earth as precipitation. That water eventually evaporates again, continuing the process.
2. Precipitation is the source of all fresh water on and below Earth's surface. The water cycle renews the supply of fresh water on Earth because when water evaporates, impurities, such as salt, are left behind.
3. The sun
4. Cutting down trees would reduce the amount of evaporation in an area because trees draw in water from the soil and give it off as water vapor in the process of transpiration.

Check Your Progress

CHAPTER PROJECT 1

Review students' choices of buildings. Help students decide whom might be best to contact to get the needed information. Lead a role-play interview or phone call with students so they can practice.

Performance Assessment

Writing Encourage students to think about the water cycle in the area where they live and write a detailed description of this water cycle.

You and Your Environment

Water From Trees

Preparing for Inquiry

Key Concept Plants play an important role in the water cycle through the process of transpiration.

Skills Objectives Students will be able to
- observe the product of transpiration in leaves;
- calculate the mass of the water transpired by leaves in 24 hours;
- infer the important role plants play in the water cycle.

Time 20 minutes for setup; 20 minutes the next day for completion

Advance Planning Ask volunteers to scout around the school for trees or shrubs with large leaves. Make a rough map of the locations of these plants and assign groups by writing their names on the map.

Alternative Materials If no trees or shrubs are available, potted plants such as geraniums can be used in the classroom.

Guiding Inquiry

Invitation To give the lab a context, ask: **How are trees part of the water cycle?** *(Trees draw in water from the soil and give it off as water vapor through the process of transpiration.)* If necessary, review the process of transpiration.

Introducing the Procedure

Have students read through the complete procedure. Then ask: **What is the purpose of determining the mass of the bags, ties, and pebbles in Step 2?** *(Determining that mass provides a basis for comparison after leaving the bags on the leaves for 24 hours.)* **Why should you be sure to make a tight seal around the stem of each leaf?** *(Making a tight seal ensures that nothing can get into or out of the bag during the 24 hours.)*

You and Your Environment

Water From Trees

Trees play many important roles in the environment—they keep the soil from washing away, remove carbon dioxide from the air, and produce oxygen. Trees are also a vital part of the water cycle. In this lab you will discover how trees help to keep water moving through the cycle.

Problem

How much water do the leaves on a tree give off in a 24-hour period?

Skills Focus

observing, calculating, inferring

Materials

3 plastic sandwich bags	balance
3 small pebbles	3 twist ties

Procedure

1. Copy the data table into your notebook.
2. Place the sandwich bags, twist ties, and pebbles on a balance. Determine their total mass to the nearest tenth of a gram.
3. Select an outdoor tree or shrub with leaves that are within your reach.
4. Put one pebble into a sandwich bag and place the bag over one of the tree's leaves as shown. Fasten the twist tie around the bag, forming a tight seal around the stem of the leaf.
5. Repeat Step 4 with the other plastic bags on two more leaves. Leave the bags in place on the leaves for 24 hours.
6. The following day, examine the bags and record your observations in your notebook.

7. Carefully remove the bags from the leaves and refasten each twist tie around its bag so that the bag is closed tightly.
8. Place the three bags, including pebbles and twist ties, on the balance. Determine their total mass to the nearest tenth of a gram.
9. Subtract the original mass of the bags, ties, and pebbles that you found in Step 2 from the mass you found in Step 8.

Analyze and Conclude

1. Based on your observations, how can you account for the difference in mass?
2. What is the name of the process that caused the results you observed? Explain the role of that process in the water cycle.
3. A single birch tree may transpire as much as 260 liters of water in a day. How much water would a grove of 1,000 birch trees return to the atmosphere in a year?
4. **Apply** Based on what you learned from this investigation, what is one reason that people may be concerned about the destruction of forests around the world?

More to Explore

Find another type of tree and repeat this experiment. What might account for any differences in the amount of water the two trees transpire?

DATA TABLE

Starting mass of bags, ties, and pebbles	
Mass of bags, ties, and pebbles after 24 hours	
Difference in mass	

Sample Data Table

Starting mass of bags, ties, and pebbles	Mass of bags, ties, and pebbles after 24 hours	Difference in mass
41.3 g	42.9 g	1.6 g

Program Resources

- **Teaching Resources** Real-World Lab blackline masters, pp. 30–31

Safety

Caution students to avoid plants such as poison ivy and poison oak. Instruct them to carry out the activity in secure, familiar places. Review the safety guidelines in Appendix A.

SECTION 1 How Is Water Important?

Key Ideas
- People use water for many purposes, including household use, industry, agriculture, transportation, and recreation.
- All living things need water to carry out their life processes.
- About 97 percent of Earth's water is salt water stored in the oceans. Less than 1 percent is usable fresh water.

Key Terms

3 irrigation   4 photosynthesis   2 habitat
5 water vapor   1 groundwater

SECTION 2 The Properties of Water
INTEGRATING **CHEMISTRY**

Key Ideas
- A water molecule consists of two hydrogen atoms bonded to an oxygen atom. The hydrogen ends of the molecule have a slight positive charge. The oxygen end of the molecule has a slight negative charge.
- The charged ends of water's polar molecules attract the charged ends of other water molecules. Water molecules are also attracted to other charged particles.
- Some properties caused by the attractions among water molecules are surface tension, capillary action, and high specific heat.
- Water dissolves so many substances that it is sometimes called the "universal solvent."
- Water on Earth exists in three states: liquid water; ice, a solid; and water vapor, a gas.
- Energy must be added or released for water molecules to change state.
- Unlike most other substances, the solid form of water is less dense than the liquid form.

Key Terms
4 polar molecule   9 surface tension   1 capillary action
4 5 solution   6 solvent   8 state
3 evaporation   2 condensation   7 specific heat

SECTION 3 The Water Cycle

Key Ideas
- In the water cycle, water evaporates from Earth's surface into the atmosphere. The water forms clouds, then falls back to Earth as precipitation. The sun's energy drives the water cycle.
- The water cycle renews Earth's supply of fresh water. In the world as a whole, the rates of evaporation and precipitation balance each other.

Key Terms
water cycle   transpiration   precipitation

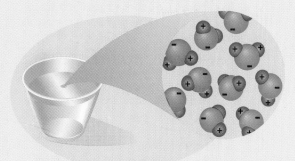

USING THE INTERNET
www.science-explorer.phschool.com

Chapter 1 **H ◆ 37**

Troubleshooting the Experiment
- The bigger the leaf, the greater the difference after 24 hours. Therefore, point students toward plants with large leaves.
- Make sure students twist the ties tightly so that the bags will be as airtight as possible.

Expected Outcome
After 24 hours, the bags should contain liquid water from transpiration. The water vapor given off by the leaves will have condensed because of the cooler temperatures overnight. Therefore, the bags will have more mass than before.

Analyze and Conclude
1. The difference in mass is a result of the water that collected in the bags after 24 hours. The water came from the leaves.
2. The name of the process is transpiration. Plants absorb water from the ground and then release water into the atmosphere through transpiration. Moving through plants is one route water takes in the water cycle.
3. 260 L/day $\times$ 1,000 trees $\times$ 365 days = 94,900,000 L
4. **Apply** Trees are part of the global water cycle. If forests are destroyed, the water cycle may be affected because trees increase the amount of water vapor in the atmosphere through the process of transpiration.

Extending the Inquiry

More to Explore Students might have different results with different types of trees. Various sizes of leaves, differences in habitats, and differences among species might account for varying results.

Program Resources
- **Teaching Resources** Chapter 1 Project Scoring Rubric, p. 14; Chapter 1 Performance Assessment Teacher Notes, pp. 160–161; Chapter 1 Performance Assessment Student Worksheet, p. 162; Chapter 1 Test, pp. 163–166

Media and Technology
- **Interactive Student Tutorial CD-ROM** H-1
- **Computer Test Bank** Chapter 1 Test

Reviewing Content: Multiple Choice

1. b 2. c 3. c 4. a 5. b

Reviewing Content: True or False

6. true 7. groundwater 8. true 9. fresh
10. transpiration

Checking Concepts

11. Plants use the water to make food, and other living things on Earth obtain food either by eating plants or by eating other organisms that eat plants.
12. Earth is called the "water planet" because oceans cover nearly 71 percent of Earth's surface.
13. More than 97 percent of the total water on Earth is salt water, which is not available for human use. About three quarters of the fresh water on Earth is ice, which is mostly unavailable for human use.
14. Students' diagrams should be similar to the illustration of a water molecule in Figure 6 on page 24, with labels for one oxygen atom and two hydrogen atoms. The hydrogen atoms should be labeled as having a positive charge; the oxygen atom should be labeled as having a negative charge.
15. Answers may vary. Properties that depend on water's polarity include surface tension, capillary action, the ability to dissolve many substances, water's unusually high specific heat, and the fact that solid ice is less dense than liquid water.
16. Students should describe the change from liquid to gas involved in evaporation and the change from gas to liquid involved in condensation.
17. Students' descriptions may vary. A typical response might mention that water is a large part of every living thing, that water is essential for living things to grow, reproduce, and carry out other important processes, and that water provides habitats for many organisms.

Thinking Visually

18. Student answers may vary. Sample:
    a. Evaporation from the ocean
    b. Precipitation onto Earth's surface
    Sample title: Path of a Water Molecule

Reviewing Content

 For more review of key concepts, see the Interactive Student Tutorial CD-ROM.

Multiple Choice

Choose the letter of the best answer.

1. The process of supplying land areas with water to make them suitable for farming is
   a. transpiration.   b. irrigation.
   c. condensation.   d. capillary action.
2. More than 97 percent of Earth's total water supply is found in
   a. ice sheets.
   b. the atmosphere.
   c. the oceans.
   d. groundwater.
3. A molecule with electrically charged parts is a
   a. nonpolar molecule.
   b. solution.
   c. polar molecule.
   d. gas.
4. When you stir salt into water, you are making a
   a. solution.   b. solvent.
   c. solid.   d. molecule.
5. The energy that drives the water cycle comes from the
   a. Earth.   b. sun.
   c. rain.   d. ocean.

True or False

If the statement is true, write true. If it is false, change the underlined word or words to make the statement true.

6. The process in which plants use water, light, and carbon dioxide to make food is called <u>photosynthesis</u>.
7. Most of Earth's liquid fresh water is found in the form of <u>lakes</u>.
8. The property of <u>surface tension</u> allows insects to walk on water.
9. In the water cycle, precipitation returns <u>salt</u> water to Earth.
10. The process by which the leaves of plants give off water into the atmosphere is <u>condensation</u>.

Checking Concepts

11. How is the water supplied to plants important for many other living things on Earth?
12. Explain why Earth is called the "water planet."
13. Explain why so little of Earth's water is available for human use.
14. Draw a diagram of a water molecule that shows how it is polar. Be sure to include labels in your diagram.
15. Give examples of two properties of water that are caused by the attractions between water molecules.
16. Describe two changes of state that occur during the water cycle.
17. **Writing to Learn** As the information officer aboard a starship, you are assigned to write a handbook describing Earth's waters to visitors from other galaxies. Write a description in which you explain how water is important to living things on Earth.

Thinking Visually

18. **Cycle Diagram** Copy the cycle diagram onto a sheet of paper and complete it to show one possible path for a water molecule. Add a title. (For more on cycle diagrams, see the Skills Handbook.)

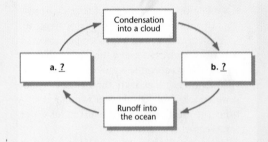

Applying Skills

19. Agriculture represents the largest use; industries and mining represent the smallest.
20. If the total use is 1,280 billion liters, then power plants use 38.7% of that: $0.387 \times 1{,}280 = 495.36$ billion liters.
21. An increase in irrigation would make the agriculture wedge bigger and all the other wedges slightly smaller.

Thinking Critically

22. Answers may vary. A typical answer might mention the availability of water for industry and transportation of people and goods.
23. Water molecules in the solid state move slowly and are arranged in a rigid structure. Water molecules in the liquid state move more rapidly and spread out to take the shape of their container. Water molecules in the gas state are moving fastest of all, and they spread out to fill an enclosed space.
24. Water is a polar substance. The charged

Applying Skills

Use this circle graph to answer questions 19–21.

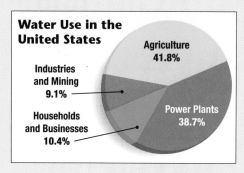

Water Use in the United States

- Agriculture 41.8%
- Power Plants 38.7%
- Households and Businesses 10.4%
- Industries and Mining 9.1%

19. **Interpreting Data** Which category represents the largest use of water in the United States? Which is the smallest?

20. **Calculating** If the total daily usage of water in the United States is 1,280 billion liters, how many liters are used each day by power plants?

21. **Predicting** How would an increase in the amount of irrigation affect this graph?

Thinking Critically

22. **Making Generalizations** Explain why towns and cities are often located along bodies of water.

23. **Comparing and Contrasting** Compare the three states of water in terms of the speed and arrangement of their molecules.

24. **Applying Concepts** You may have heard the saying, "Oil and water don't mix." Explain this statement in terms of the chemistry of water.

25. **Predicting** The city of Charleston, South Carolina, is located on the Atlantic coast. The city of Macon, Georgia, is located about 340 kilometers inland to the west. Predict which city is likely to be cooler in the summer. Explain your answer.

26. **Relating Cause and Effect** A molecule of water is likely to evaporate more quickly from the Caribbean Sea near the equator than from the Arctic Ocean. Explain why this statement is true.

Performance Assessment

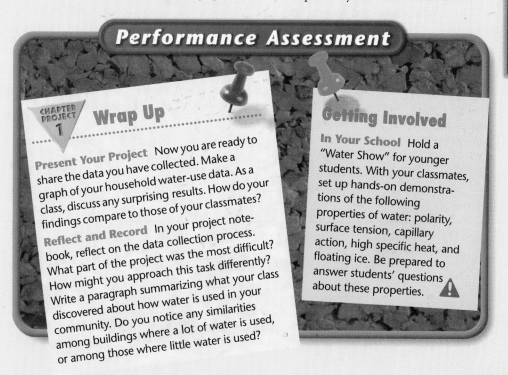

CHAPTER PROJECT 1

Wrap Up

Present Your Project Now you are ready to share the data you have collected. Make a graph of your household water-use data. As a class, discuss any surprising results. How do your findings compare to those of your classmates?

Reflect and Record In your project notebook, reflect on the data collection process. What part of the project was the most difficult? How might you approach this task differently? Write a paragraph summarizing what your class discovered about how water is used in your community. Do you notice any similarities among buildings where a lot of water is used, or among those where little water is used?

Getting Involved

In Your School Hold a "Water Show" for younger students. With your classmates, set up hands-on demonstrations of the following properties of water: polarity, surface tension, capillary action, high specific heat, and floating ice. Be prepared to answer students' questions about these properties. ⚠

ends of water molecules attract the molecules of other polar substances, allowing those substances to dissolve in water. Oil is a nonpolar substance, so its molecules are not attracted to the water molecules. Therefore the oil does not dissolve in water.

25. Charleston is likely to be cooler in summer because it is nearer to a large body of water than Macon. Because of water's high specific heat, land heats up more quickly than water. The warmer land warms the air above it, while the air above water remains cool. Breezes from the ocean, then, should keep Charleston cooler in summer.

26. The sun's heat provides the energy to evaporate water, and the sun's heat is more intense near the equator than at the Arctic Ocean.

Performance Assessment

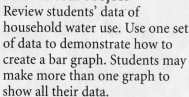

CHAPTER PROJECT 1

Wrap Up

Present Your Project Review students' data of household water use. Use one set of data to demonstrate how to create a bar graph. Students may make more than one graph to show all their data.

Reflect and Record Encourage students to evaluate how well they accomplished what they set out to do and to make whatever suggestions they think would have made the project better. In the paragraph about how water is used in the community, students should include both observations about specific uses and generalizations that demonstrate an analysis of all the data collected by class members.

Program Resources

◆ **Inquiry Skills Activity Book** Provides teaching and review of all inquiry skills

Getting Involved

In Your School Encourage students to organize the "Water Show" themselves. Explain that they should choose the time and place for the demonstrations and make sure all presentations are clear and instructive, though you should review their demonstrations for safety. Facilitate students' plans by conferring with teachers of younger students to find a good fit in their schedules for this presentation.

Sections	Time	Student Edition Activities		Other Activities
CHAPTER PROJECT 2 **Build a Watershed** p. 41	Ongoing (2–3 weeks)	Check Your Progress, p. 52 Check Your Progress, p. 64 Check Your Progress, p. 74 Wrap Up, p. 77		
1 Streams and Rivers pp. 42–52 ◆ Describe a river system and how water flows into it. ◆ Explain how a river changes the surrounding land. ◆ Describe conditions that cause floods and how floods can be controlled.	4–5 periods/ 2–3 blocks	**Discover** What Affects How Water Moves?, p. 42 **Try This** The Knuckle Divide, p. 45 **Skills Lab: Interpreting Data** How Fast Does a Stream Flow?, pp. 46–47 **Sharpen Your Skills** Inferring, p. 50	TE TE TE TE	Demonstration, p. 43 Building Inquiry Skills: Comparing and Contrasting, p. 49 Building Inquiry Skills: Making Models, p. 50 Integrating Technology, p. 52
2 Ponds and Lakes pp. 53–58 ◆ Explain how ponds and lakes form. ◆ Describe the result of lake turnover.	2–3 periods/ 1–2 blocks	**Discover** What's in Pond Water?, p. 53 **Science at Home**, p. 58	TE TE TE	Building Inquiry Skills: Comparing and Contrasting, p. 54 Including All Students, p. 55 Demonstration, p. 56
3 ⬡ **INTEGRATING LIFE SCIENCE** **Wetland Environments** pp. 59–64 ◆ Identify features of wetlands that make them suitable habitats for living things. ◆ Explain how wetlands help control flooding.	2–3 periods/ 1–2 blocks	**Discover** Wet or Dry?, p. 59 **Try This** A Natural Filter, p. 61	TE TE TE TE	Building Inquiry Skills: Measuring, p. 60 Real-Life Learning, p. 61 Demonstration, p. 62 Inquiry Challenge, p. 63
4 Glaciers and Icebergs pp. 65–67 ◆ Describe how glaciers form. ◆ Explain why icebergs are dangerous to ships.	1–2 periods/ $\frac{1}{2}$–1 block	**Discover** How Can Ice Change the Land?, p. 65 **Science at Home**, p. 67	TE	Demonstration, p. 66
5 Water Underground pp. 68–74 ◆ Describe springs, geysers, and how water moves through underground layers of soil and rock. ◆ Explain what an aquifer is and how people obtain water from an aquifer.	3–4 periods/ 1–2 blocks	**Discover** Where Does the Water Go?, p. 68 **Sharpen Your Skills** Drawing Conclusions, p. 69 **Real-World Lab: Careers in Science** Soil Testing, pp. 70–71 **Try This** An Artesian Well, p. 72	TE ISLM	Demonstration, p. 73 H-2, "Testing Water Samples"
Study Guide/Chapter Review pp. 75–77	1 period/ $\frac{1}{2}$ block		ISAB	Provides teaching and review of all inquiry skills

For Standard or Block Schedule The Resource Pro® CD-ROM gives you maximum flexibility for planning your instruction for any type of schedule. Resource Pro® contains Planning Express®, an advanced scheduling program, as well as the entire contents of the Teaching Resources and the Computer Test Bank.

CHAPTER PLANNING GUIDE

Program Resources	Assessment Strategies	Media and Technology
TR Chapter 2 Project Teacher Notes, pp. 32–33 **TR** Chapter 2 Project Student Materials, pp. 34–37 **TR** Chapter 2 Project Scoring Rubric, p. 38	**SE** Performance Assessment: Chapter 2 Project Wrap Up, p. 77 **TE** Check Your Progress, pp. 52, 64, 74 **TR** Chapter 2 Project Scoring Rubric, p. 38	Science Explorer Internet Site
TR 2-1 Lesson Plan, p. 39 **TR** 2-1 Section Summary, p. 40 **TR** 2-1 Review and Reinforce, p. 41 **TR** 2-1 Enrich, p. 42 **TR** Chapter 2 Skills Lab, pp. 59–61 **SES** Book A, *From Bacteria to Plants,* Chapters 3–5 **SES** Book B, *Animals,* Chapters 1–4	**SE** Analyze and Conclude, p. 47 **SE** Section 1 Review, p. 52 **TE** Ongoing Assessment, pp. 43, 45, 49, 51 **TE** Performance Assessment, p. 52 **TR** 2-1 Review and Reinforce, p. 41	Audiotapes, English-Spanish Summary 2-1 Transparency 4, "Exploring a River" Transparency 5, "Meander Formation" Interactive Student Tutorial CD-ROM, H-2
TR 2-2 Lesson Plan, p. 43 **TR** 2-2 Section Summary, p.44 **TR** 2-2 Review and Reinforce, p. 45 **TR** 2-2 Enrich, p. 46 **SES** Book B, *From Bacteria to Plants,* Chapters 3 and 4 **SES** Book E, *Environmental Science,* Chapter 1	**SE** Section 2 Review, p. 58 **TE** Ongoing Assessment, pp. 55, 57 **TE** Performance Assessment, p. 58 **TR** 2-2 Review and Reinforce, p. 45	Audiotapes, English-Spanish Summary 2-2 Interactive Student Tutorial CD-ROM, H-2
TR 2-3 Lesson Plan, p. 47 **TR** 2-3 Section Summary, p. 48 **TR** 2-3 Review and Reinforce, p. 49 **TR** 2-3 Enrich, p. 50	**SE** Section 3 Review, p. 64 **TE** Ongoing Assessment, pp. 61, 63 **TE** Performance Assessment, p. 64 **TR** 2-3 Review and Reinforce, p. 49	Exploring Life Science Videodisc, Unit 3 Side 1, "pH in Aquaria" Audiotapes, English-Spanish Summary 2-3 Interactive Student Tutorial CD-ROM, H-2
TR 2-4 Lesson Plan, p. 51 **TR** 2-4 Section Summary, p. 52 **TR** 2-4 Review and Reinforce, p. 53 **TR** 2-4 Enrich, p. 54	**SE** Section 4 Review, p. 67 **TE** Performance Assessment, p. 67 **TR** 2-4 Review and Reinforce, p. 53	Audiotapes, English-Spanish Summary 2-4 Interactive Student Tutorial CD-ROM, H-2
TR 2-5 Lesson Plan, p. 55 **TR** 2-5 Section Summary, p. 56 **TR** 2-5 Review and Reinforce, p. 57 **TR** 2-5 Enrich, p. 58 **TR** Chapter 2 Real-World Lab, pp. 62–63 **SES** Book F, *Inside Earth,* Chapter 1	**SE** Analyze and Conclude, p. 71 **SE** Section 5 Review, p. 74 **TE** Ongoing Assessment, pp. 69, 73 **TE** Performance Assessment, p. 74 **TR** 2-5 Review and Reinforce, p. 57	Audiotapes, English-Spanish Summary 2-5 Transparency 6, "Underground Zones" Transparency 7, "Wells and Springs" Interactive Student Tutorial CD-ROM, H-2
TR Chapter 2 Performance Assessment, pp. 167–169 **TR** Chapter 2 Test, pp.170–173	**SE** Chapter Review, pp. 75–77 **TR** Chapter 2 Performance Assessment, pp. 167–169 **TR** Chapter 2 Test, pp. 170–173 **CTB** Test H-2	Interactive Student Tutorial CD-ROM, H-2 Computer Test Bank, Test H-2 Got It! Video Quizzes

Key: **SE** Student Edition   **TE** Teacher's Edition   **TR** Teaching Resources
     CTB Computer Test Bank   **SES** Science Explorer Series Text   **ISLM** Integrated Science Laboratory Manual
     ISAB Inquiry Skills Activity Book   **PTA** Product Testing Activities by *Consumer Reports*   **IES** Interdisciplinary Explorations Series

Meeting the National Science Education Standards and AAAS Benchmarks

National Science Education Standards	Benchmarks for Science Literacy	Unifying Themes
Science As Inquiry (Content Standard A) ◆ **Use appropriate tools and techniques to gather, analyze, and interpret data** Students collect and interpret data about factors that affect stream flow. *(Skills Lab)* ◆ **Develop descriptions, explanations, predictions, and models using evidence** Students design and build a three-dimensional model of a watershed and river system. *(Chapter Project)* ◆ **Think critically and logically to make the relationships between evidence and explanations** Students compare the water-holding properties of different soil types to determine the best type of soil for a well. *(Real-World Lab)* **Life Science** (Content Standard C) ◆ **Populations and ecosystems** Rivers, ponds, lakes and wetlands provide habitats for many living things. *(Sections 1, 2, and 3)* **Earth and Space Science** (Content Standard D) ◆ **Structure of the Earth system** Freshwater sources include streams and rivers, ponds and lakes, wetlands, glaciers and icebergs, and groundwater. *(Sections 1, 2, 3, 4, and 5)*	**1B Scientific Inquiry** Students investigate factors that affect stream flow. Students compare water-holding properties of different soil types. *(Skills Lab; Real-World Lab)* **3C Issues in Technology** People build dams and levees to control flooding. People obtain groundwater by drilling wells. *(Sections 1 and 5)* **4B The Earth** Freshwater sources include streams and rivers, ponds and lakes, wetlands, glaciers and icebergs, and groundwater. *(Sections 1, 2, 3, 4, and 5)* **4C Processes That Shape the Earth** Rivers shape the land through erosion and deposition. Over time, glaciers change the surface of the land. *(Sections 1 and 4)* **5D Interdependence of Life** Rivers, ponds, lakes, and wetlands provide habitats for many living things. *(Sections 1, 2, and 3)* **11B Models** Students design and build a watershed model. Students build a stream trough to investigate stream flow. Students explore the water-holding properties of different soil types. *(Chapter Project; Skills Lab; Real-World Lab)*	◆ **Systems and Interactions** As fresh water moves over Earth's surface, it forms streams and rivers; collects in ponds, lakes, and wetlands; forms glaciers; and moves underground. *(Chapter Project; Sections 1, 2, 3, 4, and 5)* ◆ **Modeling** Students design and build a watershed model. Students build a stream trough to investigate stream flow. Students explore the water-holding properties of different soil types. *(Chapter Project; Skills Lab; Real-World Lab)* ◆ **Patterns of Change** Rivers shape the land through erosion and deposition. Lake turnover seasonally refreshes the supply of nutrients throughout a lake. Lakes change over time through eutrophication. Glaciers also change the land through erosion. *(Sections 1, 2, and 4)* ◆ **Unity and Diversity** Rivers, ponds, lakes, and wetlands provide habitats for many living things. *(Sections 1, 2, and 3)* ◆ **Scale and Structure** Water soaks down through permeable materials until it reaches a layer of impermeable materials. *(Section 5; Real-World Lab)*

Media and Technology

Exploring Life Science Videodiscs
◆ **Section 3** "pH in Aquaria" demonstrates the difficulty of creating natural conditions in the lab through a segment showing the rescue and rehabilitation of a manatee.

Interactive Student Tutorial CD-ROM
◆ **Chapter Review** Interactive questions help students to self-assess their mastery of key chapter concepts.

Student Edition Connection Strategies

◆ **Section 1** Integrating Life Science, p. 50
Integrating Technology, p. 52

◆ **Section 2** Integrating Life Science, pp. 54, 56–57
Social Studies Connection, p. 57

◆ **Section 3** Integrating Life Science, pp. 59–64

USING THE INTERNET

www.science-explorer.phschool.com

Visit the Science Explorer internet site to find an up-to-date activity for Chapter 2 of *Earth's Waters*.

ACTIVITY	Time (minutes)	Materials Quantities for one work group	Skills
Section 1			
Discover, p. 42	15–20	**Consumable** mixture of sand and pebbles, clump of grassy soil, water **Nonconsumable** large rectangular pan, small piece of porcelain tile, books to prop up pan, watering can	Predicting
Try This, p. 45	10	**Consumable** paper towel, water **Nonconsumable** spoon	Making Models
Skills Lab, pp. 46–47	40	**Consumable** food coloring, water **Nonconsumable** meterstick, pencil with eraser, several wooden blocks, 2 100-mL beakers with pour spouts, rain gutter section (120 cm or longer), stopwatch, plastic tub	Making Models, Calculating, Interpreting Data
Sharpen Your Skills, p. 50	10	No special materials are required.	Inferring
Section 2			
Discover, p. 53	20	**Consumable** pond water **Nonconsumable** plastic petri dish, hand lens, microscope, eyedropper, slide and cover slip	Classifying
Science at Home, p. 58	home	**Consumable** wax paper, water **Nonconsumable** permanent marker	Predicting
Section 3			
Discover, p. 59	10–15	**Consumable** water **Nonconsumable** 2 dry kitchen sponges, pan, 2 paper cups	Observing
Try This, p. 61	20	**Consumable** newspaper, water, damp soil **Nonconsumable** loaf pan, watering can, sponge	Observing
Section 4			
Discover, p. 65	10	**Consumable** 2 ice cubes, 1 with sand and gravel frozen into it; cardboard	Inferring
Science at Home, p. 67	home	**Consumable** milk or juice carton, water, salt **Nonconsumable** large bowl, metric ruler	Making Models
Section 5			
Discover, p. 68	10	**Consumable** water, dry sand **Nonconsumable** pebbles, clear jar, metric ruler	Observing
Sharpen Your Skills, p. 69	10	No special materials are required.	Drawing Conclusions
Real-World Lab, pp. 70–71	40	**Consumable** 100 mL powdered potter's clay, 100 mL sand, 3 squares of cheesecloth, 300 mL water **Nonconsumable** hand lens, stopwatch, 3 rubber bands, 3 large plastic funnels or cut-off plastic soda bottle tops, 3 100-mL beakers, 100 mL pebbles	Observing, Measuring, Drawing Conclusions
Try This, p. 72	20	**Consumable** newspaper, plastic straw, modeling clay, water, moist sand **Nonconsumable** loaf pan, funnel, scissors	Making Models

A list of all materials required for the Student Edition activities can be found beginning on page T14. You can order Materials Kits by calling 1-800-828-7777 or by accessing the Science Explorer Internet site at **www.science-explorer.phschool.com**.

Build a Watershed

The concept of a watershed can be difficult for students to comprehend, since they cannot view an entire river system directly. This project will provide an opportunity for students to make these concepts "real" and observable.

Purpose In this project, students will apply the chapter's concepts and terms to model typical features of a watershed—a main river and its smaller tributaries, the drainage area supplying water to the system, bodies of standing water, various landforms created by the flowing water, and the changes in a river's characteristics as it flows from its headwaters to its mouth.

Skills Focus After completing the Chapter 2 Project, students will be able to
◆ create working three-dimensional models of specific watershed and river-system features;
◆ identify variables that affect the flow rates of a main river and its tributaries;
◆ describe the changes that occur in a river as it flows from its headwaters to its mouth;
◆ predict and test the effects of increased rainfall on the river system.

Project Timeline This project requires at least two to three weeks for completion. Only the presentation of the models needs to be done in class. The remaining portions can be done in or out of class, depending on available space and time. Allow at least three days for students to plan their models, including initial sketches and revisions. Building the model will require about one week. Students should complete their models one or two days before they will test and present them, since the materials may require time to dry or set. Before beginning the project, see Chapter 2 Project Teacher Notes on pages 32–33 in Teaching Resources. Also distribute to students Chapter 2 Project Student Materials and Scoring Rubric on pages 34–38 in Teaching Resources.

Possible Materials
◆ *To form the base:* cookie sheet, roasting pan, aluminum foil baking pan, sheet of corrugated cardboard covered with waxed paper or plastic wrap, or sheet of foam core, plywood, or masonite

CHAPTER 2 Fresh Water

◆ *To shape and form the land:* salt dough or papier mâché (see instructions below), modeling clay, cardboard, or wet paper
Salt dough: Mix two parts flour to one part salt; add water a little at a time to make a stiff, moldable dough.
Papier mâché: Mix plaster of paris and water to the consistency of creamed soup; tear plain newsprint paper into thin strips and soak them in the plaster solution.
◆ *To waterproof the model:* plastic wrap, clear acrylic spray, or clear waterproof varnish

Launching the Project To introduce the project and motivate student interest, show the class a satellite photograph of a river system without telling students what the subject of the photograph is. Ask: **What do you think this picture shows?** *(Since students have never directly viewed rivers and streams from the photograph's viewpoint, they may at first have difficulty identifying the subject as a river system. Acknowledge all responses but do not comment on their accuracy at this time. When students first identify the subject correctly, confirm this response.)*

Build a Watershed

The bull moose plunges into the stream, sending shimmering drops of water flying in all directions. In addition to a refreshing dip, the stream provides the moose with drinking water and a place to find food.

A stream is one place you can find fresh water on Earth. In this chapter you will explore fresh water as it moves and changes the land, as it collects in lakes and ponds and provides a home for living things, and as it flows underground. Throughout the chapter, you will be making a model showing how water moves over the land.

Your Goal To design and build a three-dimensional model of a watershed and river system.

Your model should

◆ include a main river and at least two tributaries
◆ show at least one example of a body of standing water
◆ be constructed of materials that allow water to run over it
◆ be built following the safety guidelines in Appendix A

Get Started Begin by previewing Section 1 to see some parts of a river system. Look at the shape of the land surrounding different parts of rivers. Start thinking about materials you could use to make your landscape.

Check Your Progress You'll be working on this project as you study this chapter. To keep your project on track, look for Check Your Progress boxes at the following points.

Section 1 Review, page 52: Sketch a design for your watershed.
Section 3 Review, page 64: Revise your design to include all features.
Section 5 Review, page 74: Build your model watershed.

Wrap Up At the end of the chapter (page 77), you will use a spray bottle to demonstrate your watershed in action!

A bull moose shakes himself off following a dip in an Alaskan stream.

Program Resources

◆ **Teaching Resources** Chapter 2 Project Teacher Notes, pp. 32–33; Chapter 2 Project Student Materials, pp. 34–37; Chapter 2 Project Scoring Rubric, p. 38

Allow time for students to read the description of the project in their text and in Chapter 2 Project Student Materials from Teaching Resources. During this time, pass the photograph around so students can examine it more closely. When students have finished reading the project description, encourage discussion of possible materials to use and any preliminary questions they may have.

Have students work in small groups as a cooperative learning task. To ensure that each group member will have ample opportunity to participate in both the planning and the building of the model, make sure each group consists of no more than three students.

Performance Assessment

The Chapter 2 Project Scoring Rubric on page 38 of Teaching Resources will help you evaluate how well students complete the Chapter 2 Project. Students will be assessed on

◆ how well they plan their models, including the final sketches which should include all river-system features identified in the text;
◆ the accuracy and creativity of their models;
◆ the organization and thoroughness of their presentation;
◆ their participation in their groups.

By sharing the Chapter 2 Project Scoring Rubric with students at the beginning of the project, you will make it clear to them what they are expected to do.

Objectives

After completing the lesson, students will be able to

◆ describe a river system and how water flows into it;

◆ explain how a river changes the surrounding land;

◆ describe conditions that cause floods and how floods can be controlled.

Key Terms runoff, tributary, watershed, divide, erosion, deposition, sediment, headwaters, flood plain, meander, oxbow lake, mouth, delta, levee

1 Engage/Explore

Activating Prior Knowledge

Encourage students to describe rivers they have seen. Ask questions such as, **How big is the river? How fast does it flow?** and **What is the land around it like?** List each river's characteristics on the board. Encourage students to keep these characteristics in mind as they read this section.

· · · · · · · · **DISCOVER** · · · · · · · ·

Skills Focus predicting
Materials *rectangular* ACTIVITY
pan, sand and pebbles, small piece of porcelain tile, clump of grassy soil, books to prop up pan, watering can, water
Time 15–20 minutes
Tips Provide a container for disposing of the wet sand, pebbles, and sod.
Expected Outcome Water will flow more quickly on the tile, more slowly on the sand and pebble mixture, and most slowly on the grassy soil. The sand and pebble mixture and soil will absorb some water. The water may erode the sand and pebble mixture to some degree. The sod will show less erosion.
Think It Over Both pouring all the water at once and tilting the pan at a steeper angle will produce a higher flow rate, more erosion of the sand and pebble mixture, and less absorption by the sod.

DISCOVER · ACTIVITY

What Affects How Water Moves?

1. Cover the bottom of a pan with a mixture of sand and pebbles.

2. Press a small piece of porcelain tile onto the sand mixture to represent pavement. In another area of the pan, press a clump of soil and grass into the sand.

3. Prop up one end of the pan so it slopes gently.

4. Using a watering can, sprinkle "rain" onto the pan's contents.

5. Observe how the water moves when it falls on the sand mixture, on the tile, and on the grass.

6. Wash your hands when you are finished with this activity.

Think It Over
Predicting How would the movement of the water change if you poured the water all at once? If you tilted the pan more steeply?

GUIDE FOR READING

◆ What is a river system?

◆ How does a river change the land around it?

◆ What conditions can cause a flood?

Reading Tip Before you read, use the section headings to make an outline. Leave space to take notes as you read.

Standing on a bridge in Albuquerque, New Mexico, you look through your binoculars at the waters of the Rio Grande—the "Big River." The name fits this broad, deep stretch of water. But 700 kilometers upstream, the Rio Grande looks very different. The river begins as trickles of melting snow high in the San Juan Mountains in Colorado. As more water joins the river, it carves deep, narrow canyons out of the rock.

By the time it reaches Albuquerque the river has grown wider. It continues into Texas, winding back and forth across the dusty desert valley. In places, the river is so shallow that it may even dry up during the summer. When the Rio Grande finally empties its water into the Gulf of Mexico, it is sluggish and heavy with mud.

Spanish explorers once gave different names to three parts of the Rio Grande. They thought they had seen three different rivers! In this section, you will discover how rivers change, and how they change the land around them.

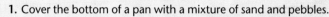

READING STRATEGIES

Reading Tip Make sure students understand that "section headings" means the headings in large type above the paragraphs of text in this section, not the titles of the five sections in the entire chapter. Students' outlines should include seven main headings: (1) *How Do Rivers Begin?* (2) *Factors That Affect Runoff,* (3) *River Systems,* (4) *Rivers Shape the Land,* (5) *Profile of a River,* (6) *Rivers and Floods,* and (7) *Can Floods Be Controlled?* Suggest

that students use the text's paragraph headings (for example, *Watersheds* and *Divides* on pages 44–45) as secondary heads in their outlines.

Study and Comprehension Encourage students to use their completed outlines to write a summary of the lesson and to generate questions to test themselves.

How Do Rivers Begin?

Have you ever helped out at a car wash for your school or youth group? Think about what happened to the water that sloshed onto the pavement. First the water ran in little trickles, which then joined together into a larger stream. The water followed the slope of the pavement down to the street or into a storm drain. A river begins in much the same way—trickles of water run over the ground and join together in larger streams.

When rain falls, some of the water evaporates immediately. Some soaks into the soil. The remaining water that flows over the ground surface is called **runoff.** Runoff also comes from melting ice and snow, like the runoff that forms the beginnings of the Rio Grande.

Figure 1 In addition to washing a car, these teens are demonstrating how ground surface affects the formation of runoff. *Applying Concepts What happens to the water that lands on the pavement? The grass?*

Factors That Affect Runoff

What determines whether water soaks into the ground or flows over it as runoff? One factor is the nature of the ground surface. Water soaks into some types of ground covering more easily than others. How much water soaks in depends on the amount of space between the particles that make up the ground cover. For example, there is more space between the particles of soil than between the particles of pavement. As a result, water soaks into soil more easily than into pavement. Since plant roots also absorb water, ground that is covered with grass or trees absorbs water more easily than bare soil.

The rate of rainfall is a second factor that affects the amount of runoff. During a heavy downpour, so much rain falls in a short time that it can't all soak into the ground. Instead some becomes runoff.

A third factor is whether the land is flat or hilly. The force of gravity pulls water downhill, just as it pulls you downhill on a sled or skateboard. Water flows faster down a steep slope than over flat ground. Because the water is moving so quickly, it runs off instead of soaking in. As runoff flows along a trench, or channel, it forms a stream. This is the beginning of the process that forms a river.

☑ *Checkpoint* *List three factors that affect the amount of runoff.*

How Do Rivers Begin?

Demonstration

Materials *hose or large watering can*
Time 10–15 minutes

For students who have not closely observed a car wash or a similar activity that produces runoff, provide direct experience: Take the class to an outdoor location that is gently sloped and has both a hard surface (such as pavement or hard-packed soil) and a looser, absorbent surface (such as a grassy lawn). Invite students to use a hose or large watering can to pour water on the ground. Ask: **What is happening to the water?** *(Small trickles are flowing across the hard surface and joining to form larger streams. The looser surface is absorbing water.)* **learning modality: kinesthetic**

Factors That Affect Runoff

Including All Students

Remind students of the Discover activity at the beginning of this section. Ask: **What variables in that activity modeled the three factors described on this page?** *(The sand and pebble mixture, tile, and clump of soil modeled the nature of the ground surface. How quickly the water was poured modeled the rate of rainfall. The tilt of the pan modeled the slope of the land.)* **learning modality: verbal**

Program Resources

◆ **Teaching Resources** 2-1 Lesson Plan, p. 39; 2-1 Section Summary, p. 40

Media and Technology

 Audiotapes English-Spanish Summary 2-1

Answers to Self-Assessment

Caption Question
Figure 1 Water that lands on pavement runs across it, with smaller trickles joining to form larger streams. Much of the water that lands on grassy soil soaks in.

☑ *Checkpoint*
Three factors that affect the amount of runoff are the nature of the ground surface, the rate of rainfall, and the slope of the land.

Ongoing Assessment

Drawing Have each student make a simple sketch showing how rivers begin, based on the text explanation on this page and on their direct observations. Advise students to save their drawings for reuse in Building Inquiry Skills on the next page.

River Systems

Building Inquiry Skills: Applying Concepts

On the drawings they made for the Ongoing Assessment on the previous page or on drawings they make specifically for this activity, students can label each feature as *small tributary, medium tributary, large tributary,* or *main river* and draw arrows to show each tributary's direction of flow. If students have difficulty fitting all the labels on their drawings, they could instead use markers to color-code the features by type and add a key to one side of the drawing. **learning modality: visual**

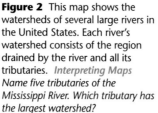 Students can save their completed drawings in their portfolios.

Using the Visuals: Figure 2

Point out that the map on this page shows *geographic* features such as rivers and mountains, not *political* features such as states, cities, and roads. Display a large political map of the United States, and invite students to compare the two maps to see where the rivers and mountains are located within states and regions. Choose volunteers to come to the large map and locate the rivers and mountain ranges shown on the text map. Ask: **What function do the Rocky Mountains and the Appalachian Mountains play in the major U.S. watersheds?** *(They are the major divides that separate these watersheds.)* Also encourage students to locate on the large map major rivers that are not labeled on the text map—for example, the Connecticut, Hudson, James, Savannah, Rio Grande, and Sacramento rivers—and try to identify their possible watersheds. Ask: **Is our area in any of these rivers' watersheds? Which river?** *(Answers will vary depending on your location.)* **learning modality: visual**

River Systems

If you were hiking in the San Juan Mountains, you could observe the path of the runoff from melting snow. As you followed one small stream downhill, you would notice that the stream reached a larger stream and joined it. You could then continue along this stream until it flowed into a small river. Eventually this path would lead you to the Rio Grande itself.

Tributaries are the smaller streams and rivers that feed into a main river. **A river and all its tributaries together make up a river system.** The tributaries flow toward the main river following a downhill path due to the pull of gravity. Even a land area that appears flat can have small differences in height that affect how water flows.

Watersheds Just as all the water in a bathtub flows toward the drain, all the water in a river system drains into the main river. The land area that supplies water to a river system is called a **watershed.** Watersheds are also called drainage basins.

A river can flow into another, larger river. When rivers join another river system, the areas they drain become part of the largest river's watershed. You can identify a river's watershed on a map by drawing an imaginary line around the region drained by all its tributaries. Some watersheds are very small. The watershed of a stream that flows down a hill into a river is just that hillside—maybe a square kilometer or two. By contrast, the watershed of the Mississippi River covers more than 3 million

Figure 2 This map shows the watersheds of several large rivers in the United States. Each river's watershed consists of the region drained by the river and all its tributaries. *Interpreting Maps Name five tributaries of the Mississippi River. Which tributary has the largest watershed?*

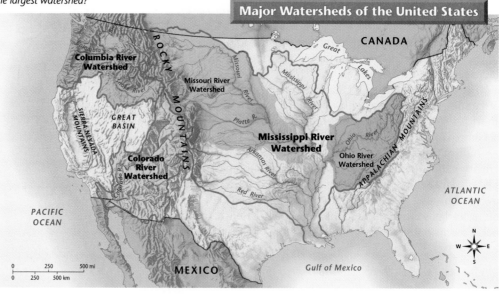

44 ◆ H

square kilometers! With your finger, trace the boundary of the Mississippi's watershed on Figure 2. Notice that it includes the watersheds of the Ohio River and the Missouri River, its two largest tributaries.

Divides One watershed is separated from another by a ridge of land called a **divide.** Streams on each side of the divide flow in different directions. The Continental Divide, the longest divide in North America, follows the line of the Rocky Mountains. Locate the Rocky Mountains on Figure 2. West of the Continental Divide, water either flows toward the Pacific Ocean or into the dry Great Basin, where the water usually evaporates. Between the Rocky Mountains and the Appalachian Mountains, water flows toward the Mississippi River or directly into the Gulf of Mexico.

☑ *Checkpoint* **Into what ocean do rivers east of the Appalachian Mountains flow?**

Rivers Shape the Land

The next time it rains, watch the rainwater flow along the side of a road. Notice how the water picks up leaves and twigs and carries them away. Bits of paper and small pebbles bounce and swirl along in the flow. Even a tiny stream has the power to move objects.

Picture a stream ten times larger, and you will start to get an idea of how running water can cause erosion. **Erosion** is the process by which fragments of soil and rock are broken off from the ground surface and carried away. These fragments are carried along by the moving water until they are eventually dropped, or deposited, in a new location. **Deposition** is the process by which soil and rock are left behind. **Rivers wear away landforms through erosion and build new landforms through deposition.** The particles of rock and soil that are picked up and moved by erosion and deposition are called **sediments.**

A river's speed affects its ability to wear away, or erode, the land. The faster the water flows, the more energy it has. A river traveling at a speed of 1 kilometer an hour

Figure 3 A hiker carefully avoids the collapsed edge of this dirt road, evidence of moving water's power to erode soil.

The Knuckle Divide

Make your hand into a fist and put it on a paper towel, knuckles facing up. With your other hand, dribble water from a spoon so that it falls onto your knuckles. Observe how the water flows over your hand.

Making a Model How are your knuckles similar to a mountain range on land? What parts of your hand represent a watershed?

TRY THIS

Skills Focus making models

Materials *paper towel, water, spoon*

Time 10 minutes

Tips Advise students to dribble the water *slowly* and to make sure it falls on the *tops* of their knuckles, not on either side.

Expected Outcome The water will flow from the tops of the knuckles to the hollows between them and to the back of the hand on one side and the spaces between the fingers on the other side. The knuckles are similar to a mountain range in that the water flows downward from them in different directions on two sides. The back of the hand represents one watershed, the fingers all represent a second watershed, and the knuckles represent a divide between the two watersheds. **learning modality: kinesthetic**

Rivers Shape the Land

Cultural Diversity

Point out that the English language includes many different names for landforms created by erosion and deposition of sediments—*canyon* and *delta,* for example. Ask: **What other names can you think of?** *(Students might suggest* gully, sandbar, mudflat, *and others.)* Emphasize that other languages also include such names, including *arroyo* (Spanish for dry gully), *wadi* (Arabic for river channel), and *billabong* (Native Australian for dead-end channel leading out from a river). Encourage students to suggest other non-English examples from their own cultures or personal reading. Interested volunteers could compile a master list of landform names in English and their corollaries in other languages. **limited English proficiency**

Answers to Self-Assessment

Caption Question

Figure 2 Five tributaries of the Mississippi are shown: the Missouri, Platte, Arkansas, Red, and Ohio rivers. The Missouri River has the largest watershed.

☑ *Checkpoint*

Rivers east of the Appalachian Mountains flow into the Atlantic Ocean.

Ongoing Assessment

Writing Have students briefly describe the processes of erosion and deposition in their own words.

How Fast Does a Stream Flow?

Preparing for Inquiry

Key Concept Increasing a stream's volume and increasing its slope both increase the water's speed.

Skills Objectives Students will be able to
◆ build a model stream trough;
◆ calculate water speed in a model stream;
◆ interpret test data to conclude that water speed increases when slope and water volume are increased.

Time 40 minutes

Advance Planning Obtain lengths of rain gutter and wooden blocks. Provide sponges and paper towels to wipe up spills.

Alternative Materials Instead of rain gutter, students could use large-diameter PVC piping cut in half lengthwise.

Guiding Inquiry

Invitation Show students pictures of a steeply sloped mountain stream and a wide, meandering stream. Ask: **Which stream is flowing faster? Why?** *(The mountain stream, because its slope is steeper)*

Introducing the Procedure

◆ Before students begin experimenting, let them practice using the stopwatch.
◆ Use examples to guide students through the formula for calculating stream speed.

Troubleshooting the Experiment

◆ Students may need to use two piles of blocks so the trough does not tip.
◆ Rinsing and drying the trough between trials will make the food coloring easier to see.
◆ The student in each group who is timing the movement of the colored water should look *straight down* at the trough and keep his or her head aligned with the leading edge of the colored water and be consistent in doing this for each trial.
◆ Let students use calculators for Analyze and Conclude questions 1 and 2. Have them round off to the nearest tenth for average times and the nearest tenth or hundredth for average speeds.

---

has enough energy to move pebbles along. At 18 kilometers an hour it can move a boulder the size of an armchair! When a river slows down, its energy decreases. It can no longer move heavy objects. The river deposits heavier sediment particles first, then lighter ones.

One factor that affects how fast a river flows is the steepness of its slope. Water flows faster down a mountainside than over a flat plain. A second factor that affects a river's speed is the volume of water in the river. An increase in the amount of water in a river

---

Skills Lab

How Fast Does a Stream Flow?

In this lab, you will interpret data to see how different factors affect stream flow. First, you will build a model called a stream trough.

Problem

How do the slope of a stream and the volume of water it contains affect its speed?

Materials

meterstick	water
pencil with eraser	stopwatch
several wooden blocks	plastic tub
2 100-mL beakers with pour spouts	
rain gutter section, 120 cm or longer	
food coloring in squeeze-top bottle	

Procedure

1. Copy the data table into your notebook. Label it "Experiment number 1."
2. Use the pencil to mark an "S" at one end of the gutter. This represents the stream's source. Mark an "M" at the other end of the gutter. This represents the stream's mouth.
3. About 10 cm from the source end, draw a dark line across the inside of the gutter.
4. Measure 100 cm toward the mouth end from the first line. Draw a second line across the gutter.
5. Place the plastic tub under the mouth end of the gutter to collect the water.
6. Place enough blocks under the source end to raise it 5 cm above the tub. Record the number of blocks in the data table.
7. Write "1" after "Number of beakers" in the data table.

DATA TABLE

Experiment number: _____

Number of blocks: _____

Number of beakers: _____

Trial Number	Time (seconds)
Trial 1	
Trial 2	
Trial 3	

Average time: _____

Average stream speed: _____

Program Resources

◆ **Teaching Resources** Skills Lab blackline masters, pp. 59–61

Safety

Students should wear safety goggles and lab aprons. Review the safety guidelines in Appendix A.

Sample Data Table

Experiment Number: 1
Number of blocks: 3
Number of beakers: 1

Trial Number	Time
Trial 1	2.7 seconds
Trial 2	2.5 seconds
Trial 3	3.0 seconds

Average time: 2.7 seconds
Average stream speed: 37 cm/sec

causes the river to flow faster. A third factor is the shape of the channel through which the river flows. As the water in the river rubs against the sides and bottom of its channel, it creates friction. This friction slows the water's movement. In a shallow, narrow channel, almost all the water is in contact with the sides or bottom, and it moves slowly. In a broad, deep channel, however, most of the water can flow without any friction, so the river flows faster.

8. One person should slowly pour water from one beaker into the source end of the gutter, trying not to spill any water out the back end. A second person should add one drop of food coloring at the source end, above the "S" line. A third person should begin timing when the food coloring first reaches the "S" line. Stop timing when the food coloring reaches the "M" line. Record the time on your data table. Be sure the water is collecting in the tub at the mouth end.

9. Repeat Step 8 twice, pouring the water at the same rate each time. Record your results.

10. Copy the data table again, labeling it "Experiment number 2." Repeat Steps 8 and 9 with an increased water volume in the stream. Increase the water volume by pouring water into the stream from two beakers at the same time. Try to pour both at the same rate.

11. Now increase the slope of the stream, adding blocks to raise the source end 5 cm higher.

12. Copy the data table two more times for Experiment numbers 3 and 4. For Experiment 3, repeat Steps 8 and 9 at this steeper slope. For Experiment 4, repeat Step 10.

Analyze and Conclude

1. Average the three trials for each experiment. Record the average times on your data table.

2. Calculate the average stream speed for each experiment using the following formula:

$$\text{Speed of stream (cm/s)} = \frac{\text{distance (100 cm)}}{\text{average time (s)}}$$

3. How did the speed of the stream change when you increased the volume of water?

4. How did the speed of the stream change when you increased the slope?

5. **Think About It** What errors might have affected your data? How could they be reduced?

More to Explore

The volume of sediments picked up and carried by a stream indicates how much erosion is occurring. How could you modify this experiment to test how the amount of erosion is affected by a stream's speed? Obtain your teacher's permission to try the experiment.

Expected Outcome
Specific times and speeds may vary among groups, but all should find that increasing the water volume and increasing the slope increases the water speed.

Analyze and Conclude
1. Average times may be in the range of 2.5–3.0 seconds for Experiment 1, 2.0–2.5 seconds for Experiments 2 and 3, and 1.5–2.0 seconds for Experiment 4.
2. Average speeds may be in the range of 30–40 cm/sec for Experiment 1, 40–50 cm/sec for Experiments 2 and 3, and 50–60 cm/sec for Experiment 4.
3. The speed increased.
4. The speed increased.
5. Sources of error include variations in reaction times when using the stopwatch, viewing the lines from different angles, not noticing the first trace of food coloring, and not pouring the water at the same rate every time. These errors could be reduced by paying very careful attention as each task is performed and by timing the pouring of the water.

Extending the Inquiry
More to Explore Students could test the effect of stream speed on erosion by spreading a given volume of mixed soil, sand, and small pebbles along the trough and measuring the volume of sediment that is washed into the collection tub. The faster a stream flows, the more sediments (and the larger the particles) it erodes.

Sample Data Table
Experiment Number: 2
Number of blocks: 3
Number of beakers: 2

Trial Number	Time
Trial 1	2.0 seconds
Trial 2	2.2 seconds
Trial 3	2.2 seconds

Average time: 2.1 seconds
Average stream speed: 48 cm/sec

Sample Data Table
Experiment Number: 3
Number of blocks: 6
Number of beakers: 1

Trial Number	Time
Trial 1	1.9 seconds
Trial 2	2.1 seconds
Trial 3	2.0 seconds

Average time: 2.0 seconds
Average stream speed: 50 cm/sec

Sample Data Table
Experiment Number: 4
Number of blocks: 6
Number of beakers: 2

Trial Number	Time
Trial 1	1.6 seconds
Trial 2	1.8 seconds
Trial 3	1.5 seconds

Average time: 1.6 seconds
Average stream speed: 63 cm/sec

Profile of a River

Including All Students

Call on volunteers to find and read aloud the different definitions of *profile* found in some dictionaries. *(Sample definitions: a side view or outline of an object; a concise description of a person's or thing's most noteworthy characteristics; a table or graph showing the extent to which a person or thing exhibits various tested traits)* Ask: **Which meaning fits the title "Profile of a River"?** *("A side view or outline" describes the illustration on these pages, while the caption provides "a concise description of a person's or thing's characteristics.")* Suggest that students write a brief profile in their own words of the river described in the text. **learning modality: verbal**

EXPLORING
a River

To help students focus on the major points presented in this visual essay and make comparisons among the river segments more easily, have them organize the information in a table. This could be done either as a whole-class discussion, with students suggesting the entries for you to write in a table on the board or an overhead transparency, or, preferably, as an individual activity, with each student making his or her own table independently. The terms *Headwaters, Downriver, Flood plain,* and *Mouth* could be written in a horizontal row across the top of the table as the column headings, and terms identifying the types of information presented—such as *Slope, Speed, Volume, Erosion or Deposition?* and *Typical Organisms*—could be written in the far-left vertical column (or vice versa). As students read the text on these two pages and the next page, they can add additional information to the table. If students create their tables independently, provide some follow-up class time for them to share their results and resolve any discrepancies. **learning modality: logical/mathematical**

If students create tables independently, they can save the tables in their **Portfolio** portfolios.

Profile of a River

Imagine taking a rafting trip along the entire length of a river to observe how it changes firsthand. You can follow the journey in *Exploring a River.*

The Headwaters Your trip starts near the river's beginning, or source, in the mountains. The many small streams that come together at the source of the river are called the **headwaters.** Your ride through the headwaters is quite bumpy as your raft bounces through rapids, dropping suddenly over a small waterfall. You notice how the fast-flowing water breaks off clumps of soil from

EXPLORING a River

A s you follow this river from its headwaters to its mouth, notice how its speed, volume, and shape change. Each part of the river forms a different habitat for living things.

A Headwaters
The steep slope of the land causes the river to flow quickly. The fast-moving water cuts a narrow channel.

The cold, rough water near ▶ the headwaters contains high levels of dissolved oxygen. Fish like these trout thrive here. Their streamlined bodies enable them to swim in the fast current.

B Downriver
The slope of the land is less steep. Tributaries increase the river's volume. The river erodes its channel, making it wider and deeper.

Beavers build dams out of logs and sticks held ▶ together with mud. The dams create pools of slow-moving water along the river.

Background

Facts and Figures Another set of terms used to describe a river are the stages of its development: youth, maturity, and old age. A single river may include all three stages.

At the headwaters, where the fast-moving water erodes the underlying land, the river is young. A young river has waterfalls, rapids, a narrow V-shaped valley, and a steep slope.

A mature river erodes its sides more than its bottom, creating a flood plain. A mature

river has a gentler slope and a smoother riverbed.

An old river has a flood plain that is much wider than the width of its meanders. An old river may shift course frequently. Oxbow lakes and natural levees are common.

These stages are relative; an "old" river may be more recently formed than some "young" rivers.

the riverbanks and carries them along. As the river continues this erosion, it wears away the sides and cuts into the bottom of its channel. The channel gradually becomes wider and deeper.

Downriver As you continue downriver, your ride becomes smoother. The land around the river is less steep than it was near the headwaters. Some smaller streams have joined the river, increasing the volume of water. Since less of the water is in contact with the channel, there is less friction slowing it down. As a result, although the slope is less steep, the river continues to flow fairly swiftly.

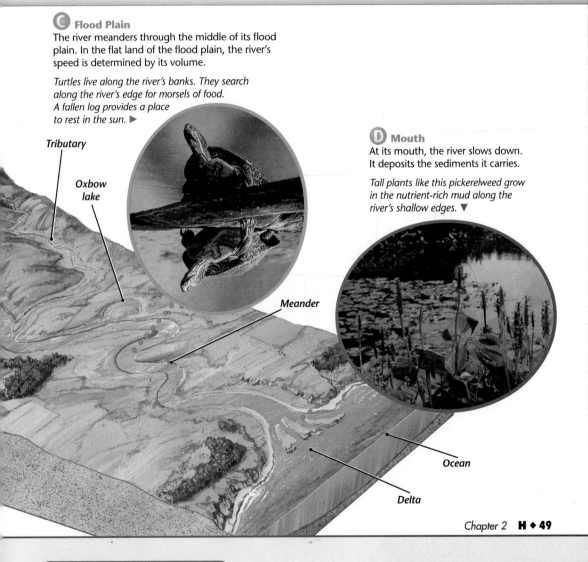

C Flood Plain
The river meanders through the middle of its flood plain. In the flat land of the flood plain, the river's speed is determined by its volume.

Turtles live along the river's banks. They search along the river's edge for morsels of food. A fallen log provides a place to rest in the sun. ▶

Tributary

Oxbow lake

Meander

D Mouth
At its mouth, the river slows down. It deposits the sediments it carries.

Tall plants like this pickerelweed grow in the nutrient-rich mud along the river's shallow edges. ▼

Ocean

Delta

Commercial businesses conduct guided rafting expeditions on many of this country's rivers. Such expeditions teach people much about the ecology of rivers and develop appreciation for our wilderness and its wildlife, but these tours can also cause ecological damage. Suggest that interested students find out more about such rafting expeditions and stage a debate on the pros and cons of wilderness rafting expeditions. **learning modality: verbal**

Building Inquiry Skills: Comparing and Contrasting

ACTIVITY

Have each group of students set up a stream trough or a long, high-sided tray with a 6-cm-deep layer of mixed sand, gravel, and small pebbles on the bottom. Instruct students to create a narrow, slightly curving river channel about 4 cm deep into the layers. With the trough or tray at a fairly steep angle, students should pour a strong, steady stream of water into the upper end of the river. Ask students: **Where is erosion occurring along the river?** *(On the outside of each curve)* **What types of materials are being eroded?** *(The sand; if the water is flowing quickly enough, gravel and small pebbles may be eroded as well.)* **learning modality: kinesthetic**

Media and Technology

 Transparencies "Exploring a River," Transparency 4

Ongoing Assessment

Writing or Drawing Challenge each student to write a brief description of the changes a river undergoes as it flows from its headwaters to its mouth, without referring to the visual essay on these pages or the tables students created in *Exploring a River* above. Allow students who learn best through a visual modality to present the information in a labeled drawing.

Profile of a River, continued

Using the Visuals: Figure 4

To make sure students understand that erosion along the *inner* curve of a river and deposition along the *outer* curve are responsible for meander formation, call on volunteers to sketch on the board the series of ever-widening loops that form between stages A and C in the figure. Next, give each student a copy of a map or an aerial photograph of a land area that has several prominent meanders and oxbow lakes. (A good choice would be eastern Louisiana, where the lower Mississippi River has formed wide loops and several large oxbow lakes on its flat flood plain.) Have each student locate these two features on the map or photograph and circle them in different colors. **learning modality: visual**

Building Inquiry Skills: Making Models

Challenge students to **ACTIVITY** devise a model to show how meanders and oxbow lakes are formed. Students' models could be as simple as a series of yarn loops to show the formation sequence or as complex as an actual working model using fine sand or silt and steadily flowing water. **learning modality: kinesthetic**

Sharpen your Skills

Inferring

Time 10 minutes
Tips If students **ACTIVITY** completed Try This on page 45, ask: **What happened when you poured water on your knuckles?** (*Some water flowed to one side and some to the other side.*) **What caused the water to flow to the sides?** (*gravity*)
Expected Outcome Students should realize that *higher* land (the divide and the Nile's headwaters) must lie to the *south* and that the land to the *north* of the Nile's source must slope *downward* to the river's mouth.
Extend Provide world atlases so students can compare the Nile's shape and direction of flow with the routes of other major rivers. **learning modality: logical/mathematical**

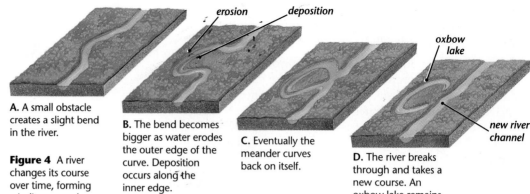

A. A small obstacle creates a slight bend in the river.

Figure 4 A river changes its course over time, forming winding meanders.

B. The bend becomes bigger as water erodes the outer edge of the curve. Deposition occurs along the inner edge.

C. Eventually the meander curves back on itself.

D. The river breaks through and takes a new course. An oxbow lake remains.

Sharpen your Skills

Inferring

Many of the **ACTIVITY** world's rivers flow from north to south. However, the Nile River in Egypt flows from south to north. What can you infer about the slope of the land through which the Nile flows? (*Hint:* Think about the factors that determine how a river system forms.)

The Flood Plain Next your raft travels through the middle of a wide valley. The river created this valley over time by eroding the land along its banks. The broad, flat valley through which the river flows is called the **flood plain.**

In places, small obstacles in the river's channel cause the water to flow slightly to one side or the other. This movement creates a bend in the river. As Figure 4 shows, the water erodes the outer edge of the curve, where it flows faster. The river deposits sediments along the inner edge, where it flows slower. This process gradually forms looping curves in the river called **meanders.** Eventually the river may break through the ends of the meander, carving a new channel. The crescent-shaped, cutoff body of water that remains is called an **oxbow lake.**

The Mouth Your raft trip is nearly over as you approach the river's mouth. The **mouth** is the point where a river flows into another body of water—a larger river, a lake, or an ocean. When the fast-moving waters of a river hit the slower waters of a lake or ocean, the river suddenly slows down. As it slows, the river deposits most of its sediment. These deposits at the river's mouth build up, forming an area called a **delta.** The sediment deposits are rich in nutrients and minerals. As a result, the soil in delta areas is very fertile for farming.

Habitats Along a River Recall that an organism's habitat **INTEGRATING LIFE SCIENCE** provides the things that the organism needs to live. As you saw in *Exploring a River*, a river provides habitats for many living things. Some organisms live in the river and obtain nutrients and dissolved gases from the water. Others find shelter and food along its banks.

☑ *Checkpoint* How does a river's volume change between its headwaters and mouth?

Background

Facts and Figures The Red River floods that devastated parts of North Dakota and Minnesota in the spring of 1997 resulted from a combination of factors. Throughout the previous winter, 13 massive storms had buried the area with record snowfalls. When the spring thaw arrived, unusually high temperatures melted the snow in days, causing rapid runoff into the Red River and its tributaries. Levees protected some towns but worsened flooding in other towns downriver.

The Red River's valley is one of the flattest on Earth, which allows floodwaters to spread out extensively. In one area close to the Canadian border, the river overflowed its 55-m channel to stretch nearly *65 km* across its valley.

The Red River flows north into Canada. Ice jams in the north slowed water flow, causing river levels to swell further.

Rivers and Floods

Spring floods occur frequently on rivers in the Midwest, but the floods of 1997 were far worse than usual. The residents of Fargo, North Dakota, had already used a million sandbags, and the Red River of the North was still rising! As the flood waters rose, people piled the sandbags higher around their houses, hoping no water would break through. People moved their belongings to their attics, then watched as water flowed through their homes.

The Red River floods went on for weeks, fed by rain and melting snow. A spring blizzard added more snow. Other nearby rivers also flooded. Parts of North Dakota, South Dakota, and Minnesota were declared a disaster area. Weary residents just waited for the waters to recede so they could start to repair the damage.

What caused the Red River to flood so badly? **A flood occurs when the volume of water in a river increases so much that the river overflows its channel.** As rain and melting snow added more and more water, the river gained in speed and strength. Recall that as the speed of a river increases, so does the amount of energy it has. A flooding river can uproot trees and pluck boulders from the ground. As it overflows onto its floodplain, the powerful water can even wash away bridges and houses.

Throughout history, people have both feared and welcomed floods. Ancient Egyptians, for instance, called their fertile cropland "the gift of the Nile." Deposition from regular floods left a layer of rich soil on each side of the river, creating a green strip of good land in the middle of the desert. But floods can also destroy farms, towns, and crops. In the United States, 20 million people live in places where flooding is likely. Even in the last century, floods have killed millions of people around the world, many of them in the heavily populated flood plains of China, Bangladesh, and India.

Figure 5 A flood can be disastrous for nearby residents, such as the owners of this house. *Making Generalizations Explain how floods can be both harmful and helpful to people.*

Program Resources

 Science Explorer Series *From Bacteria to Plants,* Chapters 3–5, and *Animals,* Chapters 1–4, have information on organisms that live in freshwater habitats.

Media and Technology

Transparencies "Meander Formation," Transparency 5

Answers to Self-Assessment

☑ Checkpoint
The volume increases.

Caption Question
Figure 5 *Harm:* injury or death of people and livestock, destruction of buildings and crops, and loss of freshwater supplies, electricity, transportation, and communication. *Help:* deposition of nutrient-rich silt

Integrating Life Science

Provide a variety of field guides so students can find out more about the animals, plants, and other organisms that live in or near rivers and streams in your area. Suggest that each student choose one organism and prepare a brief oral or written report on its physical and behavioral characteristics, its specific habitat, and its niche in the ecosystem. Monitor students' choices of organisms to minimize duplication. **learning modality: verbal**

Rivers and Floods

Real-Life Learning
Students who directly experienced the Midwest floods of 1997 or who have been personally affected by other floods (such as the flooding in California and the Southeast due to the heavy rains caused by El Niño of 1997-1998) may be uneasy or even upset by the text descriptions on this page and the next. First concentrate objectively on the physical causes of flooding described in the text. Then go on to discuss the safety precautions that should be followed in the event of a flood. Pamphlets with flood-safety guidelines may be available from your state or regional Red Cross chapter or FEMA (Federal Emergency Management Agency) office. Try to obtain such pamphlets for students to review. If students live in a flood-prone area, encourage them to copy the precautions to take home and review with their family members. **learning modality: verbal**

Ongoing Assessment

Writing Have each student summarize, in a two-column format, the hazards and benefits of flooding described in the text on this page and the next, adding others they think of on their own.

Can Floods Be Controlled?

Integrating Technology

To help students understand how difficult it is to control flooding without creating other problems, invite them to repeat Building Inquiry Skills, page 49, this time using clay to build levees along the upper and middle sections of the river and pouring more water into the upper end to simulate flood conditions. **learning modality: kinesthetic**

3 Assess

Section 1 Review Answers

1. A river and all its tributaries
2. *Erosion:* Water breaks off pieces of soil and rock and carries them away. *Deposition:* The pieces of soil and rock are carried to a new location, where they build up and form new landforms.
3. Very heavy rain could increase a river's water volume so much that the river overflows its channel and floods the land.
4. *Dam:* Redirects the river's flow or stores the water in an artificial lake. *Levees or Sandbags:* Help keep the river inside its banks by increasing height of channel walls.
5. Around its headwaters, because the water is flowing more rapidly and therefore has more energy.

Check Your Progress

CHAPTER PROJECT 2

As you review students' drawings, check for their overall understanding. Ask: **Do tributaries flow toward or away from the main river?** *(toward it)* **Are tributaries lower or higher than the main river?** *(higher)* Help them evaluate their choice of materials for cost and practicality.

Performance Assessment

Skills Check Challenge small groups to devise methods for measuring the speed of a local stream or river. Groups could present their ideas in a written report or oral presentation.

Can Floods Be Controlled?

INTEGRATING TECHNOLOGY As long as people have lived on flood plains, they have tried to control floods. Building dams is one method of flood control. A dam is a barrier across a river that may redirect the flow of a river to other channels or store the water in an artificial lake. Engineers can open the dam's floodgates to release water in dry seasons. Dams work fairly well to control small floods. During severe floods, however, powerful flood waters can wash over the top of a dam or break through it.

Sediment deposits actually build a natural defense against floods. As a river overflows onto its flood plain, it slows down, depositing the heavier sediments alongside the channel. Over time, these deposits build up into long ridges called **levees.** These natural levees help keep the river inside its banks. People sometimes build up the natural levees with sandbags or stone and concrete to provide further protection against floods.

But building up levees can sometimes backfire. These walls prevent the natural channel-widening process that rivers normally undergo as their volume increases. As a result, during a flood, the water has nowhere to go except downstream. Although built-up levees can work well to prevent small floods, they often make heavy flooding worse for areas farther downstream. The full power of the surge of flood water is passed on to flood the downstream areas.

Figure 6 These people are working together to protect their community during a flood. *Applying Concepts How do sandbags help control flooding?*

Section 1 Review

1. What bodies of water make up a river system?
2. Name and describe the two major processes by which a river changes the land.
3. How might a period of very heavy rain cause a flood to occur?
4. Describe one method of controlling floods.
5. **Thinking Critically** **Applying Concepts** Is a river more likely to erode the land around its headwaters or at its mouth? Why?

Check Your Progress

CHAPTER PROJECT 2

Begin sketching your model watershed. How will you shape the land to form the main river and tributary? What materials would be easy to shape and allow runoff to occur? Use the sketch to help estimate amounts of materials you will need. *(Hint: Decide what to use as a base for your model. Draw your sketch on a piece of paper the same size as the base.)*

Program Resources

◆ **Teaching Resources** 2-1 Review and Reinforce, p. 41; 2-1 Enrich, p. 42

Media and Technology

Interactive Student Tutorial CD-ROM H-2

Answers to Self-Assessment

Caption Question

Figure 6 Sandbags increase the height of the sides of the river channel, enabling it to hold a larger volume of water.

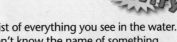

What's in Pond Water?

1. Using a hand lens, observe a sample of pond water.

2. Make a list of everything you see in the water. If you don't know the name of something, write a short description or draw a picture.

3. Your teacher has set up a microscope with a slide of pond water. Observe the slide and add any new items to your list. Wash your hands with soap when you are done.

Think It Over

Classifying Use one of these systems to divide the items on your list into two groups: moving/still, living/nonliving, or microscopic/visible without a microscope. What does your classification system tell you about pond water?

What do a glass of water, a canoe, and a snowstorm have in common? They're three things that could connect you to a nearby lake. Lake Michigan, for example, is a source of drinking water; a place to go boating and swimming; and the source of winter snowstorms on its shores.

While water in streams and rivers is always on the move, the water in lakes and ponds is still, or standing, water. Although there is no definite rule to determine whether a body of water is called a pond or a lake, ponds are generally smaller and shallower than lakes. Sunlight usually reaches to the bottom of all parts of a pond. Most lakes have parts where the water is too deep for sunlight to reach all the way to the bottom.

Ponds and lakes form when water collects in hollows and low-lying areas of land. Rainfall, melting snow and ice, and runoff supply water to ponds and lakes. Others are fed by rivers or groundwater. Eventually, water may flow out of a pond or lake into a river, or evaporate from its surface.

GUIDE FOR READING

◆ How do ponds and lakes form?

◆ What is the result of lake turnover?

Reading Tip Before you read, predict one way in which ponds and lakes are similar and one way in which they are different. As you read, add to your explanation.

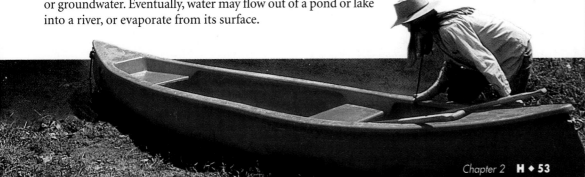

READING STRATEGIES

Reading Tip Students can set up a two-column table for recording the information, using the column headings *Predictions* and *In the Book* (or a similar descriptor) at the top of the table, and two rows labeled *Similarities* and *Differences* at the far left. Remind students to make the table large enough to write their predictions and add information from the text.

Program Resources

◆ **Teaching Resources** 2-2 Lesson Plan, p. 43; 2-2 Summary, p. 44

Media and Technology

 Audiotapes English-Spanish Summary 2-2

Objectives

After completing the lesson, students will be able to
◆ explain how ponds and lakes form;
◆ describe the result of lake turnover.

Key Terms reservoir, eutrophication

1 Engage/Explore

Activating Prior Knowledge

As you did with rivers and streams in Section 1, encourage students to describe some of the lakes and ponds they have seen. Ask questions such as, **How large is the lake?** and **What types of plants and animals live in or around it?**

 DISCOVER

Skills Focus classifying
Materials *pond water, plastic petri dish, hand lens, microscope, eyedropper, slide and cover slip*
Time 20 minutes
Tips Collect water from a local pond, making sure you obtain some bottom mud and suspended particles. (As an alternative, you can prepare a hay infusion or use prepared slides.) *To prepare the slide:* Use an eyedropper to place a drop of pond water on the slide. Hold one edge of the cover slip on the slide and drag it toward the water drop. When the slip comes into contact with the drop, let the slip's other edge down slowly. Avoid trapping air bubbles under the cover slip.
Expected Outcome Students should be able to see some larger organisms with the hand lens and a greater variety with the microscope.
Think It Over Students could use movement or the consumption of smaller particles as criteria for deciding whether items are alive. Whichever classification criteria they use, students should recognize that pond water contains a variety of living and nonliving things.

2 Facilitate

Ponds

EXPLORING
a Pond

After students have read the text in the visual essay, ask: **What are some different habitats that are described?** *(The shore, the shallow water near shore, the bottom of the pond, the surface, and the deeper waters)* Encourage volunteers to summarize how conditions vary in the different habitats. Also encourage students to name other pond organisms they know from personal experience or their reading. **learning modality: verbal**

Building Inquiry Skills: Comparing and Contrasting

Materials *pond algae, pond plants, hand lens*
Time 10 minutes

 Provide specimens of common pond algae, such as *Spirogyra* or *Cladophora*, and plants, such as pondweeds, for students to examine. Then ask: **How are the algae and plants different?** *(The plants have stems, leaves, and roots, whereas the algae do not have any similar structures.)* **How are they alike?** *(They both are green and able to carry out photosynthesis.)* Emphasize that plants and algae are vital to pond habitats because they produce food and oxygen through photosynthesis. **learning modality: visual**

Integrating Life Science

Point out the text information about temporary ponds that appear in the spring and dry up in the summer. Then ask: **What types of organisms could find temporary homes in a spring pond?** *(Frogs, birds, flying insects, and other animals that could leave the pond when it dried up; plants whose seeds could survive dry conditions)* **What is the importance of temporary ponds?** *(They provide habitats for organisms that require water during part of their lifecycles.)* **learning modality: logical/ mathematical**

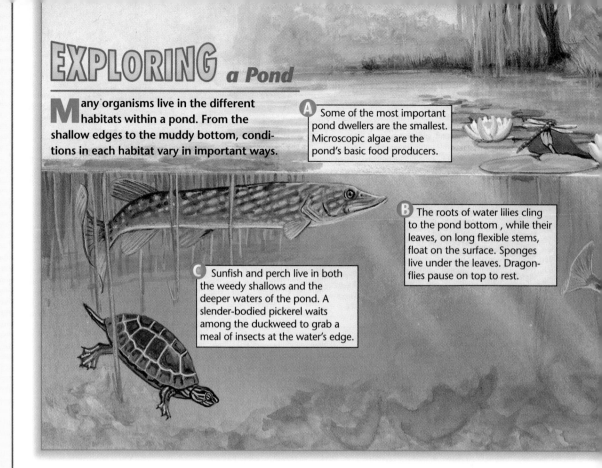

EXPLORING a Pond

Many organisms live in the different habitats within a pond. From the shallow edges to the muddy bottom, conditions in each habitat vary in important ways.

A Some of the most important pond dwellers are the smallest. Microscopic algae are the pond's basic food producers.

B The roots of water lilies cling to the pond bottom , while their leaves, on long flexible stems, float on the surface. Sponges live under the leaves. Dragonflies pause on top to rest.

C Sunfish and perch live in both the weedy shallows and the deeper waters of the pond. A slender-bodied pickerel waits among the duckweed to grab a meal of insects at the water's edge.

Ponds

INTEGRATING LIFE SCIENCE Compared to a tumbling mountain stream, a pond seems still and peaceful at first glance. Silvery minnows glide smoothly below the surface. A dragonfly touches the water, then whirs away. Lily pads with broad, green leaves and waxy, white blossoms float on the surface. This quiet pond is actually a thriving habitat, supporting a wide diversity of living things.

If you have ever waded in a pond, you know that the muddy bottom is often covered with weeds. Because the water is shallow enough for sunlight to reach the bottom, plants grow throughout a pond. Plantlike organisms called algae also live in the pond. As the plants and algae use sunlight to make food through photosynthesis, they also produce oxygen. Animals in the pond use the oxygen and food provided by plants and algae. You can see some common pond organisms in *Exploring a Pond.*

Background

Integrating Science Lakes and ponds are characterized by specific zones. Lakes have three major zones (see Background, page 56); ponds have two.

The shallow water along the edge of a pond is called the *littoral zone*. More photosynthesis occurs in the littoral zone than anywhere else in the pond, partly because nutrients wash into the pond from the land and feed the algae and plants there.

The open water away from the shore is called the *limnetic zone*. Free-floating photosynthetic bacteria and algae and animallike protists inhabit the limnetic zone, as well as animals, such as fish.

D The shore is edged with grasses and trees that require a lot of water, such as willows and maples. These plants provide shelter and nesting places for redwing blackbirds and other birds.

E Frogs lay eggs in the shallow water near shore. They hatch in the water as tadpoles and move to the land as adults.

F Snails find food on the soft bottom of the pond. Crayfish lie buried in the mud, waiting for bits of food to drift down.

Not all ponds exist year-round. For example, some ponds in the northern and western United States appear only in the spring, when runoff from spring rains and melting snow collects in low areas. The ponds dry up by midsummer as the shallow water quickly evaporates in the heat.

Ponds in colder climates often freeze over during the winter. As you learned in Chapter 1, ice floats because it is less dense than liquid water. As a result, ice forms on the surface of the pond, while the living things survive in the liquid water below.

☑ *Checkpoint* **Why can plants grow throughout a pond?**

Lakes

Suppose you suddenly found yourself on a sandy beach. Waves break on the shore. The water stretches as far as your eye can see. Gulls screech overhead. Where are you? Although you might think you're at the ocean, this immense body of water could

Lakes

Including All Students

Materials *cup of water, ice cube*
Time 5–10 minutes

Give each student a small cup of water and an ice cube. Ask students to predict what will happen when they put the ice cube in the cup. *(The cube will float.)* Let students test their predictions. Then ask: **What would have happened if ice were more dense than water?** *(The cube would have sunk to the bottom of the cup.)* **How does the lower density of ice enable lake organisms to survive through the winter?** *(Ice that forms on the lake's surface floats on the water, and shields the organisms in the water below from the cold.)*
learning modality: logical/mathematical

Program Resources

Science Explorer Series *From Bacteria to Plants,* Chapters 3 and 4, can provide more information on algae and photosynthesis.

Answers to Self-Assessment

☑ *Checkpoint*

The water in a pond is shallow enough so that sunlight reaches all areas.

Ongoing Assessment

Oral Presentation Have students pretend to be one of the organisms that lives in a pond and describe their habitat and activities.

Lakes, continued

Integrating Life Science

To help students understand the complex relationships among organisms in a lake habitat, ask: **What feeding relationships are identified in the text?** *(Loons and kingfishers eat fish; worms and mollusks feed on food particles that drift down; large, bony fish eat tiny bottom dwellers and fish and birds at the surface.)* **Why are plants and algae important to a lake habitat?** *(They carry out photosynthesis, which produces food and oxygen that other organisms depend on.)* Challenge students to draw a food chain that illustrates one set of feeding relationships that exists in a lake habitat. **learning modality: visual**

Changes in a Lake

Demonstration

Materials *large beaker, cold water, warm water, food coloring, spoon, ice*

Time 10 minutes

Make a working model of lake turnover so students can observe this process. First, fill the beaker about two thirds full of cold water. Tint the warm water with food coloring, and then hold the spoon directly over the cold water and slowly pour the warm water onto the spoon so that it flows gently into the beaker. The warm, tinted water should form a layer on top of the cold water. Next, float ice cubes in the water. The ice will cool the warm water, causing it to sink and mix with the cold water. Ask: **How is this model like lake turnover?** *(Like the model, when the warmer, top layer of a lake cools in the fall, it sinks and causes the waters of the lake to mix together.)* **How does lake turnover cause the minerals and other nutrients to be mixed through the lake?** *(When the warm layer cools and sinks, it pushes up minerals and other nutrients from the lake bottom, causing them to mix through the water.)* **learning modality: visual**

Figure 7 Standing water is found in lakes and ponds. **A.** The cold waters of Crater Lake in Oregon fill the hollow of an ancient volcano. **B.** Water lilies float in a Colorado pond. *Interpreting Photographs In which of these bodies of water does sunlight reach the bottom? Give evidence to support your answer.*

actually be a lake! You could be on a beach in Indiana, on the shore of Lake Michigan.

Although most lakes are not as large as Lake Michigan, they are generally bigger and deeper than ponds. Most lakes are deep enough that sunlight does not reach all the way to the bottom. A lake bottom may consist of sand, pebbles, or rock. The bottom of a pond is usually covered with mud and algae.

Lake Formation Lakes form in many ways. As you read in Section 1, a cut-off river meander may become an oxbow lake. Ice sheets that melted at the end of the Ice Age created depressions that became lakes. Some lakes were created by movements of Earth's crust. Such movements created the deep valleys in central Africa that lie below Lake Tanganyika and Lake Victoria. Other lakes are the result of volcanoes. An erupting volcano can cause a flow of lava or mud that blocks a river and forms a lake. Some lakes, like the one in Figure 7, form in the empty craters of volcanoes.

People can also create a lake by building a dam across a river. The lake may be used for supplying drinking water, for irrigating fields, and for boating and fishing. A lake that stores water for human use is called a **reservoir.** One of the largest reservoirs in the United States is Lake Mead in Nevada, behind Hoover Dam on the Colorado River.

Lake Habitats Like a pond, a lake provides habitats for many organisms. In the shallow water near shore, the wildlife is similar to that in a pond. Water beetles scurry over the slippery, moss-covered rocks.

INTEGRATING LIFE SCIENCE

Background

Integrating Science In addition to the two zones described for ponds in the Background on page 54, lakes have an area of deep water called the *profundal zone.* Sunlight does not reach the deeper parts of this zone, so no plants or algae live there.

Particles of food and the remains of dead organisms drift down into the profundal zone. Bacteria decompose the wastes and release the nutrients into the water.

Loons and kingfishers pluck fish from the open water. But unlike a pond, sunlight does not reach the bottom at the center of a lake. Without sunlight, plants cannot live in the deep water. As a result, fewer other organisms live in the chilly, dark depths of the lake. A few worms and mollusks do live on the bottom. They feed on food particles that drift down from the surface. The deep waters of lakes are also the home of large, bony fish such as pike and sturgeon. These fish eat the tiny bottom dwellers. They also swim to the surface to feed on fish and even small birds.

☑ *Checkpoint* *List four possible ways a lake might form.*

Changes in a Lake

Particularly in cool, northern areas of North America, many lakes undergo changes with the seasons. In the summer, the sun warms the upper layer of water in the lake. The warm water floats on top of the cooler, denser lower layer. But in the fall, the top layer cools off, too. As the water cools, it becomes denser and sinks. This causes the lake waters to mix together. **As the water mixes, minerals, plant matter, and other nutrients rise from the lake bottom to the surface. Called lake turnover, this seasonal change refreshes the supply of nutrients throughout the lake.**

A second type of change that occurs in a lake happens over a long period of time. The organisms in a lake constantly release waste products into the water. The wastes and the remains of dead organisms contain nutrients such as nitrates and phosphates. Algae feed on these nutrients. Over many years, the nutrients build up in the lake in a process called **eutrophication** (you troh fih KAY shuhn). As eutrophication causes more algae to grow, a thick, green scum forms on the

Figure 8 This island floating on Lake Titicaca is woven from totora reeds.

Social Studies CONNECTION

Imagine living on a floating island in the middle of a deep, cold lake. The island is a mat made of thick reeds you have woven tightly together. During a storm, you must anchor your island or it could be swept away. If you were a member of a group of Native Americans who live on Lake Titicaca in South America, such an island might be your home.

Lake Titicaca lies high in the Andes Mountains. Around the edges of the lake grows a hollow reed called totora. The people weave totora reeds together to form "islands" that are strong enough to hold homes and livestock. They also make ropes, boats, tea, and even medicine from the totora reeds.

In Your Journal

How would living on a totora reed island on Lake Titicaca affect your daily routine? Write a journal entry describing what a typical day might be like if you lived on a floating island.

Social Studies CONNECTION

Before students read about the totora reed islands, have them skim the first two paragraphs to find out where these islands are located. *(On Lake Titicaca in the Andes Mountains of South America)* Explain that Lake Titicaca is located on the border between Peru and Bolivia. Display a large map of South America, and have students find Peru (on the west coast), Bolivia (east and south of Peru), the border running north-south between the two countries, and Lake Titicaca itself. Lead students to conclude that this lake is high above sea level since it is in the Andes Mountains.

After students have read the two paragraphs describing the local people's way of life, ask: **Why do you think the local people first started living on reed islands centuries ago?** *(Accept a variety of reasons, and encourage creative thinking. Answers might include to provide protection against enemies, to take advantage of natural resources that were not available on shore, and to escape overcrowded conditions on the lake's shore or elsewhere.)*

In Your Journal Provide time for students to think about their entries before they begin to write. If they have difficulty coming up with ideas, ask: **Do you think the people living on the reed islands have cars? Electricity? How would these things affect your daily routine? learning modality: verbal**

Answers to Self-Assessment

Caption Question

Figure 7 The pond; the water lilies are evidence that the body of water is shallow.

☑ *Checkpoint*

A meander becomes an oxbow lake. Water fills depressions created by melting ice sheets, valleys created by crustal movements, or an empty volcanic crater. A volcano blocks a river. People build dams.

Program Resources

Science Explorer Series *Environmental Science*, Chapter 1, provides more information on interactions among living things.

Ongoing Assessment

Drawing Have each student draw two simple labeled diagrams, one showing a lake during the summer and the other showing lake turnover in the fall.

Changes in a Lake, continued

Using the Visuals: Figure 9

Emphasize that eutrophication is a natural process, though pollution can speed it up. Ask: **How would the numbers and types of plants and animals change during the process of eutrophication?** *(Gradually the number of animals in a lake would decrease as the numbers of first algae and eventually plants increased. The types of plants and animals would change as the lake became a marsh and then a meadow.)* **learning modality: logical/mathematical**

3 Assess

Section 2 Review Answers

1. Ponds and lakes form when water collects in hollows and low-lying areas.
2. As the warm and cool water mix, nutrients are brought from the lake bottom to the surface.
3. Students may name any three of the organisms and habitats presented in *Exploring a Pond* on pages 54–55.
4. (Any two) Supplying drinking water, irrigating fields, generating electricity, boating and fishing
5. The deeper the water is, the smaller the variety is of living things. Plants cannot live in deep water where sunlight does not reach. Without plants, fewer other organisms live in deep water.

Science at Home

Materials *wax paper, permanent marker, water*
ACTIVITY
Tips Review the differences between ponds and lakes and the term *divide* so students can explain them at home. Advise that the family member crumple the wax paper enough to make distinct hollows.

Performance Assessment

Skills Check Have students create a table that summarizes the similarities and differences between a lake and a pond.

A. The process begins as algae and other organisms add nutrients to the lake. These nutrients support more plant growth.

B. Soil, fallen leaves, and decaying matter pile up on the lake bottom. The lake becomes shallower and marshy.

C. Eventually, the plants completely fill the lake, creating a grassy meadow.

Figure 9 A lake environment gradually changes over time. *Predicting* Would you expect the water temperature in the lake to be higher in A or B?

surface of the water. Have you ever forgotten to clean a fish tank for a few weeks? You may have observed the process of eutrophication as algae began to grow on the sides of the tank.

When the algae layer becomes so thick that it begins to block out the sunlight, plants in the lake cannot carry out photosynthesis. They stop producing food and oxygen and die. As dead organisms in the lake decay, the amount of oxygen in the water decreases. The lake environment changes. Many of the fish and other animals no longer have enough oxygen to live. Material from decaying plants and animals piles up on the bottom, and the lake becomes more shallow. The sun warms the water to a higher temperature. Now many plants take root in the rich mud on the lake bottom. Eventually, the lake becomes completely filled with plants. The remaining water evaporates, and a grassy meadow takes the place of the former lake.

Section 2 Review

1. Explain how ponds and lakes form.
2. How does lake turnover renew the supply of nutrients in the water?
3. Give three examples of typical pond organisms. Describe where in a pond each is found.
4. What are two uses of reservoirs?
5. **Thinking Critically** **Relating Cause and Effect** How is the depth of the water in the middle of a lake related to the variety of living things there?

Science at Home

Ask a family member to crumple up a piece of waxed paper. Straighten out the paper to model a landscape with hills and valleys. Have the person use a permanent marker to draw lines along the highest divides of the landscape. Then have the person draw circles where lakes and ponds will form on the landscape. After placing the waxed paper in a sink to catch any overflow, tell the person to sprinkle water over the landscape to simulate rain. Point out where the water collects. Which would you classify as ponds and which as lakes?

Program Resources

◆ **Teaching Resources** 2-2 Review and Reinforce, p. 45; 2-2 Enrich, p. 46

Media and Technology

 Interactive Student Tutorial CD-ROM H-2

Answers to Self-Assessment

Caption Question
Figure 9 In B, the shallower stage

SECTION 3 Wetland Environments

DISCOVER ACTIVITY

Wet or Dry?

1. Hold a kitchen sponge under water until it is soaked. Then squeeze out the water until the sponge is just damp.

2. Place the damp sponge next to a dry sponge in a pan. The sponges represent areas of wet and dry land.

3. Pour water into two paper cups until each is half full.

4. Hold one cup in each hand so that the cups are about 10 centimeters above the pan. Pour the water onto both sponges at the same time.

Think It Over

Observing Which of the two sponges absorbs water faster? How would you relate your observations to what might happen in areas of wet and dry land?

Your canoe slips quietly through the brown-tinged waters of the marsh in South Dakota's Lacreek National Wildlife Refuge. Paddling among the thick clumps of velvety golden cattails, you scan for birds' nests. A spot of red catches your eye, and you realize you are only centimeters away from a black-and-white grebe sitting still atop a nest of dry rushes. Suddenly, a loud honking sound breaks the silence, as a huge flock of Canada geese flies by. You gasp as some of the black and brown birds land on a grassy mound nearby. Their outspread wings must be almost as long as your canoe!

The waters of this marsh serve as an important stopover for thousands of geese, swans, and other migrating birds. Birds stop to feed on grass and seeds as they fly south to their winter homes. Like other wetlands, the Lacreek marsh is a vital habitat for birds and many other living things.

GUIDE FOR READING

◆ What features of wetlands make them good habitats for living things?

◆ How do wetlands help control flooding?

Reading Tip Before you read, write a short description of what you think a wetland is. As you read, add details and examples to your description.

What Is a Wetland?

What image does the word *wetland* bring to mind? As the photographs on the next page show, not all wetlands are dark, smelly swamps oozing with mud. A **wetland** is an area of land that is covered with a shallow layer of water during some or all of the year. Wetlands form in places where

▼ *Western grebe*

Chapter 2 **H ◆ 59**

READING STRATEGIES

Reading Tip To provide a structured format for adding details and examples, have students write the description at the top of a sheet of paper and, below that list the following topics in a column, with space between the items for recording additional information as they read: *Definition of wetland, Types of wetlands, Characteristics of wetlands, Importance of wetlands,* and *Typical organisms.*

Program Resources

◆ **Teaching Resources** 2-3 Lesson Plan, p. 47; 2-3 Section Summary, p. 48

Media and Technology

 Audiotapes English-Spanish Summary 2-3

SECTION 3 Wetland Environments

Objectives

After completing the lesson, students will be able to
◆ identify features of wetlands that make them suitable habitats for living things;
◆ explain how wetlands help control flooding.

Key Term wetland

1 Engage/Explore

Activating Prior Knowledge

Write the terms *marsh, swamp,* and *bog* on the board, and ask: **What is similar about all three of these areas?** *(All are wet—but the water is not as deep as in a pond or lake.)* Then have students define each term in their own words. Encourage responses that identify differences between the three types of wet areas, but do not correct students' definitions or comment on their accuracy at this time.

DISCOVER

Skills Focus observing
Materials *2 dry kitchen sponges, water, pan, 2 paper cups*
Time 10–15 minutes
Tips Make sure sponges are completely dry when students begin.
Expected Outcome The damp sponge will absorb water immediately, whereas water will run off the dry sponge at first.
Think It Over The damp sponge absorbs water faster. The dry sponge models dry land. The damp sponge models the behavior of wetlands: they soak up excess water and help prevent flooding.

2 Facilitate

What Is a Wetland?

Using the Visuals: Figure 10

After students examine the photographs and read the caption and the text describing the three types of wetlands, have students review their earlier definitions (Activating Prior Knowledge on previous page). Suggest that they correct their definitions, if necessary, to reflect the differences shown and discussed here. **learning modality: verbal**

Building Inquiry Skills: Measuring

Materials *pH paper, tap water, vinegar, pond water, bog water, plastic cups*

Time 10 minutes

ACTIVITY

Point out the text statement that the water in bogs tends to be acidic. Give each group of students four strips of pH paper and four water samples: plain tap water, tap water to which you have added a small amount of vinegar, pond water (or water from a classroom fresh-water aquarium), and water taken from a bog (or aquarium water to which you have added peat moss). Then have students test each water sample and compare the pH strips. *(The strips dipped in the vinegar solution and the bog/peat water will indicate acid. The other two strips may turn slightly, but not as dramatically as the first two.)* Be sure students wash their hands after the activity. **learning modality: kinesthetic**

Including All Students

Provide students with maps of your area or of other areas with low-lying, swampy places. Direct students to the key on each map, and ask: **What is the symbol for a swamp or wetland?** *(Short wavy lines and grassy clumps drawn in blue)* Direct students to locate the wetlands on each map and circle them with a colored marker. Encourage students to make inferences about the watersheds in which the wetlands are found. **learning modality: visual**

Figure 10 Freshwater wetlands come in many forms. **A.** In Montana, colorful flowers dot a bed of velvety moss in an alpine bog. **B.** Water flows slowly through a marsh in Oregon's Willamette Valley. **C.** Curtains of Spanish moss hang from cypress trees in a Louisiana swamp. *Comparing and Contrasting How are these three environments similar? How are they different?*

water is trapped in low areas or where groundwater seeps onto the surface of the land. They can range in size from a water-filled roadside ditch to an area covering thousands of square kilometers. Some wetlands fill up during spring rains and dry up over the summer. Others, like the Lacreek marsh, are covered with water year-round.

Marshes, swamps, and bogs are three common types of freshwater wetlands. Marshes generally are grassy areas covered by a shallow layer or stream of water. They contain cattails, rushes, tule, and other tall grass-like plants. Swamps look more like flooded forests, with trees and shrubs growing in the water. In the United States, many swamps are located in the South, where trees grow quickly in the warm, humid climate. The cypress swamps of Mississippi and Louisiana are examples of wooded swamps. Bogs, which are more common in cooler northern states, often form in depressions left by melting ice sheets thousands of years ago. The water in bogs tends to be acidic. Many types of mosses thrive in the conditions found in bogs.

Wetlands along coasts usually contain both fresh and salt water. Coastal wetlands, which you will learn more about in Chapter 5, include salt marshes and mangrove forests. Salt marshes are found along both coasts of the United States. They often contain tall, strong grasses growing in a rich, muddy bottom. Mangrove forests, which are found along the central and southern coasts of Florida, consist of short trees with a thick tangle

---

Background

Integrating Science In addition to the shallowness of the water, wetlands are scientifically defined—and can be identified in nature—by the specific types of water-tolerant plants that grow there and by their characteristic soil.

The soil in a wetland is waterlogged, at least for part of the year, and thus contains very little oxygen. Because these conditions limit decomposition, wetland soil is generally rich in organic materials. In many swamps and bogs, this accumulated and partially decomposed plant matter forms layers of peat.

One fascinating group of plants commonly found in swamps and bogs is carnivorous plants. These plants have adapted to wetland soil, which lacks nitrogen, by having special organs that capture and digest insects to supply nitrogen.

of roots. The tough roots anchor the mangroves against tropical winds and storms.

☑ *Checkpoint* *Name three types of freshwater wetlands.*

Wetland Habitats

If you've ever enjoyed tart cranberry sauce or crunchy wild rice, you've eaten plants that grow in wetlands. The layer of water covering a wetland can range from several centimeters to a few meters deep. Dead leaves and other plant and animal material serve as natural fertilizer, adding nitrogen, phosphates, and other nutrients to the water and soil. Because of their sheltered waters and rich supply of nutrients, wetlands provide habitats for many living things.

Many year-round residents of wetlands are similar to those in other freshwater habitats. As in a pond, frogs, salamanders, turtles, raccoons, muskrats, and many types of insects find food and shelter among the wetland plants. Birds nest in and around the wetlands, feeding on the plants and insects there.

Wetlands also have many temporary residents. Many ducks, geese, and other waterfowl travel from Alaska and Canada to their winter homes in the South along a "flyway." For example, birds traveling along the Central Flyway through Montana, Minnesota, the Dakotas, Nebraska, and Iowa depend on the millions of small, shallow marshes called prairie potholes along their route. Like the geese at Lacreek Refuge, birds stop there to rest, feed, and mate. In the spring, thousands of birds build their nests in the prairie pothole region.

A Natural Filter

This activity demonstrates **ACTIVITY** one important role wetlands play in the environment.

1. Cover your work surface with newspaper. In one end of a loaf pan, build a sloping hill of damp soil.

2. Add water to the other end of the pan to form a lake.

3. Use a watering can to sprinkle rain onto the hill. Observe what happens to the hill and the lake.

4. Empty the water out of the pan and rebuild the hill.

5. Now push a sponge into the soil across the bottom of the hill to model a wetland.

6. Repeat Steps 2 through 4. Follow your teacher's instructions for cleaning up.

Observing What happened to the soil with and without the wetland? How did the lake look in each case?

Answers to Self-Assessment

Caption Question

Figure 10 The land in all three is covered with shallow water. Swamps are wooded, marshes are grassy, and bogs are mossy. Bogs also have acidic water.

☑ *Checkpoint*

Marshes, swamps, and bogs

TRY THIS

Skills Focus observing **ACTIVITY**
Materials *newspaper, loaf pan, damp soil, water, watering can, sponge*
Time 20 minutes
Tips Students should start over with new soil in Step 4. Provide a container for students to place wet soil in.
Expected Outcome Water will wash soil down the hill in both trials. In the first trial, the soil will wash into the lake, making it very muddy. In the second trial, the sponge will absorb some water and trap much of the eroded soil, and the lake should stay clean.
Extend Suggest that students change the slope of the hill or the width of the wetland to see how these factors affect the amount of soil erosion into the lake.
learning modality: kinesthetic

Wetland Habitats

Real-Life Learning

Give students an opportunity to examine **ACTIVITY** samples of fresh cranberries, wild rice, blueberries, peat moss, and other products harvested from wetlands. If you wish to allow students to sample any of the foods, prepare them in a nonscience classroom. Wash fruit well, and check for allergies before allowing students to taste any foods. Encourage students to find out if any of these products are commercially harvested in their area and report back to the rest of the class. **learning modality: kinesthetic**

Ongoing Assessment

Making Diagrams Have each student draw a Venn diagram to show the similarities and differences between the three types of freshwater wetlands described in this section.

 Students can save their diagrams in their portfolios.

61 ◆ H

The Importance of Wetlands

Including All Students

Let students work in small groups to create public service radio announcements, television spots, newspaper or transit ads, or educational skits designed to increase public awareness of the importance of wetlands—either wetlands in general or a specific wetland in their own community or region. Give each group an opportunity to present its product to the rest of the class. **cooperative learning**

Demonstration

Materials *clean jar with lid, soil, water, cotton batting, beaker*
Time 10 minutes

Point out the text statement that plant roots trap silt and mud in wetlands. Demonstrate this by preparing a very muddy mixture of soil and water in a screw-top jar. Place a layer of cotton batting over the top of a large beaker or other clear container. Shake the jar so the soil mixes well with the water, and ask: **How would you describe this water?** *(Very muddy, cloudy)* Wearing goggles, slowly pour the muddy water on the batting. Ask: **What does the water that collected in the bottom of the container look like?** *(A little muddy, but much clearer than the original mixture)* **What does the cotton represent in this model?** *(The network of plant roots in a wetland.)*
learning modality: visual

The Importance of Wetlands

Imagine coming home from a long trip, only to find that your house is gone and in its place is a parking lot! That happened to thousands of migrating birds before people began to understand the importance of wetlands. Farmers and builders once considered the soggy soil of wetlands to be "wasteland." This land could not be used unless it was drained and filled in. Thousands of square kilometers of wetlands were developed for farmland or for building homes and businesses. Beginning in the 1970s, however, the government enacted laws to protect wetland habitats.

Wetlands serve important functions for people as well as for wildlife. For example, wetlands provide natural water filtration. As water moves slowly through a wetland, waste materials settle out. The thick network of plant roots traps silt and mud. **Wetlands also help control floods by absorbing extra runoff from heavy rains.** They act like giant sponges, storing water and gradually releasing it as it drains or evaporates. When wetlands are drained or paved over, the water cannot be absorbed. Instead, it runs off the land quickly and can cause floods.

Figure 11 Many unusual species live in the freshwater wetland habitats of the Everglades.

Roseate spoonbills

Great egret

Snowy egret

Little blue heron

Sawgrass

Anhinga

Florida panther

Background

Facts and Figures Since the mid-1980s, the rate of wetland loss in the United States has slowed to less than an estimated 36,000 hectares a year. This is less than a quarter of the rate of loss only a few decades earlier. Wetlands may be developed only if an equal area of wetlands is restored. In addition, there are now many initiatives aimed at increasing the number and quality of wetlands. Many programs offer farmers financial incentives to restore wetlands on their property.

The Everglades: A Unique Environment

Walking down a path in Florida's Everglades National Park, you would feel the ground squish under your feet. Water is the key to the Everglades, a unique region of wetlands. A shallow layer of water moves slowly over the gently sloping land from Lake Okeechobee south to Florida Bay. Tall, sharp-edged blades of sawgrass grow in the water. The thick growth of sawgrass gave this region its Native American name, *Pa-hay-okee*, which means "river of grass." Low islands called hammocks are scattered throughout the sawgrass marsh. Trees like gumbo limbos and palms grow on the hammocks.

Everglades Wildlife As in other wetlands, water means life for many Everglades creatures. Fish and snakes gobble up tiny organisms in the warm, muddy water. Wading birds in a rainbow of colors—pink flamingoes, white egrets, and purple gallinules—stand on skinny legs in the water. A raccoon digs for alligator eggs, unaware of the alligator lying low in the sawgrass nearby.

The Everglades provide habitats for many rare or endangered species. The endangered Florida panther lives deep in the wilderness portions of the Everglades. Many species of birds, such as the wood

Figure 12 Habitats found in the Everglades include sawgrass marshes, cypress swamps, and mangrove forests. *Interpreting Maps* In which area of the park would you expect to find mangrove trees?

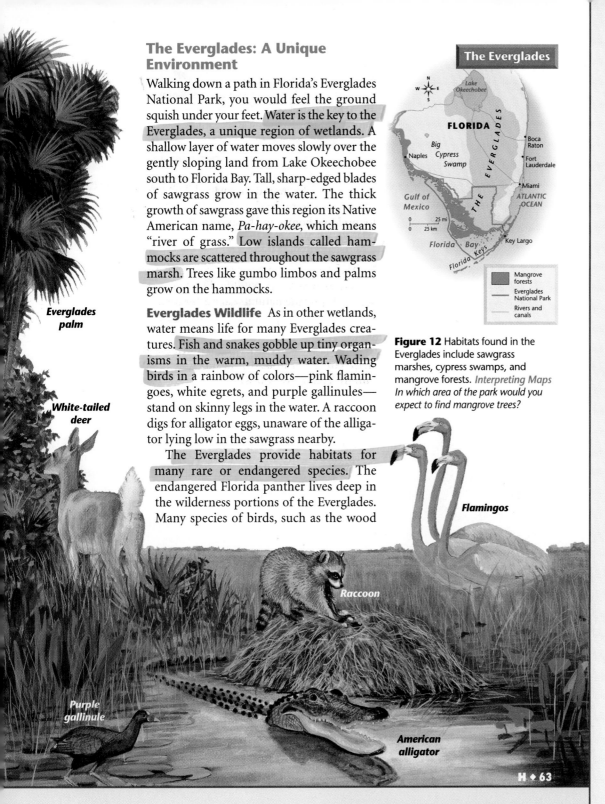

Everglades palm

White-tailed deer

Purple gallinule

Raccoon

Flamingos

American alligator

H ◆ 63

Answers to Self-Assessment

Caption Question

Figure 12 Along the southern and western coast; mangroves grow in salt water.

The Everglades: A Unique Environment

Using the Visuals: Figure 11

Ask: **What particular *type* of wetland is shown on these pages? How do you know?** (*A marsh; it is covered mostly with grass.*) **Why do you think the Everglades provides a habitat for such a variety of plants and animals?** (*There is a rich supply of nutrients to support the growth of many different plants, which in turn supply food and shelter to many different animals.*) Encourage interested students to find out more about Everglades wildlife and report to the class. **learning modality: visual**

Inquiry Challenge

ACTIVITY

After students have read about the balance of nutrients in wetlands, challenge small groups to design an experiment to answer this question: **What effect do excess fertilizers have on the growth of algae and/or water plants?** Help students recall the major steps to be completed: develop a hypothesis, describe the experiment design, control variables, record and interpret data, and draw a conclusion. Monitor the groups' experimental designs for safety and logic. Then encourage groups to conduct their experiments and report their results and conclusions to the class. **learning modality: logical/mathematical** Students can save their experiment descriptions, data, sketches, and conclusions in their portfolios.

Portfolio

Ongoing Assessment

Writing Have students write a paragraph defining and describing freshwater wetlands.

3 Assess

Section 3 Review Answers

1. Wetlands provide food, shelter, and nesting sites for year-round inhabitants and temporary resting, feeding, and mating sites for migrating birds.

2. By absorbing extra runoff from heavy rains; by acting like giant sponges, storing water, and gradually releasing it

3. The Everglades consists of a shallow layer of water that moves slowly over an enormous area of gently sloping land. Many rare and endangered species make their homes in its many habitats.

4. Answers might include the number of farmers affected and their projected losses, possible commercial uses of the restored Everglades (such as wildlife tours) and their projected revenues, and possible replacements for current agricultural practices or crops.

Check Your Progress

CHAPTER PROJECT 2

As you review students' sketches, check to see whether bodies of standing water are located in relatively level areas. Also have students describe the materials they plan to use to represent wetlands, to make sure the materials will show the specific, unique properties of wetlands. Encourage students to consider these issues carefully before they build their models.

Performance Assessment

Oral Presentation Have students give an imaginary tour of a wetland, describing its characteristics, plants and animals, and importance.

Figure 13 A manatee floats in the warm waters of Florida Bay. This species is threatened by the increased use of coastal waters around the Everglades.

stork and the roseate spoonbill (named for the unusual shape of its beak), depend on the Everglades as a nesting area. The awkward-looking manatee, or sea cow, lives in the mangrove forests along the coast, grazing on water hyacinths. Because manatees swim so slowly, they are easily injured by the propellers of powerboats. They have become an endangered species as a result of increased boating in Florida Bay.

Threats to the Everglades The Everglades are a fragile environment. Nearby farming has introduced new chemicals into the slow-moving water of the marsh, upsetting the balance of nutrients. Outside the protected limits of the national park, developers have filled in areas of wetland to build new homes and roads. New organisms brought into the area accidentally or for pest control compete with other organisms for space and food.

Water that once flowed into the Everglades from Lake Okeechobee has been diverted for farming. New canals and levees built to provide drinking water for nearby communities and to control flooding have changed the flow of water into and out of the Everglades. Some areas are drying up, while others are flooded.

Preserving the Everglades Scientists and government officials have been trying for many years to develop a plan to preserve the Everglades and save its endangered wildlife. One plan involves building an elaborate system of pipes and canals to refill some drained areas with fresh water. The National Park Service, the State of Florida, and the U.S. Army Corps of Engineers are working together to manage the supply of water to areas around and within the Everglades.

Section 3 Review

1. How are wetlands important to wildlife?
2. Explain how wetlands help control floods.
3. How are the Everglades unusual?
4. **Thinking Critically Making Judgments** Some of the plans to restore the Everglades will require millions of dollars and will negatively affect local farmers. What information would you want to have to help decide what plan of action to take to save the Everglades?

Check Your Progress

CHAPTER PROJECT 2

At this point, add the body of standing water to your watershed sketch. If your model will include any wetland areas, what materials will you use to model them? (*Hint:* Be sure to consider how water will enter and leave the body of water.)

Program Resources

◆ **Teaching Resources** 2-3 Review and Reinforce, p. 49; 2-3 Enrich, p. 50

Media and Technology

 Interactive Student Tutorial CD-ROM H-2

 Exploring Life Science Videodisc Unit 3, Side 1, "pH in Aquaria"

Chapter 7

SECTION 4 Glaciers and Icebergs

DISCOVER · ACTIVITY · · · ·

How Can Ice Change the Land?

1. Your teacher will give you two ice cubes, one of which has some sand and gravel frozen into its bottom side.
2. Rub each ice cube slowly along a piece of cardboard, pressing down slightly.
3. Observe the piece of cardboard. Wash your hands when you are finished with this activity.

Think It Over
Inferring How might a large, moving block of ice and rocks affect the surface of the land?

Standing on a mountaintop more than 4,800 meters above sea level, sparkling ice and snow surround you in every direction. The temperature is −29°C, and the wind whistles around your ears. Where is this chilly spot? It's Vinson Massif, the highest point on the continent of Antarctica.

Recall that more than two thirds of the fresh water on Earth exists in the form of ice. About 85 percent of that ice is part of the massive ice sheet that covers Antarctica. This ice sheet is larger than the United States and Europe put together! The rest of the ice on Earth is found in other ice sheets and in icebergs.

Glaciers

The ice sheet that covers Antarctica is one form of a glacier. A **glacier** (GLAY shur) is a huge mass of ice and snow that moves slowly over the land.

Glaciers form in cold places where more snow falls each year than melts. Layers of snow pile on top of more layers of snow. **Over time, the weight of the layers presses the particles of snow so tightly together that they form a solid block of ice.** If you have ever squeezed a handful of fluffy snow until it became an icy ball, you have modeled the way a glacier forms.

Ice sheets that spread over a large area of land are called continental glaciers. Today, continental glaciers are

GUIDE FOR READING

◆ How does a glacier form?
◆ Why are icebergs dangerous to ships?

Reading Tip As you read, make a list of main ideas and supporting details about glaciers and icebergs.

▲ *Gentoo penguins in Antarctica*

Chapter 2 **H ◆ 65**

READING STRATEGIES

Reading Tip Review what a "main idea" and a "supporting detail" are, using an example drawn from a previous section. Review students' lists. If any students had difficulty differentiating between main ideas and supporting details, meet with them in small groups to discuss and agree on an appropriate way to organize the list.

Program Resources

◆ **Teaching Resources** 2-4 Lesson Plan, p. 51; 2-4 Section Summary, p. 52

Media and Technology

 Audiotapes English-Spanish Summary 2-4

Objectives

After completing the lesson, students will be able to
◆ describe how glaciers form;
◆ explain why icebergs are dangerous to ships.

Key Term glacier

1 Engage/Explore

Activating Prior Knowledge

Discuss the motion picture *Titanic*, focusing on the scenes showing the ship's collision with the iceberg. Ask: **How could ice tear the thick steel of a ship's hull? Why couldn't the ship push the iceberg aside?** (*The iceberg was much larger and heavier than the ship and had jagged edges.*) **How do you think icebergs form?** (*Some students might know that icebergs form when large chunks of a glacier along a coast break off and fall into the ocean.*)

· · · · · · · · DISCOVER · · · · · · · ·

Skills Focus inferring
Materials *2 ice cubes, 1 with sand and gravel frozen into it; cardboard*
Time 10 minutes
Tips To prepare the ice cubes that represent a glacier, sprinkle some sand and gravel in the bottom of ice cube trays, then fill the trays with water and freeze.
Expected Outcome The cube that contains sand and gravel will leave scratches on the cardboard, whereas the plain cube will not.
Think It Over A large, moving block of ice and rocks could scrape gouges in the soil and rock below it, and in this way gradually change the surface of the land.

2 Facilitate

Glaciers

Demonstration

Collect a large bag of snow (or use shaved ice). **ACTIVITY** Put a layer of snow 5 cm deep in the bottom of a clear plastic container, such as a storage box, and choose one or two volunteers to push down on the snow with their hands until it is compressed as much as possible. Invite another volunteer to measure the new depth of the layer. Repeat with additional layers. Then ask: **How thick are the lower layers compared with the upper layers?** *(The lower layers are thinner.)* **What other differences do you see?** *(The particles in the lower layers are more densely packed together than the particles in the upper layers.)* **learning modality: visual**

Addressing Naive Conceptions

When students read the text statement that continental glaciers are found only in Antarctica and Greenland, some may wonder why the ice mass at the North Pole is not included. First, remind students that a continental glacier covers a large area of land. Then display a globe and direct students' attention to the North Pole region. Ask: **What land do you see at the North Pole?** *(none)* **So why can't there be a continental glacier at the North Pole?** *(The ice there is not covering land.)* Point out that the ice covering the North Pole is usually referred to as a polar ice cap or sea ice. **learning modality: visual**

Icebergs

Including All Students

To reinforce students' understanding of the danger of icebergs to ships, challenge them to write a news report summarizing the sinking of the *Titanic*, focusing on how this "unsinkable" ship was unable to survive a collision with an iceberg. **learning modality: verbal**

Figure 14 The massive Beloit Glacier towers above Prince William Sound in Alaska. *Classifying Which type of glacier is the Beloit Glacier? Explain your answer.*

found only in Antarctica and Greenland. The Antarctic glacier covers high mountain ranges and even active volcanoes. In some spots it is 3,000 meters thick. That's higher than six Empire State Buildings stacked on top of each other.

Most present-day glaciers are valley glaciers. These glaciers form in the mountains. They look like thick rivers of ice sliding down into the valley. As a valley glacier descends into warmer regions, it gradually melts. Valley glaciers are found mainly in high, cold mountain ranges such as the Alps in Europe, the Rockies in the United States, and the Himalayas in Asia.

Like moving water, moving ice can cause erosion. As a glacier forms, rocks, gravel, and other debris are frozen into the ice. Like a giant piece of sandpaper, the glacier scrapes against the ground as it moves. Over time, glaciers grind away rock and change the surface of the land.

☑ *Checkpoint* *How does a glacier change the shape of the land?*

Icebergs

It was a dark night in the spring of 1912. The gleaming new ocean liner *Titanic* sailed through the North Atlantic on its first voyage, from Southampton, England, to New York City. Suddenly a huge white wall loomed out of the darkness in front of the ship! It was an iceberg, the terror of ships at sea. Underwater, the jagged ice tore a series of cuts in the *Titanic*'s side. As the ship sank to the bottom of the ocean, nearly 1,500 people died.

Icebergs like the one that sank the *Titanic* form when a glacier reaches the seacoast. With a loud roar, large chunks

Figure 15 The *Titanic* sank on its first voyage when it hit an iceberg in the North Atlantic Ocean.

Background

Facts and Figures The British ship *Titanic* sank on the night of April 14, 1912, after striking an iceberg off the coast of Newfoundland in the North Atlantic.

Both the sinking of the ship and the devastating death toll could possibly have been avoided. According to some investigations, the ship's speed was too great considering the iceberg warnings that were received. The ship did not have enough lifeboats for the people on board, and a nearby ship, the *Californian*, apparently failed to respond to the *Titanic*'s distress signals.

As a result of the *Titanic* disaster, shipping companies took new measures to avoid disaster, including setting up iceberg patrols and radio watches.

break off, or calve, and float away. Although icebergs are found in the salty ocean, remember that they consist of fresh water.

In the North Atlantic and Arctic oceans, about 10,000 new icebergs form every year. Many of these icebergs calve from Greenland's continental glacier. As they drift south, the icebergs break into chunks as big as houses. They begin to melt in the warmer water.

The ocean around Antarctica is filled with even larger icebergs. Flat-topped pieces calve from the edges of the glaciers along the coast. In 1995, a giant iceberg broke off Antarctica's Larsen Ice Shelf. Scientists flying over the new iceberg reported that it was about 70 kilometers long and 25 kilometers wide—more than half the size of the state of Rhode Island!

The thought of a chunk of floating ice that big is scary enough, but it's more frightening to realize that only about 10 percent of an iceberg is visible above the water. **About 90 percent of an iceberg lies below the surface. The underwater part is a hazard to ships because it is often much wider than the visible part of the iceberg.** Icebergs are also a threat to floating platforms that support rigs for drilling oil from the ocean floor.

After the *Titanic* disaster, countries involved in Atlantic shipping set up the International Ice Patrol. The Patrol, which is managed by the United States Coast Guard, uses ships, planes, and satellites to track icebergs. The Patrol's warnings have saved many people aboard ships and floating oil rigs from disasters like the *Titanic*.

Figure 16 If you could see an entire iceberg at once, how would it look? An artist created this composite photograph to reveal the hidden part of the iceberg. *Applying Concepts What percentage of the ice is underwater?*

Section 4 Review

1. Describe the process by which a glacier forms.
2. Why is it hard to determine the size of an iceberg from the deck of a ship?
3. How do icebergs form?
4. Name the two types of glaciers. Where is each type of glacier found?
5. **Thinking Critically Making Judgments** How might the fact that glaciers and icebergs consist of fresh water make them useful to people?

Science at Home

With a family member, make a model iceberg. Fill the cut-off bottom of a milk or juice carton with water and freeze. When the water has frozen, peel the carton away from the iceberg. Add salt to a large bowl of water to create an "ocean." Float the iceberg in the bowl. Help your family member use a ruler to measure how much of the iceberg's thickness is above the surface of the water and how much is below. Use these measurements to explain why icebergs can be dangerous to ships.

Chapter 2 **H ◆ 67**

Answers to Self-Assessment

Caption Question

Figure 14 A valley glacier; it formed in mountains and is flowing down into the water. Also, it is located in North America.

Figure 16 About 90%

✓ *Checkpoint*

The glacier's sides and bottom scrape against the ground and erode it.

Including All Students

Point out the word *calve* used for the breaking-off of icebergs from glaciers. Ask: **What is a calf?** *(A baby cow or steer)* **What does it mean for a cow to calve?** *(To give birth to a calf)* **Why is the word "calve" a good one to use for the process of icebergs forming?** *(The glacier "gives birth" to an iceberg when it breaks off and floats away.)* **limited English proficiency**

3 Assess

Section 4 Review Answers

1. Layers of snow pile on top of each other, and, over time, the weight presses the snow into a solid block of ice.
2. Most of an iceberg—about 90 percent—is below the water surface, where it is not visible from a ship.
3. When the end of a glacier reaches the seacoast, large chunks break off and float away as icebergs.
4. Continental glaciers: found only in Antarctica and Greenland; valley glaciers: found in high, cold mountain ranges
5. People might be able to find a way to use glaciers and icebergs as sources of fresh water for drinking, industry, agriculture, and other uses.

Science at Home

Materials *empty milk or juice carton, tap water, freezer, large bowl, salt, ruler*
ACTIVITY

Tips Tell students to use about one teaspoonful of salt for each quart of water to make the "ocean." Students and their family members can calculate the percentages of ice above and below water. These calculations will be easier if the measurements are made in metric units.

Performance Assessment

Drawing Have each student make a labeled, three-step diagram of an iceberg calving from a glacier.

67 ◆ H

Objectives

After completing the lesson, students will be able to
◆ describe springs, geysers, and how water moves through underground layers of soil and rock;
◆ explain what an aquifer is and how people obtain water from an aquifer.

Key Terms pore, permeable, impermeable, saturated zone, water table, unsaturated zone, aquifer, recharge, artesian well, spring, geyser

1 Engage/Explore

Activating Prior Knowledge

Show the class a bottle of spring water you have purchased. Ask: **What was the original source of this water?** *(Students may mention wells, springs, or other sources.)* **Where does the water in springs and wells come from?** *(Students may be unsure or may suggest an underground supply; some may know the term "aquifer." Acknowledge all responses without comment at this time.)*

········· **DISCOVER** ·········

Skills Focus observing
Materials *pebbles, clear jar, ruler, dry sand, water*
Time 10 minutes
Tips A plastic jar is preferable to avoid the danger of broken glass. Advise students to add the water slowly.
Expected Outcome The water will seep through the sand and collect at the bottom of the jar.
Think It Over The water fills the spaces between the pebbles.

DISCOVER ·· **ACTIVITY**

Where Does the Water Go?

1. Add pebbles to a jar to form a layer about 5 centimeters deep. Cover the pebbles with a layer of dry sand about 3 centimeters thick. Pour the sand in slowly to avoid moving the pebbles. These materials represent underground soil layers.

2. Sprinkle water onto the sand to simulate rainfall.

3. Looking through the side of the jar, observe the path of the water as it soaks through the layers. Wash your hands when you are finished with this activity.

Think It Over
Observing Describe what happens when the water reaches the bottom of the jar.

GUIDE FOR READING

◆ How does water move through underground layers of soil and rock?

◆ How do people obtain water from an aquifer?

Reading Tip As you read, create a flowchart that shows one possible path of water from a rainstorm to a well.

When you were younger, did you ever dig a hole in the ground hoping to find a buried treasure? Though you probably never found a trunk full of gold, you could have found a different kind of treasure without even realizing it. If you continued to dig deeper, past tangled grass roots and small stones, you would have noticed the soil begin to feel heavier and wetter. If you dug deep enough, the bottom of your hole would have started to fill up with water. You would have "struck groundwater!" In the days before pipes and public water systems, such a discovery was like finding a treasure. A usable source of fresh water enabled people to build a house or farm and settle on that land. Today, many people still rely on the water underground to meet their water needs.

Underground Layers

Where does this underground water come from? Like the water in rivers, lakes, and glaciers, it comes from precipitation. Recall what can happen to precipitation when it falls. It can evaporate right away, run off the surface, or soak into the ground. The water that soaks in trickles downward, following the pull of gravity.

If you pour water into a glass full of pebbles, the water trickles down around the pebbles until it reaches the bottom of the glass. Then the water begins to fill up the spaces between the pebbles. **In the same way, water underground trickles down between particles of soil and through cracks and spaces in layers of rock.**

68 ◆ H

READING STRATEGIES

Reading Tip Sample flowchart steps: raindrop to ground to groundwater to well.
Vocabulary Write the terms *permeable* and *impermeable* on the board, and draw a box around the root *perme* in each word. Explain that this root comes from a Latin word meaning "to pass through." Then draw a line below the suffix *-able* in each word and ask what this suffix means. ("*Capable of

being" something) Challenge students to put the two roots together to find the meaning of *permeable*. ("*Capable of being passed through*"; correct students if they say "*capable of passing through.*") Draw a line below the prefix *im-* and ask what this prefix means. ("*not*") Again, challenge students to put the roots together to find the meaning of *impermeable*. (*Not capable of being passed through*)

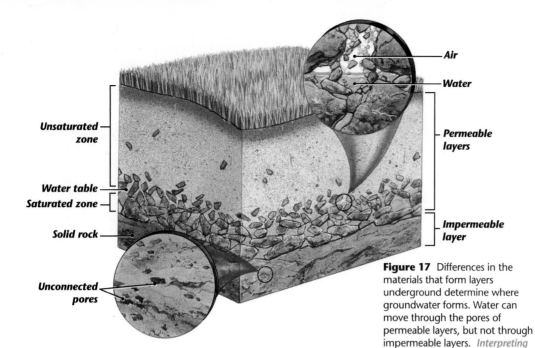

Unsaturated zone

Water table
Saturated zone

Solid rock

Unconnected pores

Air

Water

Permeable layers

Impermeable layer

Figure 17 Differences in the materials that form layers underground determine where groundwater forms. Water can move through the pores of permeable layers, but not through impermeable layers. *Interpreting Diagrams What is the difference between the saturated and unsaturated zone?*

Different types of rock and soil have different-sized spaces, or **pores,** between their particles. How easily water moves through the material depends not only on the size of the pores, but also on whether the pores are connected to each other. Materials that allow water to easily pass through, or permeate, are called **permeable.** Sand and gravel are permeable materials.

As water soaks down through permeable rock, it eventually reaches layers of material that it cannot pass through. These materials have few or no pores or cracks for the water to flow through. Materials that water cannot pass through easily are called **impermeable.** Clay and granite are impermeable materials.

Once water reaches an impermeable layer, it is trapped. It can't soak any deeper. Instead, the water begins to fill up the spaces above the impermeable rock. The area of permeable rock or soil that is totally filled, or saturated, with water is called the **saturated zone.** The top of the saturated zone is the **water table.** Knowing the depth of the water table in an area tells you how deep you must dig to reach groundwater.

Soil and rock layers above the water table contain some moisture, too. But here the pores contain air as well as water. They are not saturated with water. Therefore, the layer of rocks and soil above the water table is called the **unsaturated zone.**

☑ *Checkpoint* *Give an example of a permeable material other than sand or gravel.*

Drawing Conclusions

You have just bought some land and need to dig a well. By drilling a number of holes on your property, you learn that there is a layer of impermeable granite rock located approximately 12 meters underground. If the saturated zone is 3 meters thick, how deep should you dig your well? (*Hint:* Drawing a diagram may be helpful.)

Program Resources

◆ **Teaching Resources** 2-5 Lesson Plan, p. 55; 2-5 Section Summary, p. 56

Media and Technology

 Transparencies "Underground Zones," Transparency 6

Audiotapes English-Spanish Summary 2-5

Answers to Self-Assessment

Caption Question

Figure 17 The pores in the saturated zone are filled with water, whereas in the unsaturated zone, the pores contain air as well as water.

☑ *Checkpoint*

Other permeable materials include soil, porous rock such as sandstone, foam rubber, plastic foam, and cloth.

2 Facilitate

Underground Layers

Using the Visuals: Figure 17

Point out the two circular insets and ask: **What is different about the pores in the two pictures?** (*The pores in the top-right picture are larger and are connected to one another; the pores in the bottom-left picture are smaller and are not connected.*) **Which picture represents a permeable rock layer?** (*The top-right picture*) **In this picture, how do the pores differ above and below the water table?** (*Above, the pores contain both air and water; below, the pores contain only water.*) **learning modality: visual**

Sharpen your Skills

Drawing Conclusions

Time 10 minutes
Tips Before students attempt to solve the problem, ask: **Where is the saturated zone located, on top of the impermeable layer or below it?** (*on top of it*)

Expected Outcome The depth of the well should be at least 9 m. Some students may realize that making it exactly 9 m deep may cause it to run dry in drought conditions or if too much water is withdrawn. Accept answers ranging from somewhat more than 9 m to somewhat less than 12 m.

Extend Encourage students to make a simple three-dimensional model showing the saturated zone, the impermeable layers, and the depth of the well. **learning modality: logical/mathematical**

Ongoing Assessment

Drawing Have each student make a simple sketch of an underground water supply, without referring to Figure 17, and label its features with the terms *pores, permeable materials, impermeable materials, saturated zone, water table,* and *unsaturated zone.*

Soil Testing

Preparing for Inquiry

Key Concept Different soil materials have different permeabilities.

Skills Objectives Students will be able to
- measure how quickly water flows through sand, clay, and pebbles;
- interpret data to conclude that the sizes of a material's particles and the spaces between them determine its permeability.

Time 40 minutes

Advance Planning At least one day before students do the lab, gather sufficient materials for each group. If funnels are not available, cut the tops off plastic soda bottles, or let students do this. Have them cover the rough edge with masking tape to avoid cutting themselves.

Guiding Inquiry

Invitation After distributing the sand, clay, and pebbles, have students look at and feel them. Ask: **Which material would let water pass through it the quickest? Which do you think would hold water best?** Write their hypotheses on the board, and discuss these responses when students complete the lab.

Introducing the Procedure
- After students read the help-wanted ad, ask: **Which would be a good location for a well—in soil that lets water pass through it easily, or in soil that does not let water pass through?** *(Soil that lets water pass through easily)*
- After students read the instructions, ask: **Why should the layers of sand, clay, and pebbles be the same depth?** *(The depth is a variable that should be controlled; making the layers different depths could affect the results.)*

SOIL TESTING

In what type of soil is it best to site a well? This is a question that hydrologists, scientists who study groundwater, need to answer before new houses or other buildings can be constructed. In this lab, you will compare different soil types to learn more about their water-holding properties.

HELP WANTED

Hydrologists to conduct soil tests for new housing development. Homes will have private wells. Engineers must test soil permeability to select best locations. Please send resumé and references to

Problem

How fast does water move through sand, clay, and pebbles?

Skills Focus

observing, measuring, drawing conclusions

Materials (per group)

hand lens	3 100-mL beakers
sand, 100 mL	water, 300 mL
stopwatch	pebbles, 100 mL
3 rubber bands	

powdered potter's clay, 100 mL
3 squares of cheesecloth
3 large funnels or cut-off plastic soda bottle tops

Procedure

1. Copy the data table into your notebook.

2. Use a hand lens to observe each of the three material samples closely. Record your observations in your data table.

3. Place a piece of cheesecloth over the bottom of each funnel or bottle top and secure it with a rubber band.

4. Place the sand in one funnel, the pebbles in another, and the clay in another. Be sure that there is at least 5 cm of space above the material in each funnel.

5. Place each funnel on top of a beaker.

6. Slowly pour 100 mL of water into the funnel containing the sand. Do not let the water overflow the funnel.

7. Start the stopwatch when the water begins to flow or drip out of the bottom of the funnel.

DATA TABLE		
Material	Observations	Time for Water to Stop Dripping
Sand		
Clay		
Pebbles		

Program Resources

- **Teaching Resources** Real-World Lab blackline masters, pp. 62–63

Safety

Have students wear safety goggles. Review the safety guidelines in Appendix A.

8. Stop the stopwatch when the water stops dripping out of the funnel or after 5 minutes. Record the time to the nearest second in your data table.

9. Repeat Steps 6 through 8 with the pebbles and then with the clay. When you are finished with this activity, dispose of your materials according to your teacher's instructions. Wash your hands thoroughly with soap.

Analyze and Conclude

1. Through which material did water move the fastest? The slowest?

2. What can you conclude about the permeability of the three materials?

3. Based on your observations of each sample, suggest an explanation for the differences in their permeability.

4. Based on the results of this lab, would you expect to get more water from a well dug in sand, pebbles, or clay? Explain.

5. **Apply** Why might gardeners and landscapers need to know about the permeability of different soil types?

More to Explore

Which of the soil samples that you tested do you think the soil of the grounds at your school most resembles? Design an experiment to test your hypothesis. With your teacher's permission, carry out your experiment.

Sample Data Table

Material	Observations	Time for Water to Stop Dripping
Sand	small grains, irregular shapes, whitish to brownish	9 minutes
Pebbles	large pieces, smooth shapes, various colors	2 minutes
Clay	tiny particles, regular shapes, tannish color	greater than 15 minutes

Troubleshooting the Experiment

◆ In Step 1, suggest that students make the Observations section of their tables larger so they have more room to record.

◆ If necessary, demonstrate how to make sure the beaker is filled exactly to the 100-mL mark in Step 6. Also remind students to stop pouring the water if it comes close to overflowing the funnel.

Expected Outcome

Times will vary. Sample data might show that it takes about 9 minutes for 100 mL of water to flow through sand, 2 minutes to flow through pebbles, and 15 minutes to flow through clay.

Analyze and Conclude

1. The fastest through pebbles, the slowest through clay

2. A layer of pebbles is the most permeable, a layer of clay the least permeable, and a layer of sand somewhere between those two.

3. The sizes of the particles and of the spaces between them determine a material's permeability. Clay is least permeable because it has the smallest particles and the smallest spaces. Pebbles are the most permeable because they are the largest particles and have the largest spaces between them.

4. You would get more water from a well dug in pebbles because there are larger pores that can hold more water, and the water moves through the pebbles faster into the well as water is pumped out.

5. Some plants may survive and grow best in sandy soils that let water drain away from their roots, while other plants grow best in clay soils that hold water.

Extending the Inquiry

More to Explore Students should be able to estimate the soil's permeability by observing whether water is absorbed after a rain or pools on top. Each group could test an actual sample and compare results with the data using sand, pebbles, and clay.

Aquifers

Skills Focus making models

Materials *newspaper, loaf pan, modeling clay, moist sand, funnel, plastic straw, scissors, water*

Time 20 minutes

Tips Before students begin, slowly add a little water to the sand to moisten it. Make extra clay available for students to stop any leaks that occur. Also provide paper towels so students can remove any water that overflows the funnel.

Expected Outcome Water will flow from the funnel into the sand layer at the high end, downhill through the sand layer, and then up the straw at the low end. The layers of clay and sand represent impermeable and permeable layers under ground. The water represents rain or other precipitation. The flow of the water downhill through the sand layer represents real water movement in an aquifer. The model is like a real aquifer in that water moves through a permeable layer. It is different because water would fall as precipitation and soak through permeable material until it reaches a layer of impermeable rock.

Extend Ask students: **What do you think would happen if you cut the straw below the water level of the funnel?** Suggest that students test their predictions. *(Cutting the straw below the water level will produce a gushing artesian well.)*
learning modality: kinesthetic

Including All Students

Choose a volunteer to find the derivation of the word "aquifer" in a dictionary. *(From the Latin* aqua, *meaning "water")* Ask: **What other English words do you know that have "aqua" in them?** *(Examples include aquarium, the colors aqua and aquamarine, the astrological sign Aquarius, aquatic, and aqueduct.)* **What non-English words for** *water* **do you know that are similar to** *aqua?* *(Students may suggest the Spanish word* agua.)
limited English proficiency

An Artesian Well

In this activity you will build a model of an artesian well. Before you start, cover your desk or table with newspaper.

1. Cover the bottom of a loaf pan with clay. Pile the clay higher at one end.
2. Cover the clay with about 4 cm of moist sand.
3. Cover the sand with a thin sheet of clay. Seal the edges of the clay tightly against the sides of the pan.
4. Push a funnel into the high end so that the bottom of the funnel is in the sand.

5. Insert a short piece of plastic straw through the clay and into the sand layer at the low end. Remove the straw, discard it, and then insert a new piece of straw in the same hole.
6. Slowly pour water into the funnel. Do not let the water overflow the funnel.
7. Observe the level of water in the straw. Wash your hands after this activity.

Making a Model What real-world feature does each part of your model represent? How is your model like a real artesian well? How is it different?

Aquifers

Any underground layer of rock or sediment that holds water is called an **aquifer.** Aquifers can range in size from a small underground patch of permeable material to an area the size of several states. The huge Ogallala aquifer lies beneath the plains of the midwest, stretching from South Dakota to Texas. Millions of people obtain their drinking water from this underground storehouse. The Ogallala aquifer also provides water for crops and livestock.

Maybe you picture groundwater as a large, still pool beneath Earth's surface. In fact, the water is actually in motion, seeping through the layers of rock. How fast it moves depends largely on how steeply the aquifer slopes and how permeable the rocks are. Groundwater in some aquifers moves only a few centimeters a day. At that rate, the water moves about 10 meters a year—less than the length of a typical classroom. Groundwater may travel hundreds of kilometers and stay in an aquifer for thousands of years before coming to the surface again.

☑ *Checkpoint* *What factors affect how fast water moves in an aquifer?*

Bringing Groundwater to the Surface

Look at Figure 18 and notice how the level of the water table generally follows the shape of the underground rock layers. The depth of the water table can vary greatly even over a small area of land. Heavy rain or lots of melting snow raise the level of the water table. The level falls in dry weather.

In places where the water table meets the ground surface, groundwater seeps onto the surface. The groundwater may feed a stream or pond, or form a wetland. People can also bring groundwater to the surface.

Wells Since ancient times, people have brought groundwater to the surface for drinking and other everyday uses. **People can obtain groundwater from an aquifer by drilling a well below the water table.** Locate the well near the center of Figure 18. Because the bottom of the well is in the saturated zone, the well contains water. Notice the level of the bottom of the dry well in the diagram. Because this well does not reach below the water table, water cannot be obtained from it.

Long ago, people dug wells by hand. They lined the sides of the well with brick or stone to keep the walls from collapsing. To bring up water, they lowered and raised a bucket. Today, most wells are dug with well-drilling equipment. Pumps bring up the groundwater.

Background

Facts and Figures Taking more groundwater from an aquifer than can be naturally recharged is known as *aquifer depletion.* Wells running dry is not the only serious consequence. When water is depleted from an aquifer, the land above it may settle, a condition called subsidence. In California's San Joaquin Valley, for example, aquifer depletion has caused some land areas to sink nearly 10 meters in a 50-year period. When groundwater is depleted in coastal areas, salt water is drawn into the aquifer. This makes the groundwater salty and unfit for drinking.

Aquifer depletion is due largely to withdrawing water for irrigation. With traditional irrigation methods, more than 50 percent of the water applied to fields simply evaporates. Recent advances in irrigation technology are improving the efficiency of water use.

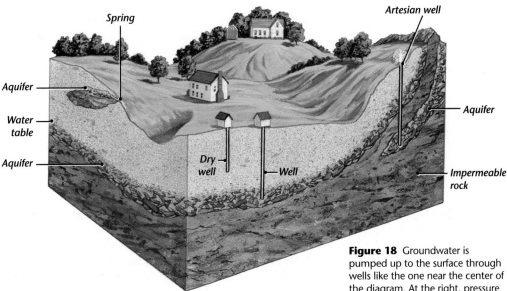

Spring

Artesian well

Aquifer

Aquifer

Water
table

Aquifer

Dry
well

Well

Impermeable
rock

Figure 18 Groundwater is pumped up to the surface through wells like the one near the center of the diagram. At the right, pressure causes water to spurt from an artesian well. Where an aquifer meets the ground surface, at the left, a spring may form.
Interpreting Diagrams Why does the dry well not contain any water?

Pumping water out of an aquifer lowers the water level near the well. If too much water is pumped out too fast, the well may run dry. It will be necessary either to dig deeper to reach the lowered water table, or to wait for rainfall to refill the aquifer. New water that enters the aquifer from the surface is called **recharge.**

Artesian Wells In some aquifers, groundwater is trapped between two layers of impermeable rock or sediment. This water is under great pressure from the weight of the water above it. If the top layer of rock is punctured, the pressure sends water spurting up through the hole. Water flows without pumping from a well dug in such an aquifer. A well in which water rises because of pressure within the aquifer is called an **artesian well** (ahr TEEZH uhn well).

Springs and Geysers

Imagine that you are walking through a strange-looking land full of bubbling mud pools and mineral-filled ponds. With a loud roar, a column of boiling hot water and white steam suddenly erupts from the ground in front of you. The towering fountain soars high into the air as the hot steam blows around you. Although you might think you've landed on another planet, these are common sights in Wyoming's Yellowstone National Park.

Springs In Yellowstone, groundwater seeps, flows, and erupts onto the surface in very dramatic ways. But in most other places, groundwater comes to the surface more quietly. Places

Bringing Groundwater to the Surface

Using the Visuals: Figure 18

Call students' attention to the two wells in the figure. Ask: **Why is the one well dry?** *(The well does not reach to the water table.)* **How could that well become a working well?** *(It could be dug deeper, or it could pump water if the water table rose.)* **Why is the water from the artesian well spurting up?** *(The water at the bottom of the aquifer is under pressure from the water at the top of the aquifer.)* **Where is water flowing gently from the rock?** *(From the spring)* **learning modality: visual**

Springs and Geysers

Demonstration

 Do the following activity immediately before or after students read about geysers on the next page. Heat some water in a teakettle on a hot plate. When the water boils and the kettle releases steam, ask the class: **What would happen if I plugged the kettle's spout?** *(The pressure of the steam would build up to the point where it would blow the plug out of the spout. CAUTION: Do not try this.)* Emphasize that this is what happens in a geyser eruption. Ask: **What supplied the heat to boil the water in the kettle?** *(The hot plate, electricity, electrical energy)* **What do you think heats water deep underground?** *(Students might say magma, molten rock, lava, or hot rocks.)* **learning modality: logical/mathematical**

Program Resources

◆ **Integrated Science Laboratory Manual** H-2, "Testing Water Samples"

Media and Technology

Transparencies "Wells and Springs," Transparency 7

 Interactive Student Tutorial CD-ROM H-2

Answers to Self-Assessment

✓ *Checkpoint*
How fast the water moves in an aquifer depends on how steeply the aquifer slopes and how permeable the rocks are.

Caption Question

Figure 18 The dry well does not reach below the water table.

Ongoing Assessment

Writing or Drawing Have each student write a paragraph or draw and label a sketch to explain why water flows from an artesian well without needing to be pumped.

3 Assess

Section 5 Review Answers

1. The pull of gravity causes water to trickle down between particles of soil and through cracks and spaces in rock until it reaches impermeable materials.

2. Without knowing the depth of the aquifer, the drillers don't know how deep they must drill the well to be below the water table.

3. Students' drawings should show the layers in the following sequence from top to bottom: permeable layer; within the permeable layer—unsaturated zone, water table, saturated zone; impermeable layer.

4. The pressure of boiling water deep underground

5. The water table must fall below the level of the spring in summer and rise above it in winter. Factors such as precipitation and human water use could also affect the depth of the water table.

Check Your Progress

CHAPTER PROJECT 2

Make sure you give students' sketches a final approval. Consult with students as they build their models to see if they are encountering any problems with the materials and to provide positive feedback, encouragement, and assistance as needed. Establish a plan for students to present their models at the conclusion of the chapter.

Performance Assessment

Drawing Have each student draw a simple sketch of the artesian well model he or she made in Try This, page 72, and add labels and captions explaining how a real artesian well works.

Figure 19 A crowd of tourists is amazed by Yellowstone's most famous geyser, Old Faithful. The geyser's regular eruptions can reach as high as an eight-story building.

where groundwater bubbles or flows out of cracks in the rock are called **springs.** Most springs contain water at normal temperatures, but some springs, like those in Yellowstone, contain water that is warmed by the hot rocks deep below the surface. The heated water bubbles to the surface in hot springs. Not surprisingly, two places in the United States where such springs occur are Warm Springs, Georgia, and Hot Springs, Arkansas!

Geysers The fountain in Yellowstone that shot into the air is a geyser. A **geyser** (GY zur) is a type of hot spring from which the water bursts periodically into the air. The word *geyser* comes from an Icelandic word, *geysir,* which means "gusher."

A geyser forms when very hot water that has been circulating deep underground begins to rise through narrow passages in the rock. Heated gases and bubbles of steam are forced up these passages by the pressure of the hot water boiling below. Just as pressure builds up in a partly blocked water pipe, the pressure within these narrow openings in the rock increases. Finally the gases, steam, and hot water erupt high into the air. Outside the United States, many dramatic geysers are found in Iceland, New Zealand, Kenya, and Indonesia.

Section 5 Review

1. Describe what happens to water that soaks into the ground.
2. Why is it important to know the depth of an aquifer before drilling a well?
3. Draw a cross section of the ground that includes the following labeled features: permeable layer, saturated zone, unsaturated zone, impermeable layer, and water table.
4. What force causes a geyser to erupt?
5. **Thinking Critically** **Inferring** During the winter, a small spring flows on your property. Every summer, the spring dries up. What might be the reason for the change?

Check Your Progress

CHAPTER PROJECT 2

Now you are ready to build your model watershed. Be sure to follow the plan you have drawn. When your model is finished, do a practice run of your demonstration. (*Hint:* Some materials need to be worked with quickly before they harden. Others need time to dry before you can pour water over them. Be sure to leave yourself enough time to build your model and let it dry before your presentation.)

Program Resources

◆ **Teaching Resources** 2-5 Review and Reinforce, p. 57; 2-5 Enrich, p. 58

Science Explorer Series *Inside Earth,* Chapter 1, can provide information to help students better understand geysers.

SECTION 1 — Streams and Rivers

Key Ideas
◆ Runoff from precipitation forms streams, which flow together to form rivers. The area drained by a river system is its watershed.
◆ Rivers wear away landforms through erosion and build new ones through deposition.
◆ As a river flows from its headwaters to its mouth, the slope, speed, and volume change.
◆ Floods occur when a river overflows its channel and spreads out over its floodplain.

Key Terms
runoff	tributary	watershed
divide	erosion	deposition
sediment	headwaters	flood plain
meander	oxbow lake	mouth
delta	levee	

SECTION 2 — Ponds and Lakes

Key Ideas
◆ Ponds and lakes are bodies of standing water that form when fresh water collects in depressions in the land.
◆ Because sunlight reaches the bottom of a pond, plants can grow throughout the pond.
◆ Lake turnover is a seasonal mixing that refreshes the nutrient supply in the lake.

Key Terms
reservoir   eutrophication

SECTION 3 — Wetland Environments
INTEGRATING LIFE SCIENCE

Key Ideas
◆ Wetlands are covered with a shallow layer of water for all or part of the year.
◆ Wetlands provide nesting and feeding areas for birds and other wildlife. Wetlands also filter water and help control floods.

Key Term
wetland

SECTION 4 — Glaciers and Icebergs

Key Ideas
◆ Glaciers form when layers of snow pile up. The pressure from the mass of the layers packs the snow into ice.
◆ Icebergs form when the edges of glaciers reach the ocean and break off. About 90 percent of an iceberg is located underwater.

Key Term
glacier

SECTION 5 — Water Underground

Key Ideas
◆ As water soaks into the ground, it moves through the pores between particles of soil and rock. Water moves easily through permeable materials, but does not move easily through impermeable materials.
◆ People dig wells to obtain groundwater from aquifers. To supply water, a well must reach below the level of the water table.
◆ Water pressure brings groundwater to the surface naturally in artesian wells, springs, and geysers.

Key Terms
6 pore	5 permeable	4 impermeable
8 saturated zone	unsaturated zone	
11 water table	1 aquifer	7 recharge
2 artesian well	9 spring	3 geyser

USING THE INTERNET
www.science-explorer.phschool.com

Program Resources
◆ **Teaching Resources** Chapter 2 Project Scoring Rubric, p. 38; Chapter 2 Performance Assessment Teacher Notes, pp. 167–168; Chapter 2 Performance Assessment Student Worksheet, p. 169; Chapter 2 Test, pp. 170–173

Media and Technology
Interactive Student Tutorial CD-ROM H-2

Computer Test Bank Test H-2

Reviewing Content: Multiple Choice

1. b **2.** b **3.** a **4.** d **5.** c

Reviewing Content: True or False

6. true **7.** levees **8.** valley **9.** true
10. true

Checking Concepts

11. Any two: The nature of the ground surface, the rate of rainfall, and the slope of the land affect the amount of runoff.

12. An obstacle in a river causes the water to flow to one side, creating a bend in the river. The water erodes the outer edge of the curve, where it flows faster, and deposits sediments along the inner edge, where it flows slower. This process forms looping curves.

13. In the fall, the top layer of water in a lake cools off, becoming denser, and sinks. This causes the lake's layers to mix together. As they mix, minerals, plant matter, and other nutrients are brought from the lake bottom to the surface, refreshing the supply of nutrients throughout the lake.

14. Many migratory waterfowl stop in wetlands to rest, feed, mate, and build nests.

15. Any one: *Artesian well:* Groundwater is trapped between two layers of impermeable rock or sediment. This water is under great pressure from the weight of the water above it. If the top layer of rock is punctured, the pressure sends water spurting up through the hole. *Spring:* Groundwater bubbles or flows out of cracks in the rock. *Geyser:* Very hot water that has been circulating deep underground begins to rise through narrow passages in the rock. Heated gases and bubbles of steam are forced up these passages by the pressure of the hot water boiling below. Eventually enough pressure builds up to blow the gases, steam, and hot water high into the air.

16. Students' descriptions of sports and other activities will vary. The following wildlife is cited in the text for each location. *River:* fish (trout), beavers, turtles, tall plants (pickerelweed); *pond:* algae, grasses, trees (willows, maples), birds (redwing blackbird), frogs and tadpoles,

---

Reviewing Content

 For more review of key concepts, see the Interactive Student Tutorial CD-ROM.

Multiple Choice
Choose the letter of the best answer.

1. Rain that falls on a steep, paved street during a thunderstorm will most likely become
  a. groundwater. **b.** runoff.
  c. a spring. **d.** a reservoir.

2. Which of the following features is most typical of the headwaters of a river?
  a. broad flat valley
  b. waterfalls and rapids
  c. winding meanders
  d. muddy, slow-moving water

3. Lakes that store water for human use are called
  a. reservoirs. **b.** aquifers.
  c. oxbow lakes. **d.** wetlands.

4. More than two thirds of Earth's fresh water is found in
  a. rivers and streams.
  b. ponds and lakes.
  c. wetlands.
  d. glaciers and icebergs.

5. Groundwater is stored in
  a. wetlands.
  b. water tables.
  c. aquifers.
  d. impermeable layers.

True or False
If the statement is true, write true. If it is false, change the underlined word or words to make the statement true.

6. In the process of <u>erosion,</u> moving water breaks off rocks and soil and carries them downstream.

7. <u>Dams</u> are ridges that build up naturally alongside rivers that frequently flood.

8. <u>Continental</u> glaciers move like rivers of ice down mountain slopes.

9. Water moves easily through <u>permeable</u> rock layers.

10. To supply water, the bottom of a well must be located in the <u>saturated zone</u>.

Checking Concepts

11. What are two factors that affect amount of runoff?

12. Explain how a meander forms in a river.

13. Describe how temperature changes in the fall and spring can help distribute nutrients throughout a lake.

14. Explain how wetlands are important to migrating birds.

15. Describe one way that groundwater can come to the surface naturally.

16. Writing to Learn Imagine that you are on summer vacation in one of three different places: a river valley, a pond, or a lake. Write a letter to a friend describing the kinds of wildlife you see and the sports and other activities you are enjoying at the spot you chose.

Thinking Visually

17. Concept Map Copy the concept map about wetlands onto a sheet of paper. Complete it and add a title. (For more on concept maps, see the Skills Handbook).

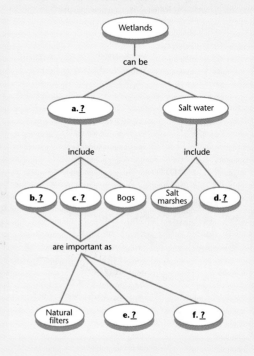

---

snails, worms, crayfish, water lilies, spiders, sponges, insects (dragonflies), fish (sunfish, perch, pickerel, minnows), duckweed; *lake:* insects (water beetles), birds (loons, kingfishers), worms, mollusks, large bony fish (pike, sturgeon).

Thinking Visually

17. a. Fresh water; **b.** and **c.** Marshes, Swamps; **d.** Mangrove forests; **e.** and **f.** Wildlife habitats, Flood control; Sample title: Wetlands

Applying Skills

18. Accept Point D or Point E: Point D, because the distance down to the saturated zone is less, although Point E has a much larger water supply to draw from.

19. Point C; a spring

20. Students' drawings should show a higher water table and thicker saturated zone. They might show a pond at point B.

Applying Skills

Use the diagram of underground layers to answer Questions 18–20.

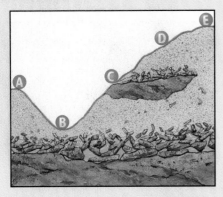

18. **Drawing Conclusions** Would point D or point E be a better location to dig a well? Explain your reasoning.
19. **Inferring** At which location could you obtain groundwater without having to pump it up? What is such a place called?

20. **Predicting** Draw a simple diagram showing how this area might look during a very rainy season.

Thinking Critically

21. **Comparing and Contrasting** How is the variety of organisms you would find in the center of a pond different from those you would find in deep water at the center of a lake?
22. **Classifying** Which of the following materials are permeable? Which of the materials are impermeable? Aluminum foil, cotton, plastic wrap, glass, paper towel, and bread.
23. **Problem Solving** Suppose that the water table in your area is located 8 meters below the ground surface in the spring. By the end of the summer, the level of groundwater drops 2 meters. How deep should you dig a well to be sure that it does not run dry?

Performance Assessment

Wrap Up

Present Your Project Before presentation day, show your watershed model to a classmate. Ask your classmate to predict how the water will flow over the model. Can your classmate identify the features of the watershed? If you need to make any final adjustments to your model, do so now. On presentation day, use a spray bottle to spray rain onto your model.

Reflect and Record In your notebook, explain what you would change about your model now that you have demonstrated it. What aspect of freshwater flow was most difficult to model? What other watershed features might you add?

Getting Involved

In Your Community Obtain permission from your teacher and family to conduct a survey of lakes, ponds, and wetlands in your community. Choose one location and, with an adult family member, take an inventory of the wildlife you find there. If possible, sketch or photograph plants, birds, small mammals, frogs, and other wildlife. Prepare an exhibit for your local library that highlights the natural features of this water environment.

Performance Assessment

Wrap Up

Present Your Project To maximize sharing of information and to give students an opportunity to compare their models, try to schedule all the presentations in no more than two class periods or one block, allocating a specific maximum amount of time for each model. If possible, arrange the room with the students forming a large circle so everyone can see each model as it is presented.

Prompt students to identify the specific features in the model by name, explain how the features are formed in nature, and describe the role they play in the river system. Encourage the other students to ask questions about each model as it is presented. Make sure you provide all students with positive feedback about their model. Suggest that students save their models for presentation on Parents' Night or at a science fair.

Reflect and Record Encourage students to use the Chapter 2 Project Scoring Rubric to help assess their models. Suggest that they review their sketches to make sure their models accomplished what they planned. Students might also evaluate the materials they used to make the models for their effectiveness to the application.

Thinking Critically

21. The variety of organisms in the center of a pond is much greater because sunlight reaches the bottom. Sunlight does not reach the deep water at the center of a lake, so plants and algae and the organisms that depend on them cannot live there.
22. *Permeable:* cotton, paper towel, bread; *impermeable:* aluminum foil, plastic wrap, glass
23. It should be more than 10 meters deep.

Program Resources

◆ **Inquiry Skills Activity Book** Provides teaching and review of all inquiry skills

Getting Involved

In Your Community Before students begin, obtain a map of your local area and give each student a copy. Review the map with the class so students are sure of the locations of the lakes, ponds, and wetlands nearby. Monitor students' choices to avoid duplication. As a cooperative learning activity, students could share their information and work together to create the exhibit.

Freshwater Resources

Sections	Time	Student Edition Activities	Other Activities
CHAPTER PROJECT 3 **A Precious Resource** p. 79	Ongoing (2–3 weeks)	Check Your Progress, p. 89 Check Your Progress, p. 104 Check Your Progress, p. 108 Wrap Up, p. 111	
1 **Water to Drink** pp. 80–89 ◆ Describe sources of drinking water and how it is treated and distributed. ◆ Explain what happens to wastewater in most large communities.	3–4 periods/ 2–3 blocks	**Discover** How Hard Is It to Move Water?, p. 80 **Real-World Lab: You, the Consumer** Testing the Waters, pp. 82–83 **Try This** Moving Water Uphill, p. 86	TE Inquiry Challenge, pp. 81, 84 TE Addressing Naive Conceptions, p. 84 TE Building Inquiry Skills: Predicting, p. 85 TE Integrating Physics, p. 86 TE Real-Life Learning, p. 87 TE Using the Visuals, p. 87 TE Building Inquiry Skills: Controlling Variables, p. 88 PTA "Testing Shampoos," pp. 1–8
2 **Balancing Water Needs** pp. 90–96 ◆ Describe conditions that can result in a water shortage and list sources of fresh water for the future. ◆ Explain how water can be conserved.	3–4 periods/ 2–3 blocks	**Discover** Can You Reach a Balance?, p. 90 **Sharpen Your Skills** Predicting, p. 93 **Science at Home,** p. 94 **Skills Lab: Making Models** Getting the Salt Out, p. 95	TE Integrating Technology, p. 91 PTA "Testing Bottled Waters," pp. 1–8
3 **Freshwater Pollution** pp. 97–104 ◆ Describe what water pollution is and list some of its sources. ◆ Explain how runoff affects ponds and streams. ◆ Describe how pollution can be prevented and how polluted water can be cleaned up.	2 periods/ 1 block	**Discover** Will the Pollution Reach Your Wells?, p. 97 **Sharpen Your Skills** Classifying, p. 99 **Try This** How Do Your Algae Grow?, p. 102	TE Using the Visuals, pp. 98, 104 TE Demonstration, p. 100 TE Real-Life Learning, p. 101 TE Integrating Chemistry, p. 101 ISLM H-3, "Examining Pollution of the Water" IES "Where River Meets Sea," pp. 28–30
4 **INTEGRATING PHYSICS** **Water As an Energy Resource** pp. 105–108 ◆ Explain how moving water can produce electricity. ◆ List ways in which hydroelectric power is a good source of energy. ◆ Describe the impact of dams.	2 periods/ 1 block	**Discover** Can Water Do Work?, p. 105 **Try This** Making a Water Wheel, p. 106	TE Exploring a Hydroelectric Power Plant, p. 107 IES "Mill Life in the 1840s," pp. 12–13 IES "Back to the Thirties," pp. 38–39
Study Guide/Chapter Review pp. 109–111	1 period/ $\frac{1}{2}$ block		ISAB Provides teaching and review of all inquiry skills

 For Standard or Block Schedule The Resource Pro® CD-ROM gives you maximum flexibility for planning your instruction for any type of schedule. Resource Pro® contains Planning Express®, an advanced scheduling program, as well as the entire contents of the Teaching Resources and the Computer Test Bank.

CHAPTER PLANNING GUIDE

Program Resources	Assessment Strategies	Media and Technology
TR Chapter 3 Project Teacher Notes, pp. 64–65 **TR** Chapter 3 Project Student Materials, pp. 66–69 **TR** Chapter 3 Project Scoring Rubric, p. 70	**SE** Performance Assessment: Chapter 3 Project Wrap Up, p. 111 **TE** Check Your Progress, pp. 89, 104, 108 **TR** Chapter 3 Project Scoring Rubric, p. 70	🌐 Science Explorer Internet Site
TR 3-1 Lesson Plan, p. 71 **TR** 3-1 Section Summary, p. 72 **TR** 3-1 Review and Reinforce, p. 73 **TR** 3-1 Enrich, p. 74 **TR** Chapter 3 Real-World Lab, pp. 87–89 **SES** Book A *From Bacteria to Plants,* Chapter 2 **SES** Book M *Motion, Forces, and Energy,* Chapter 3	**SE** Analyze and Conclude, p. 83 **SE** Section 1 Review, p. 89 **TE** Ongoing Assessment, pp. 81, 85, 87 **TE** Performance Assessment, p. 89 **TR** 3-1 Review and Reinforce, p. 73	💿 Exploring Life Science Videodisc, Unit 2 Side 2, "Positive Bacteria" 🎧 Audiotapes, English-Spanish Summary 3-1 📽 Transparency 8, "Exploring Drinking-Water Treatment" 📽 Transparency 9, "Exploring Wastewater Treatment" 📽 Transparency 10, "Cutaway View of a Septic Tank" 💽 Interactive Student Tutorial CD-ROM, H-3
TR 3-2 Lesson Plan, p. 75 **TR** 3-2 Section Summary, p. 76 **TR** 3-2 Review and Reinforce, p. 77 **TR** 3-2 Enrich, p. 78 **TR** Chapter 3 Skills Lab, pp. 90–91 **SES** Book K *Chemical Building Blocks,* Chapter 2	**SE** Section 2 Review, p. 94 **SE** Analyze and Conclude, p. 95 **TE** Ongoing Assessment, pp. 91, 93 **TE** Performance Assessment, p. 94 **TR** 3-2 Review and Reinforce, p. 77	💿 Exploring Life Science Videodisc, Unit 2 Side 2, "Xeriscape" 🎧 Audiotapes, English-Spanish Summary 3-2 💽 Interactive Student Tutorial CD-ROM, H-3
TR 3-3 Lesson Plan, p. 79 **TR** 3-3 Section Summary, p. 80 **TR** 3-3 Review and Reinforce, p. 81 **TR** 3-3 Enrich, p. 82 **SES** Book E *Environmental Science,* Chapters 1, 2, 5, 6 **SES** Book D *Human Biology and Health,* Chapter 6 **SES** Book G *Earth's Changing Surface,* Chapter 3	**SE** Section 3 Review, p. 104 **TE** Ongoing Assessment, pp. 99, 101, 103 **TE** Performance Assessment, p. 104 **TR** 3-3 Review and Reinforce, p. 81	💿 Exploring Earth Science Videodisc, Unit 4 Side 2, "Rain, Rain, Go Away" 🎧 Audiotapes, English-Spanish Summary 3-3 💽 Interactive Student Tutorial CD-ROM, H-3
TR 3-4 Lesson Plan, p. 83 **TR** 3-4 Section Summary, p. 84 **TR** 3-4 Review and Reinforce, p. 85 **TR** 3-4 Enrich, p. 86 **SES** Book N *Electricity and Magnetism,* Chapter 3	**SE** Section 4 Review, p. 108 **TE** Ongoing Assessment, p. 107 **TE** Performance Assessment, p. 108 **TR** 3-4 Review and Reinforce, p. 85	💿 Exploring Physical Science Videodisc, Unit 3 Side 1, "Energy" 🎧 Audiotapes, English-Spanish Summary 3-4 📽 Transparency 11, "Exploring a Hydroelectric Power Plant" 💽 Interactive Student Tutorial CD-ROM, H-3
TR Chapter 3 Performance Assessment, pp. 174–176 **TR** Chapter 3 Test, pp. 177–180	**SE** Chapter 3 Review, pp. 109–111 **TR** Chapter 3 Performance Assessment, pp. 174–176 **TR** Chapter 3 Test, pp. 177–180 **CTB** Test H-3	💽 Interactive Student Tutorial CD-ROM, H-3 💾 Computer Test Bank, Test H-3 📼 Got It! Video Quizzes

Key: **SE** Student Edition
CTB Computer Test Bank
ISAB Inquiry Skills Activity Book

TE Teacher's Edition
SES Science Explorer Series Text
PTA Product Testing Activities by *Consumer Reports*

TR Teaching Resources
ISLM Integrated Science Laboratory Manual
IES Interdisciplinary Explorations Series

Meeting the National Science Education Standards and AAAS Benchmarks

National Science Education Standards	Benchmarks for Science Literacy	Unifying Themes
Science As Inquiry (Content Standard A) ◆ **Use appropriate tools and techniques to gather, analyze, and interpret data** Students test and compare various types of water. *(Real-World Lab)* ◆ **Think critically and logically to make the relationships between evidence and explanations** Students investigate desalination. *(Skills Lab)* **Science and Technology** (Content Standard E) ◆ **Design a solution or product** Students design and build a model water treatment system. *(Chapter Project)* ◆ **Understanding about science and technology** Various processes are used to treat drinking water and wastewater. Hydroelectric power plants generate electricity. *(Sections 1 and 4)* **Science in Personal and Social Perspectives** (Content Standard F) ◆ **Personal health** Water supplies often need treatment to make water safe. Water pollution makes water unsafe. *(Sections 1 and 3)* ◆ **Populations, resources, and environments** Water shortages occur due to supply and demand. *(Section 2; Science and Society)* ◆ **Science and technology in society** There are various ways to conserve water. Human activities can cause water pollution. *(Sections 2 and 3)*	**1B Scientific Inquiry** Students test and compare various types of water. Students investigate desalination. *(Real-World Lab; Skills Lab)* **3A Technology and Science** Water undergoes treatment before and after people use it. There are various ways to conserve water. Hydroelectric power plants generate electricity. *(Sections 1, 2, and 4)* **3B Design and Systems** Students build a water treatment system. *(Chapter Project)* **3C Issues in Technology** Water pollution can be caused by human activities. Hydroelectric power plants have both positive and negative effects. *(Sections 3 and 4)* **4B The Earth** Water shortages occur when there is too little water or too great a demand. *(Section 2; Science and Society)* **8C Energy Sources and Use** Hydroelectric power plants change the energy of moving water into electricity. *(Section 4)*	◆ **Systems and Interactions** Various processes are used to treat drinking water and wastewater. Water pollution can affect surface water, groundwater, and even rain. *(Sections 1 and 3)* ◆ **Patterns of Change** Water shortages occur when there is too little water or too great a demand. High demands on the Ogallala Aquifer have caused water levels to drop there. *(Section 2; Science and Society)* ◆ **Modeling** Students design and build a model of a water treatment plant. Students investigate desalination using a distillation model. *(Chapter Project; Skills Lab)* ◆ **Unity and Diversity** Students test and compare various types of water. Sources of water pollution include point and nonpoint sources. *(Real-World Lab; Section 3)* ◆ **Energy** Hydroelectric power plants capture the energy of moving water and change it into electrical energy. *(Section 4)*

Media and Technology

Exploring Life Science Videodiscs
◆ **Section 1** "Positive Bacteria" tells how bacteria help in wastewater treatment.
◆ **Section 2** "Xeriscape" illustrates a landscaping technique that helps conserve water.

Exploring Earth Science Videodiscs
◆ **Section 3** "Rain, Rain Go Away" describes acid rain.

Exploring Physical Science Videodiscs
◆ **Section 4** "Energy" defines kinetic and potential energy.

Interactive Student Tutorial CD-ROM
◆ **Chapter Review** Interactive questions help students self-assess their mastery of key chapter concepts.

Student Edition Connection Strategies

◆ **Section 1**   Math Toolbox, p. 84
                  Integrating Physics, p. 86
◆ **Section 2**   Integrating Technology, p. 91
                  Social Studies Connection, p. 92
                  Integrating Chemistry, p. 94
◆ **Section 3**   Integrating Life Science, pp. 98, 102
                  Integrating Health, pp. 99–100
                  Integrating Chemistry, p. 101
◆ **Section 4**   Integrating Physics, pp. 105–108
                  Integrating Life Science, pp. 106–107

USING THE INTERNET

www.science-explorer.phschool.com

Visit the Science Explorer internet site to find an up-to-date activity for Chapter 3 of *Earth's Waters*.

ACTIVITY	Time (minutes)	Materials Quantities for one work group	Skills
Section 1			
Discover, p. 80	20	**Consumable** 2 heavy plastic trash bags, water **Nonconsumable** 2 large trash barrels, large plastic pitcher with lid	Calculating
Real-World Lab, pp. 82–83	40	**Consumable** liquid soap, 200 mL tap water, 200 mL distilled water, 200 mL spring water, 200 ml mineral water, 4 pieces of pH paper, 4 paper cups **Nonconsumable** hot plate, ruler, wax pencil, 4 200-mL beakers, 4 test tubes and stoppers, pH indicator chart, 25-mL graduated cylinder	Observing, Inferring, Drawing Conclusions
Try This, p. 86	20	**Consumable** water **Nonconsumable** books, 2 large bowls, pitcher, plastic tubing	Observing
Section 2			
Discover, p. 90	15	**Consumable** water **Nonconsumable** large measuring cup, plastic dropper, 2 small bowls, spoon, stopwatch	Predicting
Sharpen Your Skills, p. 93	5, 5	**Nonconsumable** large measuring cup	Predicting
Science at Home, p. 94	home	**Consumable** toothpaste, water, tape, toothbrush	Comparing and Contrasting
Skills Lab, p. 95	40	**Consumable** aluminum foil, water, ice, salt **Nonconsumable** hot plate, 250-mL beaker, plastic spoon, shallow pan, plastic tube, 500-mL flask, stirring rod, rubber stopper, rubber tubing	Making Models
Section 3			
Discover, p. 97	15	**Consumable** coffee filter, paper plate, food coloring **Nonconsumable** permanent marker, wet sponge, plastic dropper	Observing
Sharpen Your Skills, p. 99	10	No special materials required.	Classifying
Try This, p. 102	15, 5	**Consumable** masking tape, tap water, pond or aquarium water, liquid fertilizer **Nonconsumable** 2 wide-mouth jars with tops, permanent marker, graduated cylinder	Drawing Conclusions
Section 4			
Discover, p. 105	10	**Consumable** large plastic trash bag, water **Nonconsumable** various cylindrical objects, plant sprayer	Observing
Try This, p. 106	15	**Consumable** aluminum pie plate, small foam ball, 2 toothpicks, running water **Nonconsumable** tin snips or heavy scissors, metric ruler, marker	Developing Hypotheses

A list of all materials required for the Student Edition activities can be found beginning on page T14. You can order Materials Kits by calling 1-800-828-7777 or by accessing the Science Explorer Internet site at **www.science-explorer.phschool.com**.

A Precious Resource

In this chapter, students will be introduced to the concepts that water quality can vary widely and that drinking water must be treated for both safety and taste. This project will give students a tangible sense of what the treatment of water entails.

Purpose In this project, students will design a water treatment system with at least two steps. Then, they will assemble and demonstrate a model water treatment system that cleans and recovers as much of 1 liter of dirty water as possible. In doing so, they will gain a better understanding of the processes involved in water treatment.

Skills Focus Students will be able to
♦ observe the characteristics of dirty water;
♦ design a model water treatment system;
♦ create a flow chart that represents the treatment system;
♦ make a working model of a water treatment system;
♦ communicate the workings of the treatment system to the class;
♦ compare and contrast their design with that of others;
♦ draw conclusions from the experiences of their classmates.

Project Timeline The entire project will require at least two weeks. On the first day, distribute Chapter 3 Project Overview, pages 66–67 in the Teaching Resources. Allow class time for students to discuss what the project will entail and the possible materials needed to carry it out. At this time, you may wish to distribute Chapter 3 Project Scoring Rubric, page 70 in Teaching Resources, so students are clear about what will be expected of them. Students will be doing the Chapter 3 Project Worksheet 1, page 68 in Teaching Resources and Chapter 3 Project Worksheet 2, page 69 in Teaching Resources.

Once they've completed Worksheet 2, allow class time for students to decide on a design and begin assembling the treatment system model. Students will need more time during the second week to test the model, to make any changes necessary to improve the design, and finally to prepare for the presentation to the class. At least

CHAPTER 3 Freshwater Resources

WHAT'S AHEAD

SECTION 1 **Water to Drink**
Discover How Hard Is It to Move Water?
Real-World Lab Testing the Waters
Try This Moving Water Uphill

SECTION 2 **Balancing Water Needs**
Discover Can You Reach a Balance?
Sharpen Your Skills Predicting
Skills Lab Getting the Salt Out

SECTION 3 **Freshwater Pollution**
Discover Will the Pollution Reach Your Wells?
Sharpen Your Skills Classifying
Try This How Do Your Algae Grow?

one class period will be needed for students to present their water-treatment models. End with a class discussion that focuses on a comparison of all the models.

Suggested Shortcuts You can simplify the project by limiting the model to filtration as the only treatment method. You also may wish to divide students into groups of three or four to design and build their system to save time. Students can complete Chapter 3 Project Worksheet 1 in their groups, and then present their results to the class.

Possible Materials Because students design their own treatment systems, materials may vary widely. In fact, you should encourage students to think of unique materials as long as they are not too difficult to obtain. All students, though, will need certain materials, especially for Chapter 3 Project Worksheet 1, in which they experiment with a variety of filtration materials.

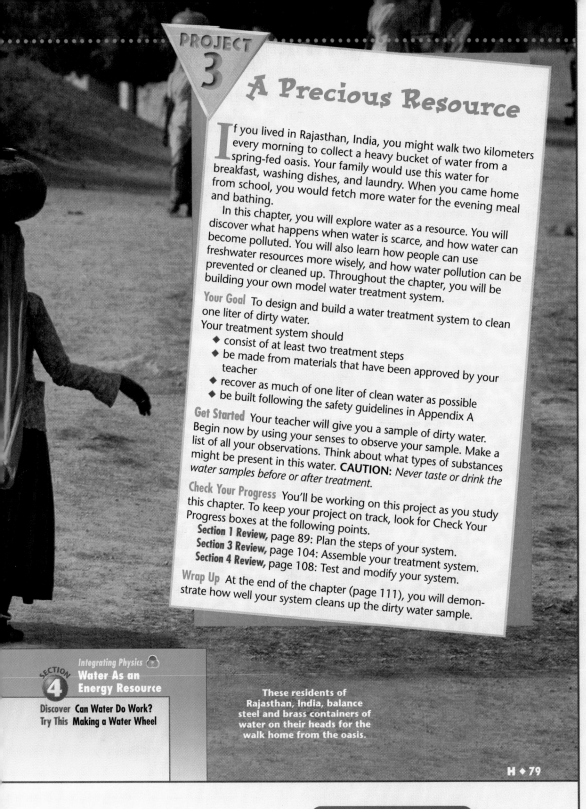

A Precious Resource

If you lived in Rajasthan, India, you might walk two kilometers every morning to collect a heavy bucket of water from a spring-fed oasis. Your family would use this water for breakfast, washing dishes, and laundry. When you came home from school, you would fetch more water for the evening meal and bathing.

In this chapter, you will explore water as a resource. You will discover what happens when water is scarce, and how water can become polluted. You will also learn how people can use freshwater resources more wisely, and how water pollution can be prevented or cleaned up. Throughout the chapter, you will be building your own model water treatment system.

Your Goal To design and build a water treatment system to clean one liter of dirty water.

Your treatment system should
◆ consist of at least two treatment steps
◆ be made from materials that have been approved by your teacher
◆ recover as much of one liter of clean water as possible
◆ be built following the safety guidelines in Appendix A

Get Started Your teacher will give you a sample of dirty water. Begin now by using your senses to observe your sample. Make a list of all your observations. Think about what types of substances might be present in this water. **CAUTION:** Never taste or drink the water samples before or after treatment.

Check Your Progress You'll be working on this project as you study this chapter. To keep your project on track, look for Check Your Progress boxes at the following points.
Section 1 Review, page 89: Plan the steps of your system.
Section 3 Review, page 104: Assemble your treatment system.
Section 4 Review, page 108: Test and modify your system.

Wrap Up At the end of the chapter (page 111), you will demonstrate how well your system cleans up the dirty water sample.

SECTION 4 *Integrating Physics* 🌐
Water As an Energy Resource
Discover Can Water Do Work?
Try This Making a Water Wheel

These residents of Rajasthan, India, balance steel and brass containers of water on their heads for the walk home from the oasis.

Program Resources

◆ **Teaching Resources** Chapter 3 Project Teacher Notes, pp. 64–65; Chapter 3 Project Student Materials, pp. 66–69; Chapter 3 Project Scoring Rubric, p. 70

All students will need a supply of dirty water. You can make such water by mixing 1 tablespoon of fuller's earth per cup of tap water. You could also use water from a local river or pond, making sure to include mud from the bottom.

Filtration materials include sand, gravel, charcoal or activated charcoal, window screening, various fabrics, and coffee filters or other papers. Each student or group will need a 2-L clear plastic soda bottle with the bottom cut off. The bottles will work as filter supports when held upside down on a ring stand.

If students want to include a coagulation step in the system, they will need alum (aluminum sulfate) or baking soda (sodium bicarbonate).

Launching the Project To introduce this project, show students a container of tap water and a container of dirty water. Ask: **What are some methods by which you could make this dirty water as clean as the tap water?** (*Accept any suggestion. Many students will mention methods of filtration. Some students might suggest a distillation method.*) Write the list on the board. At this point, you might also prepare the "cleanness scale" as described in the Teacher's Notes on page 64 of Teaching Resources. Ask: **Would adding tap water to the dirty water be a way to make the water safe to drink?** (*Some students may correctly suggest that simply diluting the water would not be sufficient.*)

Finally, have students read the description of the project in the text and in the Chapter 3 Project Overview. Encourage them to begin thinking of steps they could include in their water treatment system.

Performance Assessment

To assess students' performance in this project, use the Chapter 3 Project Scoring Rubric on page 70 of Teaching Resources. Students will be assessed on
◆ their treatment system design and flow chart;
◆ their treatment system model;
◆ their class presentation;
◆ their group participation, if they worked in groups.

Objectives

After completing the lesson, students will be able to
◆ describe sources of drinking water and how it is treated and distributed;
◆ explain what happens to wastewater in most large communities.

Key Terms water quality, pH, hardness, concentration, filtration, flocs, coagulation, sewage, sludge, septic tank, leach field

1 Engage/Explore

Activating Prior Knowledge

Display a glass of water, and tell students that it came from a school drinking fountain. Ask: **Where did this water come from before that?** (*Answers will vary. A typical answer might mention a local river or reservoir.*) Have students make a flowchart of a possible route by which the water came to the school, including any treatment the water received on its journey.

⋯⋯ DISCOVER ⋯⋯

Skills Focus calculating
Materials *2 large trash barrels, 2 heavy plastic trash bags, water, large plastic pitcher with lid*
Time 20 minutes
Tips Spilled water is to be expected in this activity, so it would be best to do this outdoors on a warm day. Bigger pitchers will result in fewer passes. To save time, students could pass multiple pitchers, as long as someone keeps count.
Expected Outcome Students will experience the amount of time and effort needed to move water.
Think It Over Answers will vary depending on the size of the pitcher. Students should make this calculation using the number of passes it took to transfer the 100 L of water. For example, if it took 50 passes to transfer 100 L, then it would take 2.5 times that to transfer 250 L.

DISCOVER ⋯⋯⋯⋯⋯⋯⋯⋯⋯⋯⋯⋯ ACTIVITY ⋯

How Hard Is It to Move Water?

1. Line two large trash barrels with heavy plastic bags. Fill one barrel with about 100 liters of water. This is about how much water a person uses during a five-minute shower.

2. Form a line of students between the barrels. Your goal is to transfer all the water from the first barrel to the second barrel. Avoid spilling the water. Be careful of slippery floors if you are doing this activity indoors.

3. The first person in line should fill a large plastic pitcher with water, put the cover on, and hand it to the next person.

4. Pass the pitcher to the end of the line, where the last person should empty it into the second barrel. Hand the empty pitcher back down the line to the first person.

5. Repeat Steps 3 and 4 until all the water has been transferred to the second barrel. How many times did you pass the pitcher down the line?

Think It Over

Calculating Suppose a person uses an average of 250 liters of water a day. How many times would you have to pass the pitcher to move the amount of water this person would use in a day? In a year?

GUIDE FOR READING

◆ What is the goal of drinking-water treatment?

◆ What happens to wastewater in most large communities?

Reading Tip Before you read, rewrite the section headings as how, why, or what questions. As you read, find answers to these questions.

At first, doctors in Milwaukee, Wisconsin, thought that 1993 was just a bad year for the flu. Patient after patient complained of nausea, fever, and other flulike symptoms. Within just a few weeks, about 400,000 people came down with symptoms of the disease. Public health officials began looking for another explanation for the epidemic.

The investigators discovered that all the victims had drunk water from the same water treatment plant. Tests revealed that the water contained a tiny parasite, a protist called *Cryptosporidium*. One sip of water could contain enough *Cryptosporidium* to make a person ill! This parasite had not been killed by the chemicals used to treat water at the plant. The scientists hypothesized that the *Cryptosporidium* might have come from runoff from fields where cows grazed. Although most of the victims recovered after a few weeks, about 100 deaths were blamed on the contamination.

READING STRATEGIES

Reading Tip Student's questions and answers may vary. Typical questions and answers: What are the sources of drinking water? (*Rivers, lakes, reservoirs, and aquifers*) How is drinking water treated? (*Treatment ranges from a simple filter on a household well to complex processes at public treatment plants.*) What steps does a typical treatment plant carry out? (*First filtration, coagulation, second filtration, chlorination, aeration, and*

additional treatment.) What does water distribution involve? (*Water goes from a treatment plant to a central pumping station, where it is pumped through water mains and smaller pipes to houses and buildings.*) How is wastewater treated? (*Through settling, filtration, and the addition of chemicals*) What is a septic system? (*A septic system is a method to dispose of sewage used by people not connected to a public sanitary sewer system.*)

Figure 1 An aqueduct carries water from one place to another. This aqueduct, the Pont du Gard in France, was built by the Romans more than 2,000 years ago. *Inferring Why do you think the Romans found it necessary to construct aqueducts?*

Milwaukee's experience was a reminder of the importance of a safe, clean water supply. In this section, you will follow drinking water on its journey to and from homes, schools, and businesses.

Sources of Drinking Water

Where does the water in your kitchen faucet come from? The first step in tracing the path of your water supply is to identify its source. Recall that Earth's liquid fresh water is found on the surface in rivers, lakes, and reservoirs, and underground in rock layers called aquifers. Most people in the United States get their drinking water from one of these sources.

If you live near a large lake or river, your water may come from that source. A distant lake or reservoir could also supply your drinking water. For instance, the city of Los Angeles draws much of its water from the Sierra Nevada Mountains, halfway across California. Or you may rely on groundwater as a source of drinking water. About half the people in the United States, including most people in rural areas, pump drinking water from aquifers.

Your drinking water comes from either a public or private water supply. Most large communities maintain public water supplies. These communities collect, treat, and distribute water to residents. In smaller communities and rural areas, people rely on private wells that supply water for individual families.

☑ *Checkpoint* **List three possible sources of drinking water.**

Treating Drinking Water

After you have identified the source of your drinking water, what is the next step in its journey to your faucet? **Water from both public and private supplies often needs some treatment to ensure that the water is safe and appealing to drink.** Treatment can range from a simple filter on a household well to complex processes at public treatment plants.

Program Resources

◆ **Teaching Resources** 3-1 Lesson Plan, p. 71; 3-1 Section Summary, p. 72
◆ **Product Testing Activities by** *Consumer Reports* "Testing Shampoos," pp. 1–8

Media and Technology

 Audiotapes English-Spanish Summary 3-1

Answers to Self-Assessment

Caption Question

Figure 1 The Romans needed a way to transport water to places where there was not enough water to meet their needs.

☑ *Checkpoint*

A typical answer should include three of the following: rivers, lakes, reservoirs, and aquifers.

2 Facilitate

Sources of Drinking Water

Real-Life Learning

To familiarize students with the source of their own drinking water, display a large map of your area. Ask: **What bodies of water in our area could be the source of our drinking water?** (*Students should point out any reservoir, lake, or major river in the area.*) **Is there any other possible source of drinking water?** (*groundwater*) Designated students could call the local water department, find out the source of your water, and report to the class. If students live in an area where there is no water department and most people get water from private wells, have students contact a nearby state geological survey office or drilling company to find out about local aquifers. **learning modality: verbal**

Treating Drinking Water

Inquiry Challenge

Materials *lake or river water, slide, plastic dropper, microscope*
Time 15 minutes

Have students examine untreated water from a local surface water source to make inferences about why the water would need to be treated. Place several beakers of this water around the classroom, where students can examine it closely and smell it. Then each student can make a slide to examine under a microscope. Each student should conclude by writing a short description of the water and why they think it is not safe to drink. Caution students never to taste the water and to wash their hands after the activity. **learning modality: visual**

Ongoing Assessment

Oral Presentation Call on students at random to explain why communities treat drinking water and to identify the sources of drinking water.

You, the Consumer

Testing the Waters

Preparing for Inquiry

Key Concept Bottled waters, including distilled water, spring water, and mineral water, differ from tap water and from each other in a number of ways.

Skills Objectives Students will be able to
◆ observe that samples of different kinds of water differ in a variety of ways;
◆ infer that dissolved solids may affect other water qualities;
◆ draw conclusions about the differences among different types of water.

Time 40 minutes

Advance Planning Bring to class unopened bottles of distilled water, spring water, and noncarbonated mineral water. Obtain a pump bottle of liquid soap, such as a nondetergent hand-washing soap. Make sure to have enough unused, small paper cups. Obtain narrow-range (6–8) pH paper, which can detect subtle differences in similar samples.

Alternative Materials Burners and stands can be used in place of hot plates. Use small jars in place of test tubes. Instead of stoppers, use plastic wrap or wax paper held in place with rubber bands.

Guiding Inquiry

Invitation To give the lab a context, ask: **Why do many people buy costly bottled water instead of always using relatively inexpensive tap water?** *(People buy bottled waters for taste, health purposes, use in appliances, and a variety of other reasons.)*

Introducing the Procedure

◆ Ask students: **Why is it important to use the same amount of water in each beaker when heating the water?** *(The goal is to boil away the same amount in each beaker.)*

◆ Ask: **What factors might influence the taste test?** *(Dissolved substances in the different waters, individual tastes among students)*

Appearance and Taste Picture a glass of water. What observations would affect whether or not you were willing to take a sip? What if the water were cloudy, or had a funny smell? What if the water were rust-colored? Cloudiness, odor, and color are three factors that affect water quality. **Water quality** is a measurement of the substances in water besides water molecules. Some substances, such as iron, can affect the taste or color of water but are harmless unless present at very high levels. Other

You, the Consumer

Testing the Waters

How does the bottled water sold in supermarkets differ from the water that comes out of your kitchen faucet? In this lab, you will discover some differences among various types of water.

Problem

How do distilled water, spring water, and mineral water differ from tap water?

Skills Focus

observing, inferring, drawing conclusions

Materials

hot plate	liquid soap
ruler	wax pencil
tap water, 200 mL	distilled water, 200 mL
spring water, 200 mL	mineral water, 200 mL
4 200-mL beakers	4 test tubes and stoppers
4 pieces of pH paper	pH indicator chart
25-mL graduated cylinder	
4 paper cups per person	

Procedure

1. Copy the data table into your notebook.

2. Label the beakers A, B, C, and D. Pour 100 mL of tap water into beaker A. Pour 100 mL of the other water samples into the correct beaker (refer to the data table).

3. Heat each water sample on a hot plate until about 20 mL remains. Do not allow the water to boil completely away. **CAUTION:** *Do not touch the hot plate or beakers.*

4. After the water samples have cooled, look for solids that make the water cloudy. Rank the samples from 1 to 4, where 1 has the fewest visible solids and 4 has the most visible solids. Record your rankings in the data table.

5. Label the test tubes A, B, C, and D. Pour 10 mL of each water sample from the source bottle into the correct test tube.

6. Dip a piece of pH paper into test tube A to measure its acidity. Match the color of the pH paper to a number on the pH indicator chart. Record the pH (1–14) in your data table.

Troubleshooting the Experiment

◆ Heating the water in Step 3 may take 15–20 minutes, and then cooling may take another 10–15 minutes. During those periods, have students continue with the rest of the steps of the Procedure. That is, after beginning Step 3, they should do Steps 5–12 and then return at the end to do Step 4.

◆ If wide-opening droppers are available, have students use them to add soap to samples. For instance, have students add 4 drops to each sample instead of 5 mL.

Sample Data Table

Water Sample	Visible Solids (1–4)	pH (1–14)	Soap-sud Height (cm)	Taste
A Tap water	3	7.0	11	metallic, refreshing
B Distilled water	4	7.0	10	tasteless, flat
C Spring water	2	7.5	9	refreshing
D Mineral water	1	8.0	8	salty, bitter

substances, such as certain chemicals and microorganisms, can be harmful to your health.

Acidity The **pH** of water is a measurement of how acidic or basic it is, on a scale of 1 to 14. Pure water is neutral, meaning it is neither an acid or a base, and has a pH of 7. The lower the pH, the more acidic the water. Acidic water can cause problems by dissolving lead or other metals from the pipes it passes through. The higher the pH, the more basic the water.

DATA TABLE

Water Sample	Visible Solids (1–4)	pH (1–14)	Soapsud Height (cm)	Taste
A - Tap water				
B - Distilled water				
C - Spring water				
D - Mineral water				

7. Repeat Step 6 for the other samples.
8. Add 0.5 mL of liquid soap to test tube A. Put a stopper in the test tube and shake it 30 times. With the ruler, measure the height of the soapsuds in the test tube. Record the measurement in your data table.
9. Repeat Step 8 for the other samples.
10. Label the four cups A, B, C, and D. Write your name on each cup.
11. Pour a little tap water into cup A directly from the original source bottle. Taste the tap water. In your data table, describe the taste using one or more of these words: salty, flat, bitter, metallic, refreshing, tasteless. **CAUTION:** *Do not conduct the taste test in a lab room. Use a clean cup for each sample and discard it after use.*
12. Repeat Step 11 with the other samples.

Analyze and Conclude

1. Review your data table. Compare each of the bottled water samples to the tap water sample. What similarities and differences did you detect?
2. Rank the samples from the one with the fewest soapsuds to the one with the most. Compare this ranking to the one for visible solids. What pattern do you see? What do both of these tests have to do with the hardness of water?
3. What other information about the water samples might you need before deciding which one to drink regularly? Explain.
4. **Apply** Based on your results, which sample would you most want to use for (a) drinking, (b) boiling in a kettle, and (c) washing laundry? Which sample would you least want to use for each purpose? Explain.

Getting Involved

Conduct a survey to find out what percentage of people buy bottled mineral water, distilled water, and spring water. Why do they buy each type of water and how do they use it in their homes?

Safety

Emphasize that in Step 3 students should not let the water boil away completely. Advise that an oven mitt is essential to use when handling hot beakers. Caution students to be careful using the electric hotplates. Students should pour tasting samples only from the original bottles and always use a new cup. Review the safety guidelines in Appendix A.

Expected Outcome

The different kinds of water will differ in amount of dissolved solids, pH value, ability to produce soapsuds, and taste. See Sample Data Table.

Analyze and Conclude

1. Answers may vary. A typical answer: Distilled water has fewer visible solids, lower pH, greater soapsud height than tap water, and flatter taste than tap water. Both spring water and mineral water have more visible solids, higher pH, lower soapsud height, and more salty or refreshing taste than tap water.
2. Answers may vary. See Sample Data Table for typical rankings. Students should observe that the sample with the most visible solids has the fewest soapsuds, and vice versa. Both tests measure the hardness of water. The more visible solids, the harder the water; the fewer soapsuds, the harder the water.
3. Answers may vary. A typical answer may mention testing for the concentrations of other substances, such as lead and nickel, as well as for the coliform count.
4. Answers may vary. A typical answer: (a) The spring water is best for drinking because it tastes best; the distilled water is worst because it is tasteless. (b) The distilled water is best for boiling because it contains the least solids; the mineral water is worst because its minerals leave a residue. (c) The distilled or tap water is best for washing because they produce the most soapsuds; the mineral water is worst because it produces the fewest soapsuds.

Extending the Inquiry

Getting Involved Students could collaborate on constructing a simple survey with such questions as these: Do you ever buy bottled water? What kind? How often? For what use? Several questions could be constructed so that they can be answered with a "yes" or "no." For those questions, students could circle or check the appropriate response. Other questions could elicit short-answer responses. Once students have constructed the survey, help them make copies and decide where they could do the survey. Local grocery stores are good places to begin.

Treating Drinking Water, continued

Addressing Naive Conceptions

Materials *noncarbonated mineral water, softened water, 2 beakers, non-detergent soap*

Time 10 minutes

Ask students: **What does the term hard water mean?** *(Some students may take the term literally and think it is harder to the touch than soft water.)* Explain that water is called "hard" because minerals are dissolved in it, not because it is harder to the touch. Then give each student the opportunity to compare mineral water and softened water. (Buy commercial mineral water; bring softened water to school from a home that has soft water or a water softener.) Have students pour a sample of each type of water into a beaker. Encourage students to compare the two samples. Then have students add a small amount of soap to each sample, stir, and compare. Students should observe more suds in the soft water. **limited English proficiency**

Inquiry Challenge

Materials *muddy water, large beaker, alum crystals, stirring rod*

Time 20 minutes

Invite students to investigate coagulation. First have them hypothesize what will happen when alum is added to muddy water. Then they can add one tablespoon of alum crystals to a beaker of muddy water and stir slowly for 5 minutes. Students will observe large clumps settle quickly and smaller clumps later. **learning modality: kinesthetic**

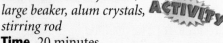

Time 15 minutes

Tips Have students rewrite as fractions the following concentrations:

♦ 2 ppm of copper *(2/1,000,000)*
♦ 0.09 ppm of cyanide *(0.09/1,000,000)*
♦ 0.24 ppb of arsenic *(0.24/1,000,000,000)*

learning modality: logical/ mathematical

Math TOOLBOX

Parts per . . .

Concentrations are often measured in parts per million (ppm) or parts per billion (ppb). What do these units mean? If you own one compact disc by your favorite band, and the disc sells one million copies, your disc is one of the one million sold, or one part per million. When you see a concentration written in this form, you can rewrite it as a fraction:

1. Suppose the concentration of iron in a water sample is 500 parts per million.

2. Write this concentration as a fraction by putting the number of parts on top, and the "whole" on the bottom:

$$500 \text{ parts per million} = \frac{500}{1,000,000}$$

Figure 2 The EPA has set standards for the amounts of various substances in drinking water. *Interpreting Data Based on this table, is a concentration of 0.09 ppm of arsenic in drinking water acceptable? Is a concentration of 0.05 ppm of cyanide acceptable?*

Hardness The level of two minerals—calcium and magnesium—in water is referred to as **hardness.** Hard water contains high levels of these minerals. The minerals come from rocks such as limestone that water flows through. For most people, the main drawback of hard water is that it does not form suds well when mixed with soap. That means that it takes more soap or detergent to get laundry clean in hard water. The minerals in hard water also form deposits that can clog pipes and machinery. Soft water, on the other hand, contains lower levels of calcium and magnesium. Soft water leaves fewer deposits and forms better soapsuds than hard water.

Disease-Causing Organisms Another factor affecting water quality is the presence of disease-causing organisms. The coliform count measures the number of *Escherichia coli* bacteria. Since these bacteria are found in human and animal wastes, their presence in the water shows that it contains waste material. A high coliform count is an indicator, or sign, that the water may also contain other disease-causing organisms.

Standards of Quality The Environmental Protection Agency (EPA), which is responsible for protecting the quality of water and other natural resources in the United States, has developed water-quality standards for drinking water. These standards set concentration limits for certain chemicals, minerals, and bacteria in drinking water. A **concentration** is the amount of one substance in a certain volume of another substance. For example, the concentration of letters in alphabet soup might be written as the number of letters per liter of soup. Figure 2 shows the standards for some different substances.

Checkpoint *List five factors that affect water quality.*

Selected Water-Quality Standards

Substance	Limit
Arsenic	0.05 parts per million (ppm)
Carbon tetrachloride	0.005 ppm
Copper	1.3 ppm
Cyanide	0.2 ppm
Lead	0.015 ppm
Coliform count	No more than 5% of samples taken in a month can be positive.
pH	6.5–8.5

Source: U.S. Environmental Protection Agency, National Primary and Secondary Drinking-Water Standards.

Background

Facts and Figures The standards in Figure 2 represent maximum contaminant levels (MCLs) except for copper and lead, which are action levels requiring treatment. In 1998, the U.S. Environmental Protection Agency announced regulations requiring community water agencies to inform customers of basic facts regarding their drinking water, including: (1) the source of the water, (2) what contaminants were in the water and which exceeded EPA health standards, (3) what health risks were associated with those contaminants that exceeded standards, and (4) any violations and actions that had been taken against the water agency that year.

A Typical Treatment Plant

Follow the water from river to faucet in *Exploring Drinking-Water Treatment* to see what happens in a typical water treatment plant.

The first step in treating water from a lake or river is usually filtration. **Filtration** is the process of passing water through a series of screens that allows the water through, but not larger solid particles. During this first step, trash, leaves, branches, and other large objects are removed from the water.

In the second step, a chemical such as alum is added to cause sticky globs, called **flocs,** to form. Other particles in the water stick to the flocs, a process called **coagulation.** The heavy clumps sink to the bottom in the settling basins. The water is then filtered again.

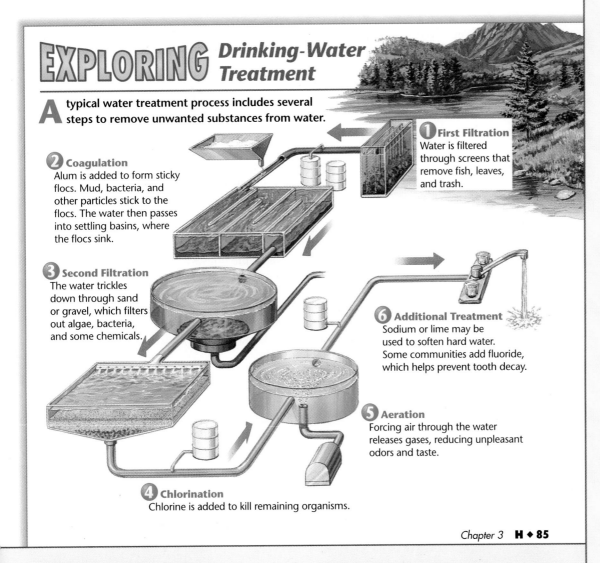

EXPLORING Drinking-Water Treatment

A typical water treatment process includes several steps to remove unwanted substances from water.

① First Filtration
Water is filtered through screens that remove fish, leaves, and trash.

② Coagulation
Alum is added to form sticky flocs. Mud, bacteria, and other particles stick to the flocs. The water then passes into settling basins, where the flocs sink.

③ Second Filtration
The water trickles down through sand or gravel, which filters out algae, bacteria, and some chemicals.

④ Chlorination
Chlorine is added to kill remaining organisms.

⑤ Aeration
Forcing air through the water releases gases, reducing unpleasant odors and taste.

⑥ Additional Treatment
Sodium or lime may be used to soften hard water. Some communities add fluoride, which helps prevent tooth decay.

Chapter 3 **H ◆ 85**

A Typical Treatment Plant

EXPLORING
Drinking-Water Treatment

As students read aloud the descriptions of the steps in drinking-water treatment, have other students create a table on the blackboard showing each step and its results. Encourage students to investigate the process used at the local drinking-water treatment plant, if there is one. Students can compare the process shown here with the local process by making flow charts of each. **learning modality: visual**

Building Inquiry Skills: Predicting

Materials *pond water, 2 L plastic bottle with top, funnel, 2 large plastic jars*
Time 15 minutes

Challenge students to model aeration. First, invite them to examine and smell the pond water and predict how the pond water will change after being aerated. To aerate the water, students can pour it through a funnel into a clean, 2-L plastic bottle. Then with the top on, students should shake the bottle vigorously. After shaking, they should pour the water into a jar. Finally, students should pour the water back and forth between that jar and another 10 times. Then have students examine and smell the water to test their predictions. **learning modality: kinesthetic**

Program Resources

Science Explorer Series *From Bacteria to Plants,* Chapter 2, has more information about bacteria.

Media and Technology

Transparencies "Exploring Drinking-Water Treatment," Transparency 8

Answers to Self-Assessment

✓ *Checkpoint*

Any five: Cloudiness, odor, color, acidity, hardness, and presence of disease-causing organisms

Caption Question

Figure 2 A concentration of 0.09 ppm of arsenic is unacceptable. A concentration of 0.05 ppm of cyanide is acceptable.

Ongoing Assessment

Writing Have students explain in writing how each step in drinking-water treatment affects water quality by describing how the step affects appearance, taste, acidity, hardness, and/or the presence of disease-causing organisms.

85 ◆ H

TRY THIS

Skills Focus observing

Materials *books, 2 large bowls, water, pitcher, plastic tubing*

Time 20 minutes

Tips Cut lengths of tubing before class, at least 50–60 cm each. Demonstrate how to fill the siphon with water by completely immersing it in the water of the higher bowl. Emphasize that the finger must completely cover the end of the siphon and that no air should be allowed inside the tube.

Expected Outcome Water will flow through the siphon from the higher bowl into the lower bowl, eventually emptying the higher bowl.

Extend Students can experiment with longer siphons and circuitous routes, such as holding the middle of the tubing above the higher bowl. **learning modality: kinesthetic**

Integrating Physics

After students have read **ACTIVITY** about water pressure and distribution, divide the class into groups of three or four. Then have each group consider this hypothesis derived from a statement in the text: *In an enclosed space, water exerts pressure in all directions.* Challenge groups to design an experiment that could test this hypothesis. A design should consist of a description and a drawing. Once the designs are finished, groups could evaluate one another's experiments. Finally, encourage students to perform the experiments that seem most likely to test the hypothesis. **cooperative learning**

TRY THIS

Moving Water Uphill

In this activity you will see **ACTIVITY** how a device called a siphon can be used to move water.

1. Pile a stack of books on a table. Place one bowl on top of the books and another bowl on the table. Pour water into the higher bowl until it is about half full.

2. Submerge a piece of plastic tubing in the water in the upper bowl. When the tubing is full of water, put a finger over each end.

3. Keeping one end of the tubing underwater, place the other end in the lower, empty bowl. Release both fingers and watch what happens.

Observing In what direction does the water first have to travel to get out of the higher bowl? Can you explain this movement?

The next step is to chlorinate the water. If you have ever been to a public swimming pool, you are familiar with the smell of chlorine. Chlorine is added to drinking water for the same reason it is added to swimming pools—to kill disease-causing microorganisms. At this point, the water is usually ready to be distributed to homes. Sometimes other chemicals are added to kill specific organisms, such as the *Cryptosporidium* you read about earlier.

Water from an aquifer may require less treatment than water from a lake or river. Flowing through the rocks or sand naturally filters and purifies the water. However, most public water supplies that use a groundwater source still add chlorine to kill disease-causing organisms.

Public health officials regularly test samples from water treatment plants to assess water quality. They test for the substances covered by the drinking-water standards, including chemicals, dissolved solids, pH, hardness, and disease-causing organisms. Private well owners should also test their water regularly to make sure no treatment is needed.

✓ *Checkpoint* *What is the goal of most drinking-water treatment systems?*

Water Distribution

 INTEGRATING PHYSICS Once it has been treated, the water is ready to be distributed to homes and businesses. From a treatment plant, water goes to a central pumping station. There the water is pumped into an underground network of steel or concrete pipes called water mains. The water mains branch off to smaller pipes. These feed into smaller copper or plastic pipes that carry water into houses and other buildings.

Water pressure causes the water to move through this system of pipes. Whenever water is in an enclosed space, it exerts pressure in all directions. For example, water pressure pushes water through a garden hose. If the hose springs a leak, a jet of water sprays out of the hole into the air. The pressure pushes the water out through the hole.

Pumping stations are designed to keep water pressure steady throughout the system. If there is a leak in one of the pipes, water escapes—just as it did from the garden hose—and the pressure drops. A typical distribution system can push water up against the downward force of gravity about five or six stories. High-rise buildings must use additional pumps to raise the water to higher floors.

Rather than use a central pumping station, some communities store their water high in the air! No, not as clouds or water vapor, but in a water tower or tank on top of a hill. Treated

Background

Facts and Figures The use of chlorine as a disinfectant in drinking-water treatment began in the United States in 1908. Chlorination has proved quite effective in reducing the outbreak of waterborne diseases caused by bacteria and other pathogens, though such diseases still sicken an estimated 940,000 Americans every year. Filtration of the water before chlorination is important. First, it removes organisms that chlorine might not destroy. Second, it removes organic matter that might react with chlorine and form harmful compounds. Because these compounds may cause diseases in humans, treatment plants add as little chlorine as possible. Ozone (O_3) is being used as a disinfectant instead of chlorine in some cities. As it kills microorganisms, it breaks down into oxygen gas, which improves water quality.

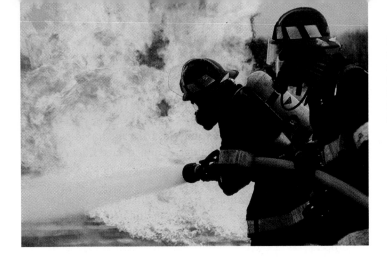

Figure 3 These firefighters rely on water pressure to force streams of water through the air. *Predicting If the diameter of the firehose were larger, would the spray be more powerful or less powerful?*

water is pumped up into the water tower. When the water is released, the weight of the water supplies additional pressure that sends the water rushing downward, filling the town's water mains and pipes.

Treating Wastewater

Finally, after a long journey, the water reaches your house. You take a shower, flush the toilet, or wash a load of laundry. What happens now to the used water that goes down the drain? That wastewater and the different kinds of wastes in it are called **sewage.** You might be surprised to learn that this water could someday return as part of your drinking water! No need to worry, however. The wastewater goes through many changes to make this possible.

In many communities, a network of pipes called sanitary sewers carries sewage away from homes. Sanitary sewers are separated from storm sewers, which drain rainwater and runoff from sidewalks, lawns, and parking lots.

Cities and towns have had sanitary sewer systems for only about the last 200 years. Before then, wastewater was often dumped into open gutters and allowed to run directly back into rivers or oceans. Although people eventually realized that this practice helped spread disease, it still occurs in some places, both in the United States and the rest of the world. Coastal cities, in particular, sometimes still pump untreated sewage into the oceans.

Most communities treat their wastewater to make it safe to return to the environment. Different communities may use different treatment processes.

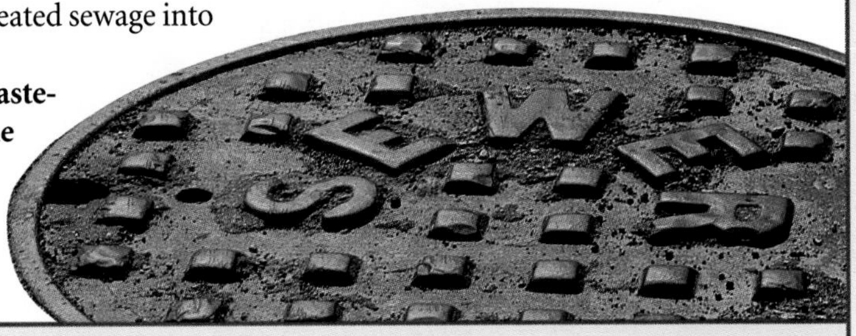

Figure 4 If your community has a sanitary sewer system, you may have seen a sewer cover like this one in the street. Sanitary sewers carry wastewater away from homes and businesses.

Treating Wastewater

Real-Life Learning

ACTIVITY

Some students may have little experience or understanding of the plumbing of a building. Have a member of the school's custodial staff lead students on a tour of the separate water and sewage pipes running into and out of the school. This could begin in a school restroom and end in the school basement. Encourage students to develop a list of questions about construction and maintenance before the tour begins. **learning modality: kinesthetic**

Using the Visuals: Figure 4

ACTIVITY

Help students understand that a sewer cover functions as a door into the sanitary sewer system. Ask: **What is the purpose of this removable cover?** *(To function as a point of access for workers to maintain the system.)* Then have students identify the location of such sewer covers on their way home from school or near their homes. In class the next day, make a list on the board of the locations they have found. Then challenge students to use the locations to make inferences about the underground sewer system. **learning modality: visual**

Program Resources

Science Explorer Series *Motion, Forces, and Energy,* Chapter 3, can provide more information about pressure in fluids.

Answers to Self-Assessment

Checkpoint

The goal is to make the water safe and appealing to drink.

Caption Question

Figure 3 The spray would be less powerful because water would move more slowly through a hose with a larger diameter.

Ongoing Assessment

Skills Check Invite students to predict what would happen if the wastewater that goes down the drain somehow got into the underground network of water mains *without* going to a treatment plant. *(The drinking water would become contaminated with waste material and disease-causing organisms.)*

Treating Wastewater, continued

EXPLORING
Wastewater Treatment

Ask volunteers to read aloud the descriptions of the steps in wastewater treatment. Then ask: **In drinking-water treatment, bacteria are eliminated in three of the steps. Why are bacteria used as part of wastewater treatment?** *(In drinking-water treatment, bacteria that could be harmful to health are eliminated. In wastewater treatment, the bacteria serve the beneficial purpose of breaking down sewage.)* Challenge students to find out about the process used at the local wastewater treatment plant. Students can compare the process shown here with the local process by making flowcharts of each. **learning modality: visual**

Building Inquiry Skills: Controlling Variables

Materials *2 clear plastic soda bottles with caps, pond water with mud, funnel, permanent marker*

ACTIVITY

Time 10 minutes for setup; 5 minutes each day for 5 days

Divide students into groups and have each group investigate the settling process. First, have students mark the two bottles as A and B. Next, they should use a funnel to pour pond water into the bottles, making each about half full. Caps should then be screwed tightly onto both bottles. Finally, students should place both bottles on a table for two days. Bottle A should be left undisturbed; bottle B should be shaken three times a day each day. After two days, have students describe the experiment, identify a variable and a control, and draw conclusions about differences in the water of the two bottles. Tell students not to taste the pond water and to wash their hands after handling it. **cooperative learning**

You can follow one typical wastewater treatment process, called a trickling filter system, in *Exploring Wastewater Treatment*.

During primary treatment, deposits of fine solids called **sludge** settle out from the wastewater. Despite its unappetizing name, sludge is a useful material. It can be treated with heat and chemicals and used as fertilizer. Sludge can also be reused in secondary treatment. In one method, bacteria are added to the sludge to create "activated sludge." The activated sludge is mixed into the wastewater. The bacteria then break down the remaining sewage in the water.

If necessary, additional treatment may remove other substances from the water, such as metals and industrial chemicals. Once wastewater has gone through an effective treatment process, it is safe to return to the environment. It may be released

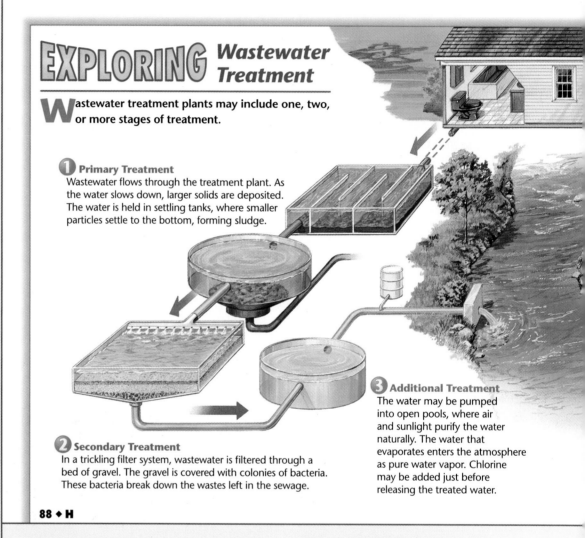

EXPLORING Wastewater Treatment

Wastewater treatment plants may include one, two, or more stages of treatment.

1 Primary Treatment
Wastewater flows through the treatment plant. As the water slows down, larger solids are deposited. The water is held in settling tanks, where smaller particles settle to the bottom, forming sludge.

2 Secondary Treatment
In a trickling filter system, wastewater is filtered through a bed of gravel. The gravel is covered with colonies of bacteria. These bacteria break down the wastes left in the sewage.

3 Additional Treatment
The water may be pumped into open pools, where air and sunlight purify the water naturally. The water that evaporates enters the atmosphere as pure water vapor. Chlorine may be added just before releasing the treated water.

88 ◆ H

Background

Facts and Figures Raw wastewater is about 1,000 parts water for every 1 part waste; that is, about 99.9 percent of wastewater is water. During primary treatment of wastewater, 30–50 percent of the organic matter present in raw sewage settles to the bottom of the settling tanks. By the end of secondary treatment, as much as 90 percent of the total organic matter has been removed.

Media and Technology

 Transparencies "Exploring Wastewater Treatment," Transparency 9; "Cutaway View of a Septic Tank," Transparency 10

Exploring Life Science Videodisc Unit 2, Side 2, "Positive Bacteria"

Chapter 4

back into lakes, rivers, and oceans or pumped back into the ground. The water rejoins the water cycle. Eventually, it could return to the same reservoir or aquifer that is the source of your water supply.

Treated wastewater that is not quite clean enough for drinking can still be used in other ways. For instance, some communities use this "gray water" to water the grass on golf courses or public parks. Gray water can also be used for irrigation or as cooling water in factories.

Septic Systems

Just as some people rely on private wells rather than public water supplies, many people are not connected to public sanitary sewer systems. They use other methods to dispose of sewage, such as a septic system. A septic system like the one in Figure 5 includes a **septic tank,** an underground tank containing bacteria that treat wastewater as it passes through. Sludge settles to the bottom of the tank and must be cleaned out regularly so it does not fill up the tank. The remaining water filters out through holes in the septic tank into the ground around it. The area around the septic tank that the water filters through is called a **leach field.** Over time, the remaining wastes break down naturally in the soil of the leach field.

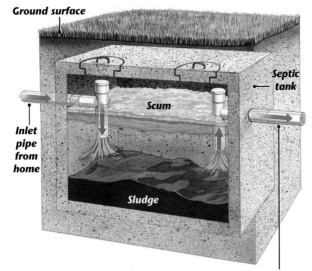

Ground surface

Septic tank

Scum

Inlet pipe from home

Sludge

Outlet pipe to leach field

Figure 5 Sewage flows into a septic tank, where bacteria break down the waste material. Cleaner water leaves the tank and flows into a leach field. There, the water slowly releases the remaining dissolved minerals into the soil.

Section 1 Review

1. How does drinking-water treatment improve water quality?
2. What is the goal of wastewater treatment?
3. List the main sources of drinking water. Classify each source as surface water or groundwater.
4. Describe how drinking water is delivered to homes and businesses in a community.
5. **Thinking Critically** **Inferring** Explain why it is important to know the depth and location of drinking-water wells before deciding where to build a septic tank.

> **Check Your Progress** CHAPTER PROJECT 3
>
> Now you are ready to plan the steps of your water treatment system. What will each step accomplish? What materials will you use to perform each step? Draw a diagram of your system and a flow-chart showing how it will work. Check your plans with your teacher. (Hint: Be sure to consider how your treatment unit will be constructed. How will you hold the pieces in place?)

Program Resources

◆ **Teaching Resources** 3-1 Review and Reinforce, p. 73; 3-1 Enrich, p. 74

Media and Technology

 Interactive Student Tutorial CD-ROM H-3

3 Assess

Section 1 Review Answers

1. Drinking-water treatment removes unwanted substances from the water and makes it safe and appealing to drink.
2. The goal of wastewater treatment is to make it safe to return to the environment.
3. The main sources are rivers, lakes, and reservoirs, which are surface water, and aquifers, which are groundwater.
4. From a treatment plant, water goes to a central pumping station, where it is pumped to homes and businesses through an underground system of pipes.
5. Water from a septic tank flows through holes into a leach field. If a septic tank is built too close to a well, the wastewater from the tank could mix with the water around the well and make the water unsafe to drink.

> **Check Your Progress** CHAPTER PROJECT 3
>
> Review each students' flow chart and water-treatment design. Make sure each design has at least two steps. Help students evaluate their designs by asking them to explain what each step is supposed to accomplish. When satisfied that a design has been well thought out, give the go-ahead to begin assembling the system.

Performance Assessment

Drawing Have students make a drawing of a fictional town, focusing on its water source, how its water is treated, how its water is distributed, and how its wastewater is treated. In their drawings, students can use representative illustrations to stand for the various parts, such as a treatment plant, water mains, a home, and so on. Portfolio Students can save their drawings in their portfolio.

Objectives

After completing the lesson, students will be able to

◆ describe conditions that can result in a water shortage and list sources of fresh water for the future;

◆ explain how water can be conserved.

Key Terms drought, conservation, desalination

1 Engage/Explore

Activating Prior Knowledge

Begin by eliciting a list of common household uses of water. Write this list on the board. Ask: **How could you use less water for each of these uses?** *(Students should propose ways to conserve water for each use, such as taking shorter showers, not running water while brushing teeth, and not watering the yard in the bright sun.)* Then challenge students to think of reasons why water should not be wasted.

········· **DISCOVER** ·········

Skills Focus predicting
Materials *large measuring cup, water, plastic dropper, 2 small bowls, spoons, stopwatch*
Time 15 minutes
Tips Use a relatively small plastic dropper in order to accentuate the drop in the level of the water in the cup when the rate is increased in Step 4. Tell students to clean up any water spills, using a sponge or paper towel.
Expected Outcome Students should infer that increased demand will diminish the amount of water if the supply is constant over time. They should also infer that decreasing demand is one way to keep the supply at a constant level.
Think It Over Answers may vary. A typical answer might suggest that the water user must decrease the rate of use by removing a spoonful every two or three dropperfuls, depending on dropper size.

SECTION 2 Balancing Water Needs

DISCOVER ·················· **ACTIVITY**

Can You Reach a Balance?

1. Fill a large measuring cup with water to represent a reservoir. Record the level of the water. One partner, the water supplier, should have a plastic dropper and a small bowl of water. The other partner, the water user, should have a spoon and an empty bowl.

2. Start a stopwatch. For two minutes, the water supplier should add water to the measuring cup one dropperful at a time. Each time the water supplier adds a dropperful of water, the water user should remove one spoonful of water from the reservoir.

3. At the end of two minutes, record the level of water in the cup.

4. Now increase the rate of water use by removing two spoonfuls of water for every dropperful added.

5. After another two minutes, record the level of water in the cup again.

Think It Over
Predicting What changes will you need to make so that the water level in the reservoir stays constant?

GUIDE FOR READING

◆ What conditions can result in a water shortage?

◆ What are some ways industries can conserve water?

Reading Tip Before you read, write an explanation of what you think water conservation means. As you read, add to your explanation.

Has this ever happened to you? You're eating dinner with your family and you ask someone to pass the rolls. As the basket makes its way around the table, each person takes a roll. By the time it gets to you, there's nothing left in the basket but crumbs!

This scenario is an example of a limited resource, the rolls, being used by many people. The same thing can happen to a river! For example, the Colorado River holds a resource that is precious in the Southwest—water. In this desert region there is little precipitation to provide water for people's needs. As the river flows through seven states and into Mexico, it is tapped again and again to provide water for drinking, irrigation, and other uses. The river's mouth at the Gulf of California is now often only a dry riverbed.

Figure 6 Cracks appear in the dry soil of an empty riverbed.

90 ◆ H

READING STRATEGIES

Study and Comprehension Help students to distinguish between supply and demand by making an analogy to basketball shoes on sale in a sports store. The basketball shoes represent the supply of a resource, while the buyers of basketball shoes represent the demand. If the demand from buyers is great—if many people want to buy the shoes—then the limited supply of shoes on sale might result in a shortage of basketball shoes on sale.

Vocabulary Call students' attention to the boldface term *desalination* on page 94. Explain that *de* is a word part from Latin that means "away," and *sali* is also from Latin and means "salt." Thus, *desalination* of water is a process that removes salt from water.

Water Supply and Demand

States along a river such as the Colorado have to decide how much water each one can take from the river. The deserts of Nevada and Arizona are home to some of the fastest-growing cities in the country. As more people move to Las Vegas, Phoenix, and Tucson, these cities need more water. They increase their demand on already scarce water supplies. Meanwhile, farmers claim a large share to irrigate their fields. Mining companies use water to cool down machinery and flush out the mines they dig. The cities, farms, and mines compete for water rights—the legal right to take water from a particular source.

The Southwest is just one of many places in the world where there doesn't seem to be enough water to go around. As you know, the water cycle ensures that water is a renewable resource. However, the water supply in a specific area is only renewed when there is enough time for rainfall to replace what has been used. **A water shortage occurs when there is too little water or too great a demand in an area—or both.**

Drought Places that normally get enough precipitation may experience a few years of scarce rainfall, a condition known as a **drought.** A drought affects the supply of groundwater as well as surface water. Without precipitation to recharge the aquifer, the amount of groundwater in the aquifer decreases. What happens to a well as the level of the water table falls? Imagine trying to drink from a tall glass of milk through a straw the length of a toothpick. When the level of the milk falls below the bottom of the straw, you can no longer reach it to drink. In the same way, when the water table falls below the bottom of a well, the well runs dry.

Aquifer Overuse Even without droughts, the demands of **INTEGRATING TECHNOLOGY** growing populations can result in overuse of aquifers. When water is used up faster than the aquifer can be recharged, the aquifer is depleted, or emptied.

When too much water is pumped out of an aquifer, the ground above the aquifer can sink or collapse. The ground is no longer supported by the pressure of the water inside it. To

Figure 7 Farmers require large amounts of water to irrigate crops in the dry desert. *Relating Cause and Effect What are two factors that might result in a shortage of water available for irrigation?*

---

2 Facilitate

Water Supply and Demand

Using the Visuals: Figure 7

After students have studied this figure, have them turn back to the *Science & History* feature on irrigation in Chapter 1, pages 18–19. Point out that Israel is a desert nation. Ask: **How does the irrigation technique used in Israel take into account that most of the country is very dry?** (*One purpose of the technique described is to waste as little water as possible.*) Help students understand that in Israel, the demand for irrigation water is great because the supply is short. **learning modality: verbal**

 Integrating Technology

Materials *10 2-L plastic soda bottles, box, concrete block, water*
Time 15 minutes

To model how groundwater can support the weight of the land above it, fill a box with empty plastic bottles with caps on. Have students predict what will happen when you place a concrete block on top of the bottles. Then place the block on the bottles. The bottles will collapse under its weight. Next, fill the bottles with water, screw on the caps tightly, and return them to the box. Again ask students to predict what will happen. This time when you place the block on top of the bottles, they will not collapse. **learning modality: logical/mathematical**

Program Resources

◆ **Teaching Resources** 3-2 Lesson Plan, p. 75; 3-2 Section Summary, p. 76
◆ **Product Testing Activities by** *Consumer Reports* "Testing Bottled Waters," pp. 1–8

Media and Technology

 Audiotapes English-Spanish Summary 3-2

Answers to Self-Assessment

Caption Question

Figure 7 Both too little water and too great a demand in an area could result in a shortage of water available for irrigation.

Ongoing Assessment

Writing Have each student write a TV news reporter's script for each of the following situations: too great a demand for water results in a water shortage, too little water results in a water shortage. Students should make up the details for each situation.

Social Studies
CONNECTION

After students have read the feature, ask: **What is a miller?** (*A person who grinds grain to make flour*) Explain that flowing water can be used to supply energy to run a mill. Then challenge students to come up with their solutions. Students' solutions may vary, but they should each take the following into consideration. Of the four possible uses of water, those of both the fisherman and the miller would not take water from the river. Because the fisherman needs the river to be half full, no more than 5,000 L can be withdrawn per day. The total needed by the grain farmer and the livestock owner add up to 5,100 L per day. Thus, students could assign less water to one or the other of those two in order to keep the river half full or consider reusing the water for washing animals for one of the other purposes.

Extend Students could return to this problem after reading Section 3. In a reconsideration, they could propose ways by which the grain farmer and livestock owner would not return polluted water to the river. **learning modality: logical/mathematical**

Conserving Water

Using the Visuals: Figure 8

After students have considered the conservation suggestions in the figure, have them meet in the same groups that carried out the Chapter 1 Project, Every Drop Counts. Have students review their data tables of the home water audit. Challenge group members to collaborate on a conservation suggestion for each item on their data tables. Have groups present their suggestions to the class. **cooperative learning**

Social Studies
CONNECTION

Laws regarding the use of water are a very old concept. Nearly 4,000 years ago in ancient Mesopotamia, now modern-day Iraq, a ruler named Hammurabi wrote in his code of laws:

> "If a man neglects the canal so that water floods a neighboring field, he shall repay the loss with his own grain."

In Your Journal

A river carries 10,000 liters of water a day through your village. Imagine that you are a member of the village council. Propose a fair way to assign water rights to the following people. (*Hint:* Think about which uses will return water to the river and which will not.)

◆ Grain farmer, wants 4,000 liters a day for watering crops

◆ Livestock owner, wants 600 liters a day for washing animals and 500 liters a day for animals to drink

◆ Fisherman, needs to keep the river at least half full for the fish to survive

◆ Miller, needs 3,500 liters a day to turn waterwheel

prevent collapse, engineers can artificially recharge an aquifer. One method is to pump water from wastewater treatment plants or industrial cooling water into shallow ponds that feed the aquifer. Another method is to inject water down wells directly into the saturated zone. However, because these techniques require expensive equipment and additional water, it is a better solution not to overuse the aquifer.

✓ *Checkpoint* *How can a drought cause a well to run dry?*

Conserving Water

During a water shortage, people often pay more attention to how they use water. They look for ways to avoid wasting water both at home and at work. Using a resource wisely so that it will not be used up is called **conservation.**

In the Home Most people in the United States have access to as much clean, safe water as they want. As a result, it is often easy to use more water than needed without thinking much about it. But as Figure 8 shows, there are some simple things you can do to help conserve water around your home.

Can these suggestions really make a difference? Figure it out. How long do you stand under the shower? For every minute, you use about 18 liters of water. If you stand under the shower for 10 minutes, that's about 180 liters. But if you showered for 5 minutes instead, you would use only 90 liters. And if each student in a class of 25 showered for 5 minutes instead of 10, they would save a total of 2,250 liters of water—enough to fill 22 trash barrels! As you can see, small efforts by many individuals can add up to a lot of water savings.

In Agriculture As you learned in Chapter 1, the biggest use of water in the United States is for agriculture. In the last few decades, farmers have found new ways to use less water. When water is carried into fields in open canals or ditches, much of it is lost through evaporation. Using pipes to carry water reduces the time that water is exposed to the air. Two such methods are sprinkler irrigation and drip irrigation. Sprinkler irrigation sprays water onto crops from overhead pipes. Drip irrigation distributes water through pipes with tiny holes. The water drips directly onto the soil near the plants' roots so that very little is wasted.

In Industry Paper mills, oil refineries, chemical factories, and other industries have made changes in manufacturing processes to use less water. For example, in the 1950s it took about 227,000 liters of water to make 1,000 kilograms of

Background

Facts and Figures An estimate from the World Resources Institute is that 65–70 percent of water used by people throughout the world is wasted, through leaks, evaporation, runoff, and similar losses. The United States wastes about 50 percent of the water it withdraws. Irrigation accounts for almost 70 percent of world water use; about two-thirds of that is wasted. One way to conserve water is to use treated wastewater for irrigation. Israel projects to use 80 percent of its wastewater for this purpose by the year 2000.

In the typical U.S. home, bathing (including showering), flushing toilets, and washing hands accounts for about 78 percent of water used. Water-saving showerheads and low-flow toilets can prevent a good deal of that waste. In 1994, a federal law mandated that all new toilets sold in the U.S. would use no more than 6 L per flush.

writing paper. By the 1980s, paper mills needed only half that much water to produce the same amount of paper.

New water-saving techniques help industries save money in water costs and meet the requirements of environmental laws. **Reducing water use, recycling water, and reusing water are three major forms of water conservation by industries.** These approaches conserve water while also reducing the amount of wastewater that plants release. For example, some factories that use water to cool machinery are building lagoons on their property. The heated water cools off in the lagoons and then can be used again. Other factories are replacing water-cooling systems with cooling systems that use air. Another change is to use high-pressure water sprays to clean products and equipment instead of dipping the objects in large tanks of water.

Fresh Water for the Future

As the number of people in the world increases, so does the need for water. Where can people find new sources of water for the future? One obvious place would seem to be the other 97 percent of water on Earth—the salt water in the oceans. For thousands

Sharpen your Skills

Predicting

Find a leaking faucet in your school or home, or turn on a faucet just enough to produce a very slow drip. How much water do you think will drip from the faucet in half an hour? Write down your prediction. Place a large measuring cup under the faucet. After half an hour, check the cup. How does the result compare with your prediction? How much water would you save per day if you fixed the leaking faucet?

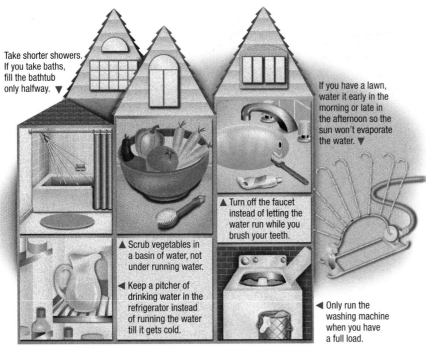

Take shorter showers. If you take baths, fill the bathtub only halfway. ▼

If you have a lawn, water it early in the morning or late in the afternoon so the sun won't evaporate the water. ▼

▲ Turn off the faucet instead of letting the water run while you brush your teeth.

▲ Scrub vegetables in a basin of water, not under running water.

◄ Keep a pitcher of drinking water in the refrigerator instead of running the water till it gets cold.

◄ Only run the washing machine when you have a full load.

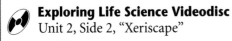
Figure 8 There are many simple ways to conserve water around the home. *Developing Hypotheses Which of these ideas do you think would save the most water per day in your home? How could you test your hypothesis?*

Predicting

Materials *large measuring cup*

Time 5 minutes for setup; 5 minutes for results

Tips Contact a member of your school's custodial staff to find a leaking faucet somewhere in the building. Students can extrapolate from their data how much water would be wasted in a month or year by multiplying by the appropriate number of minutes and days.

Expected Outcome The amount of water that drips into the cup will vary; in general, students will underestimate the amount.

Extend Ask a custodian to fix a leaking school faucet while students watch. Students can then use this knowledge to help fix a leaking faucet at home.

learning modality: logical/ mathematical

Fresh Water for the Future

Integrating Chemistry

Ask students: **How does the process of distillation produce fresh water from salt water?** *(The saltwater solution evaporates, leaving the salt behind. When the water condenses, it is pure fresh water.)* **How does distillation compare to the water cycle you studied in Chapter 1?** *(The processes are similar since both include evaporation and condensation.)* Guide students in a comparison of the solar energy that drives the water cycle and the energy used for desalination. Ask: **What is a major drawback in using this method of desalination?** *(The cost of energy, such as electricity, needed to drive the process)* **learning modality: verbal**

Ongoing Assessment

Skills Check Have students make a concept map that includes all the suggestions mentioned in the text for how water can be conserved.

Media and Technology

Exploring Life Science Videodisc
Unit 2, Side 2, "Xeriscape"

Chapter 7

Answers to Self-Assessment

☑ *Checkpoint*

A drought can cause the water table to fall below the bottom of the well.

Caption Question

Figure 8 Answers may vary. A typical answer: Taking shorter showers would save the most water. This could be tested by measuring the water saved by each idea and then comparing.

3 Assess

Section 2 Review Answers

1. Answers may vary. A typical answer might describe a drought or a situation in which there is too great a demand for the supply of water.

2. Reducing water use, recycling water, and reusing water are three major forms of water conservation by industries.

3. The aquifer can be depleted if water is used up faster than the aquifer can be recharged. Overpumping can cause the ground above the aquifer to sink or collapse.

4. Tugboats could tow a wrapped iceberg from Antarctica to a coastal region of Africa or South America and the water could be piped to shore as the iceberg melted.

5. Answers may vary. A typical answer: A community should be able to limit water use in times of shortage but not when water is in good supply.

Science at Home

Encourage students to introduce this activity at **ACTIVITY** home by explaining to family members that water is a precious resource that should not be wasted. Students might do this with more than one family member, making it into a friendly competition about who can conserve the most water. Tell students that if the tape will not stick to the wet sink, they could mark the levels with bar soap.

Performance Assessment

Writing Challenge each student to assume the role of a government official in a region experiencing a severe drought. Because of the water shortage, the official has been asked to recommend a set of regulations limiting water use by homes and businesses. Students should write a brief introduction to the regulations and then list ten specific recommendations.

Figure 9 The ocean is one possible source of drinking water for the future.
Applying Concepts How can ocean water be made suitable for drinking?

of years, people have tried different methods to make salty ocean water drinkable.

Desalination The process of obtaining fresh water from salt
INTEGRATING CHEMISTRY water is called **desalination.** One method of desalination, called distillation, is to boil water so that it evaporates, leaving the salt behind. The water vapor is then condensed to produce liquid fresh water. Another method involves freezing the water, which also leaves the salt behind. Still another method is to pump water at high pressure through a very fine filter. The filter separates out pure water and returns saltier water to the ocean.

Desalination is very expensive because of the energy and equipment it requires. In spite of the cost, however, Saudi Arabia, Kuwait, Israel, and other nations in the dry Middle East depend on this technology. A few cities in the United States, such as Santa Barbara, California, have also built desalination plants.

Icebergs Some people think that icebergs are another possible source of fresh water for dry regions. Tugboats could tow a wrapped iceberg from Antarctica to a coastal area of Africa or South America. An iceberg would provide millions of liters of pure water that could be piped to shore as the iceberg melted. However, such plans raise environmental questions: How would a huge mass of ice offshore affect local weather? What would happen to living things as the ice cooled the water around it? These questions need to be answered before icebergs can be seen as a solution to Earth's future water needs.

Section 2 Review

1. Describe a situation that could lead to a water shortage in a community.
2. Name three ways that industries can conserve water.
3. Describe the possible effects overpumping might have on an aquifer.
4. Explain how an iceberg might provide drinking water in the future.
5. **Thinking Critically Making Judgments** Do you think communities should be able to limit how often people water their lawns or wash their cars? Why or why not?

Science at Home

Place a stopper over the drain in a sink. Ask a family member to brush his or her teeth over the sink, allowing the water to run until he or she is done. Mark the level of the water in the sink with a small piece of tape. Remove the stopper and let the water drain. Replace the stopper and have the person repeat the brushing, this time turning the water on only when needed. Mark the water level with another piece of tape. Point out the difference in the amount of water used in each case.

Answers to Self-Assessment

Caption Question

Figure 9 Various methods of desalination can make ocean water suitable for drinking.

Program Resources

◆ **Teaching Resources** 3-2 Review and Reinforce, p. 77; 3-2 Enrich, p. 78
Science Explorer Series *Chemical Building Blocks,* Chapter 2, can provide more information about phase changes.

Media and Technology

Interactive Student Tutorial CD-ROM H-3

GETTING THE SALT OUT

Desalination plants use many methods to produce fresh water from ocean water. In this lab, you will make a model of a desalination plant using the method of distillation.

Problem

How can distillation be used to obtain fresh water from salt water?

Materials

hot plate	aluminum foil	250-mL beaker
plastic spoon	water, 100 mL	shallow pan
ice	plastic tube	500-mL flask
stirring rod	rubber stopper	salt
rubber tubing, 50 cm		

Procedure

1. Pour 100 mL of water into the flask.
2. Add one spoonful of salt to the water in the flask and stir until dissolved. The solution should not be cloudy.
3. Gently insert the plastic tube through the hole of the rubber stopper. Do not force the tube into the hole; ask your teacher for help if you are having difficulty.
4. Insert one end of the plastic tube into the rubber tubing.
5. Put the rubber stopper in the flask. The bottom of the plastic tube should be above the surface of the solution.
6. Cover the beaker with aluminum foil. Press the edges of the foil against the beaker.
7. Push the free end of the rubber tubing through the center of the aluminum foil covering the top of the beaker.
8. Place the beaker in the pan, surrounded by ice.
9. Put the flask on the hot plate, keeping it away from the pan of ice. Turn the hot plate on. Bring the solution to a boil. **CAUTION:** *Do not touch the hot plate or flask. Do not allow the solution to boil completely away.*
10. Observe what happens in the flask and the beaker. Continue heating the solution until a liquid has accumulated in the beaker.
11. Turn off the hot plate and allow the flask and the beaker to cool. What is left behind in the flask? Record your observations.

Analyze and Conclude

1. What happened to the water in the flask during the boiling process? What happened inside the beaker?
2. How does the liquid collected in the beaker differ from the liquid in the flask?
3. What is the purpose of the ice in this activity?
4. **Think About It** Imagine building a desalination plant that uses the method of distillation to produce water for a city. What difficulties might you encounter in using this process on such a large scale?

More to Explore

How could you change the setup and procedure to recover fresh water from salt water without using the hot plate? Design an experiment to accomplish this goal. Obtain your teacher's permission before carrying out your experiment.

Program Resources

◆ **Teaching Resources** Skills Lab blackline masters, pp. 90–91

Safety

Caution students to wear the oven mitt any time they touch the hot flask. Caution them to keep water away from electrical outlets and the hot plate plug. Do not allow the water to boil completely away. Review the safety guidelines in Appendix A.

Making Models

Getting the Salt Out

Preparing for Inquiry

Key Concept Distillation is one method that can be used in desalination.

Skills Objective Students will be able to
◆ make a model of a desalination plant using distillation.

Time 40 minutes

Advance Planning Obtain bags of ice on the morning of the lab. Cut the rubber tubing into 50-cm lengths.

Alternative Materials In place of salt, use "instant seawater," which can be found at pet stores.

Guiding Inquiry

Troubleshooting the Experiment

◆ Make sure students do not add too much salt to the water in the flask. The solution should not be cloudy.
◆ Demonstrate how to insert the plastic tube gently through the hole of the rubber stopper. Wetting the tube or rubbing it with glycerin can help.
◆ Warn students not to tear a large hole in the aluminum foil when they push the rubber tubing through its center.

Expected Outcome

The water in the flask should boil away, leaving the salt behind. The water vapor should move through the tubing and condense in the beaker.

Analyze and Conclude

1. It evaporated; water vapor from the flask condensed in the beaker.
2. It is fresh water; the flask has salt water.
3. The ice served to cool the water vapor, causing it to condense in the beaker.
4. Answers may vary. A typical answer: It would require a lot of heat to boil all the water required for a city. Generating this heat to run the desalination plant might prove too costly.

Extending the Inquiry

More to Explore Designs may vary. A typical design might suggest using the same setup, though with the flask placed in direct sunlight.

The Ogallala Aquifer

Purpose To provide students with an understanding of the problems associated with overuse of water resources.

Role-Play

Time a day to prepare; 30 minutes for role-play

Divide students into four groups: (1) a five-member "fact-finding committee" appointed by Congress, (2) a group to argue for more regulations and charges on water use, (3) a group to argue that different water-saving farming practices should be instituted, and (4) a group to argue that current practices should continue. Tell the first group to work out rules and an agenda for a public meeting on water use on the Great Plains. Students in each of the other groups can work together to prepare a presentation to the committee during the public meeting. Then hold the public meeting, using the rules and agenda worked out by the committee members. Encourage students to act the way they think citizens would act in a real public meeting of this kind.

Extend Challenge students to find out whether water shortages are a problem in your area. Suggest that they contact the local water department to ask what plans are in place in case of a drought or some other water problem.

You Decide

Have students individually complete the first two steps before the role-play as a way of preparing themselves for their participation. After the role-play is concluded, students can complete the last step, using what they learned in the role-play for finding a solution to the problem.

 Students can save their letters in their portfolio.

The Ogallala Aquifer

The Ogallala Aquifer lies beneath eight states of the Great Plains. It contains about 4 quadrillion liters of groundwater—about the amount of water in Lake Huron. Rainfall is scarce on the Great Plains. But by pumping water out of the aquifer, farmers can grow cotton, wheat, sorghum, and corn to feed cattle. More than one third of the nation's livestock are raised in this area.

Water in the Ogallala was trapped there during the last Ice Age, about 12,000 years ago. Now, due to the demands of irrigation, water levels are dropping much faster than the aquifer can recharge. In certain parts of the aquifer, water levels have fallen as much as 12 meters since 1980. Farmers recognize that the Ogallala cannot withstand this heavy use for long. However, not all agree on what should be done.

The Issues

Should Water Use Be Regulated? One way to reduce water use might be to charge people for water. But who owns the water and who would determine the cost? In most of the Great Plains, water has been free to anyone who dug a well on their land. To charge for water, local governments would need to construct a public water system as in most cities. This would be a very complex and costly task. Both farmers and consumers would be affected by the charge. Higher costs for growing crops would result in higher supermarket prices for grains and meat.

Should Farmers Change Their Practices? Farmers could switch to crops such as sunflowers and grains that need less water. These crops, however, are less valuable than others for producing food and for feeding livestock. As a result, they would be less profitable than traditional crops. Farmers could use water-saving methods of irrigation. Such methods are expensive to install but eventually save both water and money.

Another possibility is "dryland farming," a method that was used by pioneer farmers. This method involves keeping the soil moist using only rainwater. Because dryland farming depends on the amount of rainfall, it is unpredictable. It may not produce large harvests.

Should Current Use Continue? Many residents of the Great Plains depend on the aquifer for a living. Some people feel that farmers there must continue their present water use in order to compete with farmers elsewhere in the nation and around the world. They feel that people today should not have to suffer in order to preserve the aquifer for future generations. New sources of water may be discovered, or better methods of transporting water to the Great Plains may be developed. Better irrigation techniques that use less water may also be invented. But other people feel that since these possibilities are not certain, water use must be greatly reduced now to save the aquifer.

You Decide

1. Identify the Problem
In your own words, explain the problem facing the farmers on the Great Plains.

2. Analyze the Options
Make a chart of the solutions mentioned. List advantages and drawbacks of each. Who would benefit from each solution? Who would suffer?

3. Find a Solution
As a resident of the Great Plains, write a letter to the newspaper proposing a solution to the Ogallala problem.

Background

The Ogallala is the largest known aquifer in the world. Water from the aquifer is used to irrigate nearly 6 million hectares, or about 20 percent of all cropland in the United States. Each year, about 26 billion m³ of groundwater are pumped from the aquifer. Since 1950, the water table in the Ogallala has dropped an average of 30 m. In some places, the drop has been much greater. For example, the depth to groundwater in Floyd County, Texas, dropped from about 25 m in 1950 to about 75 m in 1984, despite a significant decrease of irrigated land during that time. Throughout the aquifer, water is being pumped out at about eight times the rate that natural recharge occurs. If all pumping ceased, some scientists have estimated it would take at least 1,000 years for the aquifer to recover to be completely recharged.

DISCOVER ······························· ACTIVITY ····

Will the Pollution Reach Your Wells?

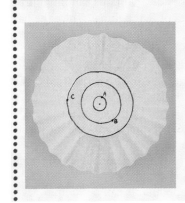

1. With a permanent marker, draw three rings on a coffee filter as shown in the picture. Draw three dots and label them A, B, and C as shown. These dots represent the locations of drinking-water supply wells.

2. Place the coffee filter on a paper plate. Moisten the coffee filter with a wet sponge. The damp coffee filter represents an aquifer.

3. Squirt five drops of food coloring onto the center of the damp coffee filter. Observe how the "pollution" travels.

Think It Over
Observing Which wells are affected by the pollution? Describe the pattern the pollution forms.

The newspaper headlines told an amazing story: "River in Flames!" "Bridges Burn As River Catches Fire!" This really happened to the Cuyahoga River in Cleveland, Ohio, in the summer of 1969. Are you wondering how a river could catch fire? What was in the Cuyahoga that allowed it to burn?

The Cuyahoga flows through a large industrial region on its way to Lake Erie. Factories along its banks used to dump their wastes into the river. Freighters spilled oil and gasoline into the water. Over time, the river became so full of chemicals and sewage that the pollution floating in it could actually burn.

Alarmed by the fire and the destruction it caused, people in Ohio began a massive campaign to clean up the Cuyahoga. Today it is safe to use for boating and fishing. The Cuyahoga River is a dramatic example of how serious water pollution can become—and of how people can work together to undo its damage.

What Is Pollution?

If you turned on your faucet and a stream of bright green water came out, you'd be fairly sure that the water contained something it shouldn't. But many things that can make water unsafe to drink don't change its color, taste, or smell. The addition of any substance that has a negative effect on water or the living things that depend on the water is called **water pollution.** Water pollution can affect surface water, groundwater, and even rain. It can result from both natural causes and human activities.

> **GUIDE FOR READING**
>
> ◆ What are some sources of water pollution?
> ◆ How does agricultural runoff affect ponds and streams?
> ◆ How can living things help clean up polluted water?
>
> *Reading Tip* As you read, make a list of sources of freshwater pollution. Write one sentence about each source.

WARNING

Fish Contaminated
DO NOT EAT

Objectives
After completing the lesson, students will be able to
◆ describe what water pollutuion is and list some of its sources;
◆ explain how runoff affects ponds and streams;
◆ describe how pollution can be prevented and how polluted water can be cleaned up.

Key Terms water pollution, point source, nonpoint source, acid rain, pesticide

1 Engage/Explore

Activating Prior Knowledge

Ask students: **What is water pollution?** *(Focus on answers that relate to the addition of any substance that has a negative effect on water or living things in the water.)* Challenge students to brainstorm a list of things that could make water polluted. List their suggestions on the board. Then as students read the section, have them classify the list by the sources of water pollution in the text.

········· DISCOVER ·········

Skills Focus observing
Materials *permanent marker, coffee filter, paper plate, wet sponge, food coloring, plastic dropper*
Time 15 minutes
Tips Students should allow time for the marker to dry before wetting the coffee filter. Make sure students moisten the filter thoroughly without making it dripping wet.
Expected Outcome Students should infer that aquifer pollution can affect more than just the place at which it first occurs.
Think It Over Answers may vary. A typical answer should mention that the "pollution" spreads out unevenly, following tiny dips and creases in the paper, just like in an aquifer. Wells closer to the center are affected more than wells farther away.

ACTIVITY

READING STRATEGIES

Reading Tip Point out that the four section heads beginning with "Human Wastes" provide a primary list of sources of freshwater pollution. The subheads under "Industrial Wastes" are specific types of pollution. For each of these heads, students should find a sentence or phrase that explains that source of pollution. For example: *Dumping human wastes into drinking water can spread disease.*

Program Resources

◆ **Teaching Resources** 3-3 Lesson Plan, p. 79; 3-3 Section Summary, p. 80
◆ **Integrated Science Laboratory Manual** H-3, "Examining Pollution of the Water"

Media and Technology

🎧 **Audiotapes** English-Spanish Summary 3-3

2 Facilitate

What Is Pollution?

 Integrating Life Science

Help students recall their knowledge of food chains and food webs by displaying an illustration of a food chain or food web from a life science text. Ask: **If you were to show this food chain as a pyramid, which of the organisms would you place at the top?** (*The large, meat-eating animals*) Challenge students to use the food chain to trace a pollutant from the producers (plants or algae) to the top consumers. **learning modality: visual**

Using the Visuals: Figure 11

Ask students: **What can you infer from the pyramid shape of the illustration?** *ACTIVITY* (*The number of organisms that make up each level decreases at each higher level of the pyramid.*) Guide students in understanding that the total mass of the organisms at a level is greater than the total mass of the level above. Thus, if the amount of DDT stays the same as it moves from a lower level to a higher level, the concentration would increase. Have students model this increase in concentration by forming a triangle: 10 students in the first row, 7 students in the next, and so on. Give a paper clip to each student in the first row, and have them pass the clips up the triangle. Students will see that the concentration of paper clips becomes greater at each succeeding level. **learning modality: kinesthetic**

The substances that cause water pollution are called pollutants. Disease-causing organisms such as the *Cryptosporidium* you read about in Section 1 are one form of pollutant. As Figure 10 shows, other types of pollutants include toxic, or poisonous, chemicals and metals, as well as radioactive substances.

INTEGRATING LIFE SCIENCE Some types of pollutants can build up in the bodies of living things. Trace the path of one such pollutant in Figure 11. The pesticide DDT dissolves in water and is absorbed by microscopic algae. The algae, which contain only low levels of the chemical, are eaten by small water animals. When frogs or fish eat these smaller animals, they also consume the chemicals from the algae these animals had eaten. The frogs and fish are in turn eaten by birds or other animals. Each larger organism consumes a greater number of the smaller organisms, and therefore more of the DDT.

When humans eat the fish from such a pond, the toxic chemicals build up in their bodies in the same way. Over a long time, even tiny amounts of certain pollutants can build up to levels that can cause birth defects or illnesses such as cancer. Drinking impure water or eating contaminated fish are not the only ways that pollutants can affect humans. Bathing or swimming in polluted water can irritate the skin or cause more serious problems.

Point and Nonpoint Sources

To clean up a polluted body of water like the Cuyahoga River, people first need to identify the source of the pollution to prevent further damage. **The major sources of water pollution are human wastes, industrial wastes, agricultural chemicals, and runoff from roads.**

Figure 10 This table lists some examples of the different types of freshwater pollutants. *Relating Cause and Effect Why might it be helpful to know the source of a particular pollutant detected in a body of water?*

Freshwater Pollutants		
Kind of Pollutant	**Examples**	**Sources**
Disease-causing organisms	*Giardia, Cryptosporidium,* bacteria	Human wastes, runoff from livestock pens
Pesticides and fertilizers	DDT, nitrates, phosphates	Runoff from farm fields, golf courses
Industrial chemicals	PCBs, carbon tetrachloride, dioxin	Factories, industrial waste disposal sites
Metals	Lead, mercury, copper	Factories, waste disposal sites
Radioactive wastes	Uranium, carbon-14	Medical and scientific disposal sites, nuclear power plants
Petroleum products	Oil, gasoline	Road runoff, leaking underground storage tanks

Background

Facts and Figures Examples of point sources of freshwater pollution include factories, mines, and wastewater treatment plants. Because these sources can be identified, they are much easier to control than nonpoint sources. Examples of nonpoint sources include septic tanks, lawns, streets and parking lots, farm fields, pastures, and construction sites. Nonpoint pollution from agriculture is responsible for about 60 percent of all pollutants entering streams and lakes.

Water pollution from the pesticide DDT is an example of a pollutant from a nonpoint source. DDT was once the most-used pesticide in the world. Its use was banned in the United States in 1972, though it is still used in other countries.

Increasing
DDT
concentration
(parts per million)

20.0

2.0

0.2

0.4

0.000003

Figure 11 A very small amount of the pesticide DDT in water can build up to harmful levels in living things. *Interpreting Diagrams Which organism ends up with the most DDT?*

Each of these sources of pollution can be a point source or a nonpoint source, depending on how the pollution enters a body of water. For example, suppose you notice a pipe gushing white sudsy water into a river. The pipe is a **point source,** a specific source of pollution that can be identified. More often, though, the source of pollution is less obvious. Pollutants may be carried along in runoff from a farm field, a street, or a construction site. The chemicals, sewage, or radioactive materials eventually flow into a lake or river or seep into groundwater and are carried far away. It's hard to trace the exact source of this pollution. A widely spread source of pollution that can't be tied to a specific point of origin is called a **nonpoint source.**

☑ *Checkpoint* *Why are nonpoint sources difficult to identify?*

Human Wastes

Today it seems obvious that dumping human wastes into drinking water can spread disease. But scientists have only understood this connection for the last 150 years.

Dr. Snow's Discovery Cholera is a disease caused by bacteria  **INTEGRATING HEALTH** that live in human wastes. Cholera causes people to become very dehydrated and can be fatal. In 1854, an English doctor named John Snow discovered the cause of a cholera outbreak in London. In the poorer

---

Sharpen your **Skills**

Classifying

Classify the following as point sources or nonpoint sources of water pollution:

◆ salt used on icy roads
◆ an open drain in a sink at a paint factory
◆ a sanitary sewer pipe with a leak
◆ fertilizer sprayed onto an orchard

Give a reason why you classified each source as you did.

Program Resources

 Science Explorer Series *Environmental Science,* Chapters 1 and 2, discuss populations, communities, and energy flow in ecosystems.

Science Explorer Series *Human Biology and Health,* Chapter 6, can provide more information on infectious diseases.

Answers to Self-Assessment

Caption Questions

Figure 10 Knowing the source might be necessary to prevent further pollution.

Figure 11 The fish-eating birds

☑ *Checkpoint*

Nonpoint sources can't be tied to specific points of origin. They may come from a widespread area.

Point and Nonpoint Sources

Sharpen your *Skills*

Classifying

Time 10 minutes

Both the salt used on icy roads and fertilizer sprayed onto an orchard are nonpoint sources, because neither can be tied to a specific point of origin. Both the open drain in a sink at a paint factory and a sanitary sewer pipe with a leak are specific sources of pollution, and thus should be classified as point sources.

Extend Have students explain what pollution would result from a leak in a sanitary sewer pipe. Then challenge them to describe how an investigator could identify the point source from a discovery of that pollution. **learning modality: logical/mathematical**

Human Wastes

Integrating Health

To familiarize students with diseases spread in water, or waterborne diseases, assign to each a disease and challenge them to make an information sheet about the disease. This sheet could include facts about the cause of the disease, the way it is spread, its symptoms, and the way it is treated and prevented. Some common waterborne diseases include cholera, typhoid fever, enteritis, bacterial dysentery, amoebic dysentery, giardiasis, schistosomiasis, and infectious hepatitis. Have students share their information sheets with the class. **learning modality: verbal**

Portfolio Students can save their information sheets in their portfolios.

Ongoing Assessment

Drawing Have students make a flow chart showing the path of a pesticide used on a farm field to water birds in a lake some distance away.

Human Wastes, continued

Using the Visuals: Figure 12

Ask students: **Where do you think this water tank might have been filled?** (*The water might have come from a well, a river, or a lake away from the city.*) Encourage students to analyze the risk to the people that the water in the tank might also be contaminated, from either human waste or animal waste. Help students understand that people in the past were always at risk because their drinking water was not treated.
learning modality: verbal

Industrial Wastes

Demonstration

Materials *2-L clear plastic soda bottle with top cut off, gravel, sand, pump sprayer from window cleaner bottle, nylon fabric, tape, water, food coloring, 2 beakers, plant sprayer*

ACTIVITY

Time 30 minutes

To show students how a chemical spill on land can pollute groundwater, make a model of groundwater contamination. Prepare the model by cutting off the top of a 2-L plastic bottle. Tape a piece of nylon fabric over the end of a pump sprayer from a bottle of window cleaner. Fill the 2-L bottle about one third full with rocks, insert the end of the pump sprayer into the rocks, and cover the rocks with an 8-cm layer of sand. Then slowly add water until the "water table" just reaches the layer of sand. Pump water out of the ground to show that the water is clear. Next, model chemical pollution by mixing food coloring with about 200 mL of water and "spilling" it onto the sand. At this point, only a little of the polluted water will seep down into the groundwater. Then model rain by spraying water onto the sand. This will move the pollution down into the groundwater. This time when you pump out groundwater, it will be polluted. Encourage students to comment on the process and the role of rain. **learning modality: visual**

sections of the city, people carried water home in buckets from public wells. After 500 people in one neighborhood died in just ten days, Dr. Snow traced the cholera to a well near a pipe carrying sewage. He ended the epidemic by removing the pump handle so no one could get water from that source. Dr. Snow's work showed the danger of releasing untreated sewage into bodies of water that might be used for drinking water.

Sewage in Cities As you know, today wastewater is usually treated before being released to the environment. However, while water treatment usually kills bacteria, some viruses and parasites are able to resist chlorine and other water treatment processes. Most of these organisms come from human or animal wastes that get into the water supply.

Figure 12 This engraving from the late 1800s shows people in Hamburg, Germany, getting water from a cart during a cholera epidemic. The city wells were closed, and water was brought in from the countryside.

During heavy rains and floods, sanitary sewers sometimes overflow and run into storm sewers. Since the storm sewers generally lead directly into surface water, the sewage from the sanitary sewers can pollute the water. For this reason, people are often told to boil water for drinking and cooking after a flood. The boiling kills many disease-causing organisms.

Sewage in Rural Areas Disposing of human waste is not just a problem in big cities. In rural areas, people must be careful where they locate septic tanks. If a tank is too near a stream or on a hill, wastewater can leak into the stream or flow into the area of a well downhill.

Wastes from cattle, pigs, and chickens can also be a problem in rural areas. They contribute disease-causing bacteria and other kinds of pollution to water that runs off from pastures and barnyards.

☑ *Checkpoint* *Why should drinking water and sewage be kept separate?*

Industrial Wastes

Most cities and towns in the United States have wastewater treatment systems that handle sewage effectively. For this reason, water pollution by factories and mines is a more serious problem than sewage in most areas of the country. Chemicals, smoke, and heated water are three types of industrial pollutants.

Background

History of Science For most of human history, people thought diseases were caused by a variety of agents, including swamp vapors and even poisons created by the movement of planets. Although John Snow proved that cholera was associated with sewage-contaminated drinking water, he did not know the actual cause of the disease. The French chemist Louis Pasteur advanced the "germ theory of disease," which states that infectious diseases are caused by specific microorganisms. In 1876, a German physician, Robert Koch, proved that bacteria can cause disease. Since then, scientists have identified the agents of most infectious diseases, including diseases associated with wastewater, such as dysentery, cholera, and typhoid fever.

Chemicals Many factory processes, especially those for making dyes and plastics or treating metals, involve toxic chemicals and strong acids. Other toxic wastes are produced as by-products, or side effects, of manufacturing and mining. Although laws now limit and control chemical pollution, some factories still release toxic chemicals directly into nearby rivers and lakes.

Another problem is leftover wastes. In the past, many industries stored toxic wastes in barrels or other containers buried underground. Over the years, however, many of these containers rusted or broke. The chemicals leaked out, polluting both the soil and the groundwater.

Smoke and Exhaust Many power plants and factories burn **INTEGRATING CHEMISTRY** coal or oil to fuel their processes. The engines of millions of cars, trucks, and buses burn gasoline. Every day, smoke and exhaust from these sources pour into the air, especially around large cities. When coal, oil, and gasoline are burned, molecules of the gases sulfur dioxide and nitrogen oxide are released into the atmosphere. There the sulfur and nitrogen react with water, forming sulfuric and nitric acids. The result is rain or other forms of precipitation that are more acidic than normal, called **acid rain.** When acid rain falls on lakes and ponds, the water can become so acidic that fish and other wildlife cannot survive. Acid rain also eats away the stone of buildings and statues.

Heat Pollution Think about how hot a metal slide gets on a sunny day. Imagine borrowing enough water from a swimming pool to cool the slide, and then returning the water to the pool. How would this change the swimming pool? Would you still want to jump in to cool off? The warm water would probably not be very refreshing.

Figure 13 Many lakes and rivers have been polluted by wastes from nearby industries. These environmental scientists are collecting water samples from a pond for testing.

Figure 14 A noisy jumble of taxis, cars, and buses crowds a city street. *Relating Cause and Effect How are these vehicles related to water pollution?*

Answers to Self-Assessment

☑ *Checkpoint*
Sewage contains bacteria, viruses, and parasites that can cause disease.

Caption Question

Figure 14 Molecules from the exhaust of vehicles pour into the air, react with water in the air to form sulfuric and nitric acids, and fall on lakes and ponds in the form of acid rain.

Real-Life Learning

ACTIVITY

Divide students into small groups and challenge each group to contact a local company to find out how it disposes of chemicals. If the companies use a hazardous waste disposal service, students might inquire about what happens to the chemicals then. Small industries and manufacturing companies might be easiest to contact. Advise groups to write a list of questions before making contact. **cooperative learning**

Integrating Chemistry

Materials *2 small potted plants, tape, marker, 2 plant sprayers, distilled water, vinegar, pH paper*

ACTIVITY

Time 20 minutes; periodic attention for 1–2 weeks

Divide students into small groups and invite each group to investigate the effects of acid rain on plants. First, students should label one plant "Water" and the other plant "Acid Rain." Then they should fill one plant sprayer with distilled water and the other with a half-and-half mixture of distilled water and vinegar. Advise students to test the two solutions with pH paper to determine the acidity of each. Then have students predict how each solution will affect the plants. Students should water each plant by spraying the soil and the plant, using distilled water on the "Water" plant and the water-vinegar mixture on the "Acid Rain" plant. Have students observe the plants for 1–2 weeks. **learning modality: kinesthetic**

Ongoing Assessment

Oral Presentation Call on students at random to explain how water can be polluted by sewage contamination, industrial chemicals, smoke and exhaust, and heat.

Agricultural Chemicals

Integrating Life Science

Bring to class several, common garden-store fertilizers. Student volunteers can read appropriate parts of the labels of the products, including the indications for use, instructions for application, and cautions if ingested or otherwise misused. Encourage students to pay special attention to how much of each product should be used and how it affects living things. In each case, ask: **If a consumer does not read the instructions, how might he or she misuse the product?** *(In most cases, consumers overapply these products.)* Have students speculate on the overuse of such products. **learning modality: verbal**

TRY THIS

Skills Focus drawing conclusions

Materials *2 wide-mouth jars with tops, masking tape, permanent marker, tap water, pond or aquarium water, liquid fertilizer, graduated cylinder*

Time 15 minutes for setup; 5 minutes every day for 1 week

Tips Use liquid fertilizer marketed for home use, which is diluted, otherwise the fertilizer may be too strong.

Expected Outcome The water in both jars will likely show algal growth, but the growth of algae in jar A will be markedly more because of the added fertilizer. Jar B is included as a control in the experiment.

Extend Aquariums often contain various water plants. Students could remove all the animals from an aquarium and add liquid fertilizer to the water, which would again encourage algal growth. That growth will eventually harm the plants, just as it would in a pond or lake.

learning modality: kinesthetic

How Do Your Algae Grow?

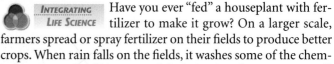

In this activity you will observe how fertilizers affect the growth of algae in pond water.

1. Label two jars A and B. Pour tap water into each jar until it is half full.

2. Add water from a pond or aquarium to each jar until it is three-quarters full.

3. Add 5 mL of liquid fertilizer to jar A only.

4. Cover both jars tightly and place them on a windowsill in the sunlight. Wash your hands with soap.

5. Observe the jars every day for a week.

Drawing Conclusions How did the fertilizer affect the growth of the algae in jar A? What was the purpose of jar B in this experiment?

Much of the water in factories is used to cool machinery or metal objects. Even if it contains no chemicals, the warm water alone can act as a pollutant. Many water organisms can live in only a narrow range of temperatures. Warm water released by a factory into a nearby river or pond raises the temperature of the water, sometimes enough to harm the living things there.

Agricultural Chemicals

INTEGRATING LIFE SCIENCE Have you ever "fed" a houseplant with fertilizer to make it grow? On a larger scale, farmers spread or spray fertilizer on their fields to produce better crops. When rain falls on the fields, it washes some of the chemicals away as runoff. Water used for irrigation also creates runoff. The fertilizers in the runoff are a nonpoint source of pollution.

The rich supply of nutrients from fertilizers encourages the growth of plants and algae in and around nearby bodies of water. As you learned in Chapter 2, ponds and lakes naturally change over time due to the process of eutrophication. As more plants grow in the water, dead plant material piles up on the bottom, making the water shallower and warmer. As the plant matter decays, the amount of oxygen in the water decreases. With the addition of fertilizers, this natural process speeds up. A thick, soupy scum of algae forms on top of the water. The scum blocks the sunlight and chokes the flow of water, changing the living conditions for other organisms.

Runoff and irrigation water also carry away other pollutants from farm fields. **Pesticides** are chemicals intended to kill insects and other organisms that damage crops. Pesticides may be sprayed on crops and then run off. Sometimes they are sprayed directly on ponds to kill mosquitoes. But at the same time, these chemicals can harm other insects or the animals that eat them.

☑ *Checkpoint* *How can chemicals used in agriculture reach streams, ponds, and lakes?*

Runoff from Roads

Have you ever noticed an oily sheen on a puddle in a parking lot after a rain shower? The sheen was probably caused by gasoline and motor oil that leaked from cars. When it rains, these oily substances are washed off along with the runoff. During cold winter weather, runoff also picks up the salt that is sprinkled on roads and sidewalks to melt ice. This runoff is a nonpoint source of pollution. Gasoline, oil, and salt pollute rivers and lakes that the runoff enters. These substances can also seep down into groundwater and pollute wells or even an entire aquifer.

Cleaning Up Polluted Water

Many pollutants are eventually removed from freshwater bodies through natural cleaning processes. **Living things in lakes, streams, and wetlands filter out and break down waste materials.** For example, plant roots filter larger particles from the water. Some plants, such as water hyacinths and duckweed, can absorb metals and chemicals. And just as certain bacteria are used in purifying wastewater, some are also useful in cleaning up toxic chemicals. Bacteria that consume oil have been used to help clean up oil spills. Waste-eating bacteria may also prove to be useful in breaking down toxic chemicals in rivers and lakes.

Pollution clean-up programs can be based on such natural treatment processes. For example, both natural and artificial wetlands are being used to clean up water pollution. Wetlands have been built near coal mines to treat acidic mining runoff before it returns to the environment.

Not only living things can help clean up polluted water. Passing through the sand or rock of an aquifer naturally filters and purifies groundwater. But natural filtering cannot remove or destroy many pollutants, such as metals or manufactured chemicals. Cleaning up this kind of pollution in groundwater is very difficult. One method involves pumping polluted groundwater to the surface, sending it through a treatment plant, and returning it to a nearby lake.

Preventing Pollution

Despite the successes in cleaning up some water pollution, most pollutants are very difficult to remove. It is often easier to avoid causing the pollution in the first place. In the late 1960s, as

Figure 15 A thick layer of red algae tints a pond the color of tomato soup. *Inferring What might be the cause of the algae growth in this pond?*

Figure 16 These purple water hyacinths can be an attractive part of a cleanup program. The plants absorb certain metals and chemicals from polluted water.

Chapter 3 **H ◆ 103**

Answers to Self-Assessment

✓ Checkpoint

When rain falls on the fields, it washes some of the chemicals away as runoff. The runoff eventually reaches streams, ponds, and lakes.

Caption Question

Figure 15 Nutrients from fertilizers from the nearby crop field might be the cause of the algae growth in the pond.

Runoff from Roads

Including All Students

Pair students who are still mastering English with native English speakers. Have each pair create a flow chart to show how gasoline, oil, and salt can travel from the surface of a road to a lake or aquifer that is a source of drinking water. After students have completed their charts, ask: **At what points could this type of pollution be controlled?** *(It could be controlled before it gets on the road by keeping motor vehicles in good running condition and by using sand and cinders on ice instead of salt. It could also be controlled along roads by catching the runoff before it goes farther.)* **limited English proficiency**

Cleaning Up Polluted Water

Building Inquiry Skills: Comparing and Contrasting

Challenge students to compare and contrast the natural process of cleaning water described on this page with wastewater treatment described in Section 1, pages 87–89. Students could describe how settling, filtration, and the breakdown of substances by bacteria are a part of both the natural and the treatment processes. **learning modality: logical/mathematical**

Ongoing Assessment

Oral Presentation Have students describe how fertilizers can cause eutrophication and how wetlands help to clean up polluted water.

Preventing Pollution

ACTIVITY

Divide students into small groups and challenge each group to design and create a poster to inform the public about how to prevent pollution.
cooperative learning

3 Assess

Section 3 Review Answers

1. The major sources are human wastes, industrial wastes, agricultural chemicals, and runoff from roads.
2. Rain washes fertilizers from farmers' fields into runoff to become a nonpoint source of pollution. The rich supply of nutrients from fertilizers encourages growth of plants and algae.
3. During floods, sanitary sewers may overflow and run into storm sewers. Since storm sewers generally lead into surface water, sewage from the sanitary sewers can pollute drinking water.
4. Students should not support this change because the industrial wastes pumped into the ground would likely pollute the groundwater.

Check Your Progress

CHAPTER PROJECT 3

Help students with any difficulties they have in assembling their treatment systems. If students experience difficulties in assembling the system, encourage them to think of alternative ways in which the system could be constructed.

Figure 17 One way you can help prevent water pollution is to educate others about its causes. This student is stenciling a storm drain to remind people of its connection to a nearby river.

people became more aware of the problems of pollution, they urged the government to create laws to control pollution. The goals of those laws include the cleanup of polluted lakes and rivers, better wastewater treatment, and limits on releasing pollutants to the environment. The government also established water-quality standards and programs to clean up waste disposal sites.

Industry and Agriculture Many recycling techniques that help conserve water also help to lessen pollution. For example, factories cool water and reuse it instead of returning it to a river, reducing heat pollution. Industries also look for ways to replace toxic materials with less harmful ones. Printing inks, for instance, can be made with water instead of chemical solvents.

Farmers are trying to reduce the problem of runoff from pastures and barnyards. Some collect and reuse this water for irrigation. Other farmers plant fields of coarse grasses that filter out pollutants before the water reaches a river or pond.

What Can You Do? You can also help keep pollutants from entering the environment. Dispose of toxic substances carefully. For example, chemicals like paint and motor oil should never be poured down the drain, but instead be taken to sites that collect hazardous waste. Avoid overfertilizing lawns or gardens. Form a group of students to educate others in your community about the causes and effects of freshwater pollution. Because many kinds of water pollution are so difficult to clean up, the most important place to stop pollution is at its source.

Section 3 Review

1. List four sources of water pollution.
2. How can fertilizers cause water pollution?
3. Explain why people are often instructed to boil drinking water after a flood.
4. **Thinking Critically Making Judgments** To prevent water pollution, a factory proposes pumping its wastes into the ground instead of into a river. Would you support this change? Why or why not?

Check Your Progress

CHAPTER PROJECT 3

At this point, you should be ready to assemble your model treatment system. Does the system include at least two treatment steps? Be sure to ask an adult to help you cut materials or assemble them if necessary. *(Hint:* Test your treatment setup for leaks using clean tap water.)

Performance Assessment

Oral Presentation Divide students into small groups and give each group a specific instance of water pollution, such as sewage in the water supply. Groups should analyze the case and prepare a presentation that classifies the pollution, explains the possible consequences, and proposes a solution.

Background

Facts and Figures Since agriculture contributes more than half of the pollution that enters U.S. lakes and streams, control of runoff from fields and feedlots would make the most difference in preventing pollution. The upgrading of sewage systems would also make a big difference. A 1994 EPA report cited 1,100 cities that dump poorly treated sewage into nearby waters. Upgrading inadequate systems could cost $500 billion.

Program Resources

◆ **Teaching Resources** 3-3 Review and Reinforce, p. 81; 3-3 Enrich, p. 82

Media and Technology

Interactive Student Tutorial CD-ROM H-3

SECTION 4 Water As an Energy Resource

DISCOVER •••••••••••••••••••••••••••••• ACTIVITY •••••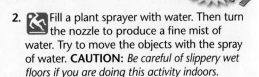

Can Water Do Work?

1. Spread out a large plastic trash bag on the ground. On top of the bag, place several cylindrical objects such as corks, spools, marbles, balls, and empty cans.

2. Fill a plant sprayer with water. Then turn the nozzle to produce a fine mist of water. Try to move the objects with the spray of water. **CAUTION:** *Be careful of slippery wet floors if you are doing this activity indoors.*

3. Now turn the sprayer nozzle to produce a narrower stream of water. Try again to move the objects. Be sure to wipe up any spilled water when you are done.

Think It Over

Observing How does changing the nozzle opening affect the stream of water? At which setting did the objects move more easily? Why?

Picture a curving wall of concrete swooping up nearly 170 meters—taller than a 40-story building. On one side of the wall is a deep reservoir. On the other side, only a narrow river trickles between rocky canyon walls. This is Grand Coulee Dam on the Columbia River in Washington. Completed in 1942, it is still one of the largest dams in the world. Behind Grand Coulee, the water in the reservoir pushes on the concrete dam. The dam's floodgates control that awesome energy. When the gates open to release the water, the water's energy is transformed into enough electricity to light thousands of homes and businesses.

For centuries, people have used the energy of moving water to turn water wheels and run machinery. Today that energy is also a source of electrical power in many parts of the world.

Power from Moving Water

Have you ever seen a fast-moving river propel a kayaker along? If so, you know how much energy moving water can have. It can move boats, carve out canyons, and sweep away cars in a flood. The energy that sends the kayak through the rapids is kinetic

GUIDE FOR READING

◆ How does moving water produce electricity?

◆ In what ways is hydroelectric power a good source of energy?

Reading Tip Before you read the section, preview *Exploring a Hydroelectric Power Plant*. Write a list of questions you have about hydroelectric power.

READING STRATEGIES

Vocabulary Call students' attention to the term *hydroelectric power*. Explain that *hydro-* derives from a Greek word for water. Thus, hydroelectric power is electric power produced from moving water. Point out that *hydro-* is also used in other words. For example, a *hydrologist* is a scientist who studies the properties, effects, and distribution of water on Earth's surface.

Program Resources

◆ **Teaching Resources** 3-4 Lesson Plan, p. 83; 3-4 Section Summary, p. 84
◆ **Interdisciplinary Explorations Series** "Mill Life in the 1840s," pp. 12–13; "Back to the Thirties," pp. 38–39

Media and Technology

 Audiotapes English-Spanish Summary 3-4

SECTION 4 Water As an Energy Resource

Objectives

After completing the lesson, students will be able to
◆ explain how moving water can produce electricity;
◆ list ways in which hydroelectric power is a good source of energy;
◆ describe the impact of dams.

Key Terms kinetic energy, potential energy, hydroelectric energy

1 Engage/Explore

Activating Prior Knowledge

Show students a picture of Niagara Falls or water flowing over a large dam. Ask: **How would you describe the force of this falling water?** *(Students should agree that the water has great force.)* Then encourage students to suggest ways in which that force could be harnessed to power machinery through the production of electricity.

•••••••• DISCOVER ••••••••

Skills Focus observing
Materials *large plastic trash bag, various cylindrical objects, plant sprayer, water*
Time 10 minutes
Tips Emphasize to students beforehand not to spray water at each other. This activity may best be done out of doors on a warm day, where spillage is not an issue.
Expected Outcome The narrower stream of water will move the objects farther and more easily than the fine mist.
Think It Over Changing the nozzle opening affects how narrow the stream of water is. The setting that produced the narrower stream moved the objects more easily because the force of the water was more concentrated.

2 Facilitate

Power from Moving Water

Including All Students

To reinforce the difference between potential and kinetic energy for students who need extra help, hold a book in the air above a desk. Ask: **What kind of energy does the book have now?** *(potential energy)* Drop the book and ask: **What kind of energy did the book have as it fell from my hand to the desk?** *(kinetic energy)* Divide students into groups and challenge them to make a list of as many examples of both kinetic and potential energy as they can. Once their lists are made, have each student read to the class one of the examples. Allow the whole class to come to a consensus on whether the example is potential or kinetic energy. **learning modality: visual**

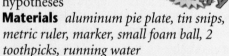

Skills Focus developing hypotheses **ACTIVITY**
Materials *aluminum pie plate, tin snips, metric ruler, marker, small foam ball, 2 toothpicks, running water*
Time 15 minutes
Tips Students should measure the squares on the plate before beginning to cut, using a marker to draw 5-cm lines. A heavy pair of scissors can be used instead of tin snips. Demonstrate how and where to push the aluminum squares and toothpicks into the ball. Remind students to be very careful of the sharp edges of the pie plate.
Expected Outcome Students' hypotheses will vary. Most will correctly hypothesize that increasing the volume of water will increase the speed of the water wheel.
Extend Students could investigate how the number of blades on the water wheel affects it speed and motion. **learning modality: kinesthetic**

Making a Water Wheel
In this activity **ACTIVITY** you will see how the kinetic energy of water can do work.
1. Put on your goggles.
2. ✂ Cut an aluminum pie plate into four squares about 5 cm on a side. **CAUTION:** *Be careful not to cut yourself on the sharp edges of the pie plate.*
3. Push the sides of the aluminum squares into a foam ball as shown. Insert two toothpicks into the sides of the ball.

4. Rest the toothpicks on top of your fingers and place the blades under a stream of slowly running water.

Developing Hypotheses How would increasing the volume of water affect the speed of the water wheel? Test your hypothesis. Describe what happens to the speed of the water wheel.

---

energy. **Kinetic energy** is the form of energy that an object has when it is moving.

Energy can change from one form to another. If the water's movement is stopped, all of its energy becomes potential energy. **Potential energy** is energy that is stored and waiting to be used. To think about potential energy in another way, imagine that you're holding a baseball bat at the top of your swing. The bat at that point has potential energy. As you swing at a ball, the bat's energy becomes kinetic energy. If you hit the ball, the energy is transferred again, becoming the kinetic energy of the ball.

Hydroelectric power is electricity produced by the kinetic energy of water moving over a waterfall or a dam. To generate hydroelectric power (or "hydropower"), engineers build a dam across a river. Water backs up behind the dam, floods the valley, and creates a reservoir. Water stored behind a dam has potential energy, which is changed to kinetic energy when the water is released. **Hydroelectric power plants capture the kinetic energy of moving water and change it into electrical energy.**

How is the kinetic energy of moving water changed into the energy that lights your house and runs your computer? Follow the path of the water in *Exploring a Hydroelectric Power Plant* on the next page to see how these energy changes take place.

✓ *Checkpoint* *What type of energy does a diver have while standing at the edge of a diving board?*

The Impact of Dams

In some ways, hydroelectric power seems like an ideal way to produce electricity. **Hydroelectric power is clean, safe, and efficient. Although building a dam is expensive, the water is free and is naturally renewed by the water cycle.** Unlike power plants that burn coal or oil, hydroelectric plants do not contribute to air pollution. In the United States, hydroelectric power accounts for about 8 or 9 percent of electricity produced, while worldwide it generates about 20 percent. Some countries, such as Norway and Brazil, produce almost all their electrical energy through hydropower.

Hydroelectric plants do have limitations, however. Only certain locations are suitable for building a dam. A fast-moving river is necessary, as is an area that can be flooded to create a reservoir.

Dams and the Environment Dams affect all living things in the area around them. Flooding the land behind a dam can destroy wildlife habitats as well as farms and towns. What was once a fast-moving river becomes the still, deep waters of a reservoir. Some organisms

---

Background

Facts and Figures The Columbia River basin has the largest hydroelectric power system in the world. The system has 100 dams, including the Grand Coulee Dam and 18 other large dams. These dams provide electricity to such large cities as Seattle, Portland, and Boise at a cost 40 percent below the national average. The dams have also reduced the number of salmon from 10–16 million before the dams to about 2.5 million now.

Program Resources

🔵 **Science Explorer Series** *Electricity and Magnetism*, Chapter 3, has more information about electric power.

EXPLORING a Hydroelectric Power Plant

Hydroelectric power is generated by changing energy from one form to another.

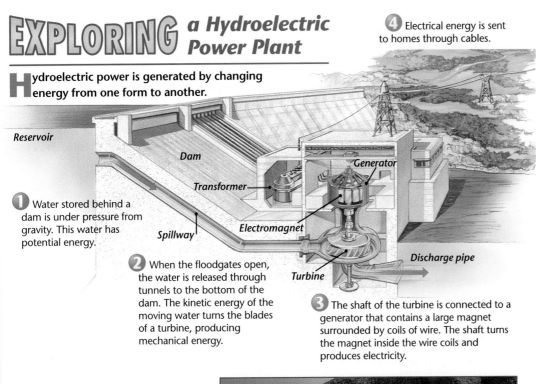

Reservoir

Dam

Transformer

Generator

Electromagnet

Spillway

Turbine

Discharge pipe

1 Water stored behind a dam is under pressure from gravity. This water has potential energy.

2 When the floodgates open, the water is released through tunnels to the bottom of the dam. The kinetic energy of the moving water turns the blades of a turbine, producing mechanical energy.

3 The shaft of the turbine is connected to a generator that contains a large magnet surrounded by coils of wire. The shaft turns the magnet inside the wire coils and produces electricity.

4 Electrical energy is sent to homes through cables.

cannot survive the change. In addition, the dam is a barrier across the river. It may prevent fish from traveling to the parts of a river where they usually lay their eggs and young fish are hatched. Dams like Grand Coulee on the Columbia River, for instance, have greatly reduced the population of salmon in the river.

As a river slows down, it deposits some of the sediments it carries. These deposits can build up behind a dam instead of being carried downstream to enrich the flood plain near the river's mouth. Since the Aswan Dam was built in Egypt, for example, farmlands near the mouth of the Nile River no longer receive the rich load of nutrients the river once brought.

Displaced by a Dam How would you feel if you discovered that your riverside home would soon be dozens of meters under the water of a lake? People whose homes or farms are located

Figure 18 This photograph shows the Theodore Roosevelt Dam in Arizona. *Interpreting Photographs What natural feature of the river made this a good location to build a dam?*

EXPLORING

A Hydroelectric Power Plant

Materials *thin insulated wire, strong bar magnet, galvanometer, wire stripper*
Time 10 minutes

✂ Invite students to read aloud the descriptions of the steps in producing hydroelectric power. Then, set up an apparatus that produces electricity from the movement of a magnet. First, remove the insulation from both ends of the insulated wire. Coil the wire into at least seven loops and connect each of the stripped ends to a galvanometer terminal. Finally, move the bar magnet into and out of the coils of wire. Students should observe the needle of the galvanometer move, evidence of an induced electric current. **learning modality: visual**

The Impact of Dams

 Integrating Life Science

Ask students: **What is a habitat?** *(The place where an organism lives and that provides it with the things it needs to survive.)* Then call on students to compare and contrast a river habitat with a lake habitat. As they describe characteristics, emphasize that different organisms are adapted to different conditions. Ask: **What happens when the conditions of a habitat changes radically?** *(Some organisms disappear while others thrive.)* **learning modality: logical/mathematical**

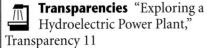 **Transparencies** "Exploring a Hydroelectric Power Plant," Transparency 11

 Exploring Physical Science Videodisc Unit 3, Side 1, "Energy"

Chapter 9

Answers to Self-Assessment

✓ *Checkpoint*

The diver has potential energy.

Caption Question

Figure 18 The banks of the river came close together at this point, making a narrow spot where a dam could be built. Also, the canyon through which the river runs might have been an area that could be flooded to create a reservoir.

Ongoing Assessment

Writing Challenge students to classify each of the following as an example of either potential or kinetic energy, giving reasons for each: (1) water flowing over a dam *(kinetic)*, (2) water in a reservoir behind a dam *(potential)*, (3) a rubber band stretched to its limit *(potential)*, and (4) a rock rolling down a hill *(kinetic)*.

3 Assess

Section 4 Review Answers

1. Hydroelectric power plants capture the energy of moving water and change it into electrical energy.

2. Students should mention two of these advantages: hydroelectric power is clean, safe, and efficient. The water is free and naturally renewed by the water cycle.

3. Answers may vary. A typical answer: A positive example is the creation of a reservoir where many types of organisms can live. A negative example is the destruction of wildlife habitats.

4. Answers may vary. A typical answer might mention a fast-flowing river, a valley behind the proposed location of the dam, a limited impact on the wildlife of an area, and the need to displace few people in building the dam.

Check Your Progress

CHAPTER PROJECT 3

Provide dirty water for students to use in testing their systems. Also set up the "cleanness scale" of grades of dirty water to help groups evaluate their results. Help groups whose systems do not yield positive results evaluate their systems and make appropriate changes.

Performance Assessment

Skills Check   Have students make a compare/contrast table that lists the benefits and the disadvantages of building a hydroelectric dam. Tell students that they may include what they learned from the text as well as any ideas they have thought of themselves.

 Students can save their tables in their portfolio.

where a dam's reservoir is planned have had to face this issue. Large dams flood hundreds or thousands of square kilometers, covering towns and valleys with water. When the Aswan High Dam was built on the Nile, about 80,000 people had to relocate. The ancient monuments of Abu Simbel had to be moved as the water in Lake Nasser rose higher and higher.

One of the largest dams ever built is now under construction on the Yangzi River in China. The Three Gorges Dam, due to be completed in 2009, could displace more than 1.5 million people.

Benefits of Dams   For countries that want to build up their industries, hydroelectric power often seems the best way to provide the electricity they need. Water power is the least expensive and least polluting large-scale energy source. Besides electricity, dams can supply water for irrigation and help in flood control.

In some places, people have suggested building small dams to supply power to a local area. Smaller dams uproot fewer people and do less harm to the environment, while still providing energy for a region to grow. However, since dams are expensive to build, small dams may not produce enough power to be worthwhile. Large dams, on the other hand, produce great amounts of power, but they also have a major effect on the land around them.

Figure 19 Building the Aswan Dam meant flooding the valley that housed these statues of ancient Egyptian rulers. Piece by piece, workers carefully dismantled the great monuments and moved them to higher ground.

Section 4 Review

1. How does a hydroelectric plant use moving water to generate electric power?

2. Name two advantages of hydroelectric power.

3. Give one positive example and one negative example of how building a dam could affect wildlife in the area.

4. Thinking Critically   **Problem Solving** Suppose you were assigned to choose a site to build a new hydroelectric plant. What features would you look for to find a good site? Be sure to consider the impact on living things as well as the physical characteristics of the site.

Check Your Progress

CHAPTER PROJECT 3

Now you are ready to test your model system, using the dirty water sample your teacher has provided. Does your treatment unit clean up the water? Measure how much of the original one liter of water is recovered. Based on your results, decide whether you need to redesign any part of your treatment system. (*Hint:* To modify your system, consider changing materials as well as adding more steps.)

Program Resources

◆ **Teaching Resources**   3-4 Review and Reinforce, p. 85; 3-4 Enrich, p. 86

Media and Technology

Interactive Student Tutorial CD-ROM   H-3

 SECTION 1 Water to Drink

Key Ideas

◆ Sources of drinking water include rivers, lakes, reservoirs, and groundwater.
◆ Many communities maintain public water supplies to collect, treat, and distribute water to residents. Some homes have private wells.
◆ Most drinking water is treated to ensure that it is safe and appealing to drink.
◆ Pumps and gravity are used to increase water pressure and move water through a system of pipes.
◆ Wastewater and sewage are treated to prevent contamination of drinking water.

Key Terms

water quality	pH	hardness
concentration	filtration	flocs
coagulation	sewage	sludge
septic tank	leach field	

SECTION 2 Balancing Water Needs

Key Ideas

◆ Water is scarce in many places, leading to competition for limited supplies.
◆ Water shortage can occur when there is too little water or too much demand in an area.
◆ Industries can conserve water by reducing water use, recycling water, and reusing water.
◆ Desalination of ocean water and icebergs are two possible future sources of fresh water.

Key Terms

drought	conservation	desalination

SECTION 3 Freshwater Pollution

Key Ideas

◆ Sources of water pollution include human and animal wastes, industrial and agricultural chemicals, and runoff from roads.
◆ Acid rain is caused by sulfur and nitrogen from smokestacks and car exhausts.
◆ Runoff of fertilizers into bodies of water can cause plants to grow too rapidly, changing the conditions for living things there.
◆ Living organisms help to naturally remove many pollutants from water, but other pollutants are difficult to remove.

Key Terms

water pollution	point source
nonpoint source	acid rain
pesticide	

SECTION 4 Water As an Energy Resource

INTEGRATING PHYSICS

Key Ideas

◆ Hydroelectric power plants capture the kinetic energy of moving water and change it into electrical energy.
◆ Hydroelectric power is a clean, renewable energy source, but dams are expensive to build and change the land around them.

Key Terms

kinetic energy	potential energy
hydroelectric power	

  ACTIVITY

USING THE INTERNET

www.science-explorer.phschool.com

Program Resources

◆ **Teaching Resources** Chapter 3 Project Scoring Rubric, p. 70; Chapter 3 Performance Assessment, pp. 174–176; Chapter 3 Test, pp. 177–180

Media and Technology

Interactive Student Tutorial CD-ROM H-3

Computer Test Bank Chapter 3 Test

Reviewing Content: Multiple Choice

1. b **2.** b **3.** d **4.** a **5.** d

Reviewing Content: True or False

6. hardness **7.** wastewater **8.** true
9. nonpoint **10.** fertilizers

Checking Concepts

11. Answers may vary. A typical answer: The water begins in a reservoir, is treated in a treatment plant, and then moves to a pumping station, where it is pumped through water mains to smaller pipes and finally into the home.

12. Sewage flows into a septic tank, where bacteria break it down and sludge settles to the bottom. Cleaner water leaves the tank and flows into a leach field.

13. There is not enough water to go around. Different types of uses must compete for the limited supply.

14. Farmers can use pipes instead of open ditches to carry water into their fields. They can use methods such as drip irrigation that waste little water.

15. Answers may vary. A typical answer should describe the build-up of a pollutant in the bodies of larger organisms that eat smaller organisms in and around a stream.

16. It might provide a clean, safe, and efficient way of producing electricity. It also might force people to move.

17. Writing to Learn Answers may vary. A typical answer should mention that a water shortage can occur when there is too little water or too great a demand, and thus people should conserve water. Suggestions of ways to conserve should reflect the ways shown in Figure 8.

Thinking Visually

18. Titles may vary. A typical title: Sources of Freshwater Pollution.
   a., b. Human wastes or sewage, Runoff from roads
   c. Fertilizers
   d., e. Smoke and exhaust, Heat

Reviewing Content

For more review of key concepts, see the Interactive Student Tutorial CD-ROM.

Multiple Choice
Choose the letter of the best answer.

1. Chlorine is added during water treatment in order to
   a. make particles form flocs.
   b. kill disease-causing organisms.
   c. improve the taste of the water.
   d. remove objects such as fish and trash.
2. Primary treatment of wastewater typically involves
   a. adding chlorine.
   b. filtering out solids.
   c. adding sludge.
   d. adding waste-eating bacteria.
3. One process used to obtain fresh water from salt water is
   a. coagulation.   b. filtration.
   c. recharge.   d. desalination.
4. The main source of acid precipitation is
   a. smoke from coal-burning factories.
   b. pesticides sprayed in the air.
   c. runoff from farm fields.
   d. toxic chemicals buried underground.
5. Water flowing swiftly possesses
   a. mechanical energy.
   b. electrical energy.
   c. potential energy.
   d. kinetic energy.

True or False
If the statement is true, write true. If it is false, change the underlined word or words to make the statement true.

6. The <u>pH</u> of water is a measurement of the amount of calcium and magnesium.
7. Sludge is produced during the treatment of <u>drinking water</u>.
8. A drought can cause wells to dry up if the level of the water table <u>falls</u>.
9. Oily runoff from highways is an example of a <u>point</u> source of pollution.
10. Agricultural runoff containing <u>pesticides</u> often results in increased plant growth in nearby ponds and streams.

Checking Concepts

11. Describe one possible path of drinking water from its source to a home.
12. Explain how a septic system works.
13. Why are water rights an important issue in dry areas?
14. Describe one way that farmers can reduce the amount of water lost during irrigation.
15. Explain how low levels of a pollutant in a stream can have harmful effects on wildlife in and around the stream.
16. How might building a dam affect people living nearby?
17. **Writing to Learn** You have been hired as a public relations specialist for the city water department. Your first assignment is to prepare a brief fact sheet for city residents about the importance of conserving water. The fact sheet should also include some simple suggestions of ways to conserve water at home.

Thinking Visually

18. **Concept Map** Copy the concept map about freshwater pollution onto a separate sheet of paper. Complete it and add a title. (For more on concept maps, see the Skills Handbook.)

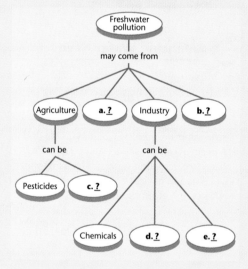

Applying Skills

19. The coliform count result supports the suspicion, because all 5 of the samples taken contained coliform bacteria. This is evidence that the water has been contaminated with waste material.

20. The source of lead might be from the pipes the water passes through. Students' suggestions for tests may vary. A typical way to test that answer would be to measure the amount of lead in a sample of water collected before the water passes through the pipes.

21. The lower the pH, the more acidic the water. Acidic water can dissolve lead from the pipes it passes through.

22. Calcium and magnesium are probably present in high levels, since hard water does not form suds well when mixed with soap.

Thinking Critically

23. When too much water is pumped out of an aquifer, the ground is no longer supported by the pressure of the water inside. As a result, the ground above the aquifer can sink or collapse.

Applying Skills

A family had their drinking-water well tested to check the water quality. The test results are shown in the table below. Use the data in the table to answer Questions 19–22.

Drinking Water Sample Test Results

Lead	0.2 parts per million
Copper	0.006 parts per million
pH	5.0
Coliform count	5 out of 5 samples positive

19. Inferring The homeowners suspect that their septic tank is polluting the well. What evidence exists to support this conclusion?

20. Designing Experiments What might be the source of the lead in the water? How could you test your answer?

21. Developing Hypotheses How might the low pH of the water be related to the lead contamination?

22. Predicting The homeowners have noticed that their water does not form suds well when mixed with soap. Predict what other substances may be present in high levels in the water.

Thinking Critically

23. Relating Cause and Effect How can increased demand for water cause the ground above an aquifer to collapse?

24. Comparing and Contrasting How is the process of desalination similar to the water cycle? How is it different?

25. Making Judgments Do you think that the benefits of hydroelectric power outweigh the disadvantages? Give reasons to support your answer.

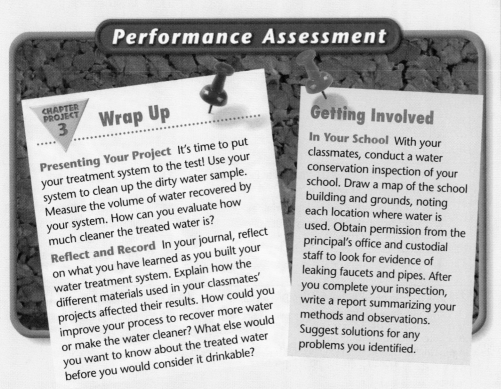

Performance Assessment

CHAPTER PROJECT 3

Wrap Up

Presenting Your Project It's time to put your treatment system to the test! Use your system to clean up the dirty water sample. Measure the volume of water recovered by your system. How can you evaluate how much cleaner the treated water is?

Reflect and Record In your journal, reflect on what you have learned as you built your water treatment system. Explain how the different materials used in your classmates' projects affected their results. How could you improve your process to recover more water or make the water cleaner? What else would you want to know about the treated water before you would consider it drinkable?

Getting Involved

In Your School With your classmates, conduct a water conservation inspection of your school. Draw a map of the school building and grounds, noting each location where water is used. Obtain permission from the principal's office and custodial staff to look for evidence of leaking faucets and pipes. After you complete your inspection, write a report summarizing your methods and observations. Suggest solutions for any problems you identified.

---

24. Answers may vary. The method of distillation is similar in that it uses evaporation and condensation to obtain fresh water from salt water. It is different in that the water is boiled instead of evaporating naturally.

25. Answers may vary. A typical answer should mention the benefits as being a clean, safe, and efficient way to produce electricity; the disadvantages as the destruction of wildlife habitats and the displacement of farms and towns.

Program Resources

◆ **Inquiry Skills Activity Book** Provides teaching and review of all inquiry skills

---

Performance Assessment

Wrap Up

CHAPTER PROJECT 3

Presenting Your Project

As students prepare to make their presentations, field any questions about what they need to present to the class. Encourage students who are having trouble with their models to make last-minute changes, but reassure them that a good effort and clear presentation can make up for disappointing results. Use the Scoring Rubric on page 70 of the Teaching Resources to help in assessing the presentations.

Reflect and Record

After all presentations have been made, encourage students in a class discussion to evaluate their own designs in light of their classmates' designs. Students can come to a consensus about what steps and materials were most effective in cleaning water. Then have all students write their reflections about the project in their journals.

Getting Involved

In Your School Divide students into small groups to carry out this inspection. Each group should be accompanied by an adult. If the school is large, divide it into sections and assign each group one section. An alternative would be to assign one group the school cafeteria, another the restrooms, and so on. Once the inspections are completed, groups can compile their reports to make a complete audit of water use at the school. Once all groups have finished, they can compare findings and collaborate on a final report.

Ocean Motions

Sections	Time	Student Edition Activities		Other Activities
CHAPTER PROJECT 4 **Protecting a Shoreline** p. 113	Ongoing (2 weeks)	Check Your Progress, p. 121 Check Your Progress, p. 126 Check Your Progress, p. 140 Wrap Up, p. 143		
1 Wave Action pp. 114–121 ◆ Describe the characteristics of waves and explain how they form. ◆ Describe how waves change near the shore and explain what a tsunami is. ◆ Identify the effects of waves on beaches and coastlines.	2–3 periods/ 1–2 blocks	**Discover** How Do Waves Change a Beach?, p. 114 **Try This** Wave Motion, p. 116	TE TE TE TE TE TE TE	Demonstration, p. 115 Including All Students, p. 115 Including All Students, p. 116 Demonstration, p. 117 Inquiry Challenge, p. 119 Visual Arts Connection, p. 119 Demonstration, p. 120
2 _INTEGRATING SPACE SCIENCE_ **Tides** pp. 122–126 ◆ Explain what causes tides and the daily and monthly tide cycles. ◆ Describe how people can use the energy of tides.	1–2 periods/ 1 block	**Discover** When Is High Tide?, p. 122 **Sharpen Your Skills** Graphing, p. 124	TE TE	Including All Students, p. 123 Including All Students, p. 124
3 Ocean Water Chemistry pp. 127–133 ◆ Identify the salinity, gas content, and temperature of ocean water. ◆ Describe how ocean conditions change with depth.	2–3 periods/ 1–2 blocks	**Discover** Will the Eggs Sink or Float?, p. 127 **Science at Home**, p. 131 **Skills Lab: Controlling Variables** Investigating Changes in Density, pp. 132–133	TE TE TE TE ISLM	Integrating Chemistry, p. 128 Including All Students, p. 129 Including All Students, p. 130 Inquiry Challenge, p. 131 H-4, "Density and Salinity"
4 Currents and Climate pp. 134–140 ◆ Identify the forces that cause surface currents and deep currents. ◆ Describe how surface currents affect climate on land.	2–3 periods/ 1–2 blocks	**Discover** Which Is More Dense?, p. 134 **Sharpen Your Skills** Drawing Conclusions, p. 136 **Real-World Lab: How Things Work** Modeling Ocean Currents, pp. 138–139	TE TE	Demonstration, p. 135 Including All Students, p. 136
Study Guide/Chapter Review pp. 141–143	1 period/ $\frac{1}{2}$ block		ISAB	Provides teaching and review of all inquiry skills

For Standard or Block Schedule The Resource Pro® CD-ROM gives you maximum flexibility for planning your instruction for any type of schedule. Resource Pro® contains Planning Express®, an advanced scheduling program, as well as the entire contents of the Teaching Resources and the Computer Test Bank.

CHAPTER PLANNING GUIDE

Program Resources	Assessment Strategies	Media and Technology
TR Chapter 4 Project Teacher Notes, pp. 92–93 TR Chapter 4 Project Student Materials, pp. 94–97 TR Chapter 4 Project Scoring Rubric, p. 98	SE Performance Assessment: Chapter 4 Project Wrap Up, p. 143 TE Check Your Progress, pp. 121, 126, 140 TR Chapter 4 Project Scoring Rubric, p. 98	🌐 Science Explorer Internet Site
TR 4-1 Lesson Plan, p. 99 TR 4-1 Section Summary, p. 100 TR 4-1 Review and Reinforce, p. 101 TR 4-1 Enrich, p. 102 SES Book I, *Weather and Climate,* Chapter 2 SES Book G, *Earth's Changing Surface,* Chapter 3 SES Book F, *Inside Earth,* Chapter 2	SE Section 1 Review, p. 121 TE Ongoing Assessment, pp 115, 117, 119 TE Performance Assessment, p. 121 TR 4-1 Review and Reinforce, p. 101	💿 Exploring Earth Science Videodisc, Unit 2 Side 2, "The Wave" 🎧 Audiotapes, English-Spanish Summary 4-1 📽 Transparency 12, "Parts of a Wave" 📽 Transparency 13, "Longshore Drift and Rip Currents" 💽 Interactive Student Tutorial CD-ROM, H-4
TR 4-2 Lesson Plan, p. 103 TR 4-2 Section Summary, p. 104 TR 4-2 Review and Reinforce, p. 105 TR 4-2 Enrich, p. 106 SES Book J, *Astronomy,* Chapter 1 SES Book N, *Electricity and Magnetism,* Chapter 3 IES "Where River Meets Sea," pp. 26–27	SE Section 2 Review, p. 126 TE Ongoing Assessment, pp. 123, 125 TE Performance Assessment, p. 126 TR 4-2 Review and Reinforce, p. 105	🎧 Audiotapes, English-Spanish Summary 4-2 📽 Transparency 14, "Spring and Neap Tides" 💽 Interactive Student Tutorial CD-ROM, H-4
TR 4-3 Lesson Plan, p. 107 TR 4-3 Section Summary, p. 108 TR 4-3 Review and Reinforce, p. 109 TR 4-3 Enrich, p. 110 TR Chapter 4 Skills Lab, pp. 115–117 IES "Where River Meets Sea," pp. 15–16, 18–21, 22–23, 24–25	SE Section 3 Review, p. 131 SE Analyze and Conclude, pp. 132–133 TE Ongoing Assessment, p. 129 TE Performance Assessment, p. 131 TR 4-3 Review and Reinforce, p. 109	💿 Exploring Physical Science Videodisc, Unit 1 Side 1, "Density" 🎧 Audiotapes, English-Spanish Summary 4-3 📽 Transparency 15, "Exploring the Water Column" 💽 Interactive Student Tutorial CD-ROM, H-4
TR 4-4 Lesson Plan, p. 111 TR 4-4 Section Summary, p. 112 TR 4-4 Review and Reinforce, p. 113 TR 4-4 Enrich, p. 114 TR Chapter 4 Real-World Lab, pp. 118–119	SE Analyze and Conclude, p. 139 SE Section 4 Review, p. 140 TE Ongoing Assessment, pp. 135, 137 TE Performance Assessment, p. 140 TR 4-4 Review and Reinforce, p. 113	🎧 Audiotapes, English-Spanish Summary 4-4 📽 Transparency 16, "Major Ocean Currents" 💽 Interactive Student Tutorial CD-ROM, H-4
TR Chapter 4 Performance Assessment, pp. 181–183 TR Chapter 4 Test, pp. 184–187	SE Chapter 4 Review, pp. 141–143 TR Chapter 4 Performance Assessment, pp. 181–183 TR Chapter 4 Test, pp. 184–187 CTB Test H-4	💽 Interactive Student Tutorial CD-ROM, H-4 💾 Computer Test Bank, Test H-4 📼 Got It! Video Quizzes

Key: **SE** Student Edition   **TE** Teacher's Edition   **TR** Teaching Resources
        CTB Computer Test Bank   **SES** Science Explorer Series Text   **ISLM** Integrated Science Laboratory Manual
        ISAB Inquiry Skills Activity Book   **PTA** Product Testing Activities by *Consumer Reports*   **IES** Interdisciplinary Explorations Series

Meeting the National Science Education Standards and AAAS Benchmarks

National Science Education Standards	Benchmarks for Science Literacy	Unifying Themes

Science As Inquiry (Content Standard A)

◆ **Design and conduct a scientific investigation** Students design an experiment and control variables to investigate density of ocean water. *(Skills Lab)*

◆ **Develop descriptions, explanations, predictions, and models using evidence** Students model ocean currents to gain an understanding of how currents affect climate. *(Real-World Lab)*

Physical Science (Content Standard B)

◆ **Properties and changes of properties in matter** The total dissolved salts in water is salinity. Water density increases when salinity or temperature decreases. *(Section 3; Skills Lab)*

◆ **Transfer of energy** Waves form when winds transmit their energy to water. The movement of water between high and low tide is a source of potential energy. Surface currents are driven mainly by winds. Students model the movement of ocean water due to surface currents. *(Sections 1, 2, and 4; Real-World Lab)*

Earth and Space Science (Content Standard D)

◆ **Earth in the solar system** Tides are caused by the interaction of Earth, the moon, and the sun. *(Section 2)*

Science and Technology (Content Standard E)

◆ **Design a solution or product** Students build a model to explore preventing shoreline erosion. *(Chapter Project)*

1B Scientific Inquiry Students build a model to explore preventing shoreline erosion. Students design an experiment and control variables to investigate water density. *(Chapter Project; Skills Lab)*

4B The Earth Tides are caused by interaction of the moon, sun and Earth. Ocean currents affect climate by moving cold and warm water around the globe. *(Sections 2 and 4)*

4C Processes that Shape the Earth Waves shape a beach through erosion and deposition. *(Section 1)*

4D Structure of Matter The total amount of dissolved salts in water is called salinity. The density of water increases when salinity increases or temperature decreases. *(Section 3; Skills Lab)*

4E Energy Transformation Waves form when winds transmit their energy to water. Surface currents are driven mainly by winds. Students model the movement of ocean water due to surface currents. *(Sections 1 and 4; Real-World Lab)*

8C Energy Sources and Use The movement of water between high and low tide is a source of potential energy. *(Section 2)*

11B Models Students build an ocean beach model to investigate erosion. Students model ocean currents to gain an understanding of how currents affect climate. *(Chapter Project; Real-World Lab)*

◆ **Energy** Waves form when winds transmit their energy to water. The movement of water between high and low tide is a source of potential energy. Surface currents are driven mainly by winds. *(Sections 1, 2, and 4)*

◆ **Patterns of Change** Waves shape a beach through erosion and deposition. Pressure increases continuously from the surface to the deepest part of the ocean. The density of water increases when salinity increases or temperature decreases. *(Sections 1 and 3; Skills Lab)*

◆ **Systems and Interactions** Tides are caused by the interaction of Earth, the moon, and the sun. Currents affect climate by moving cold and warm water around the globe. *(Sections 2 and 4)*

◆ **Stability** The daily rise and fall of Earth's waters on shores are called tides. On average, ocean water salinity is about 35 parts per thousand. *(Sections 2 and 3)*

◆ **Modeling** Students build an ocean beach model to investigate erosion. Students model ocean currents to gain an understanding of how currents affect climate. *(Chapter Project; Real-World Lab)*

Media and Technology

Exploring Earth Science Videodiscs
◆ **Section 1** "The Wave" gives information about ocean waves.

Exploring Physical Science Videodiscs
◆ **Section 3** "Density" shows how to calculate density.

Interactive Student Tutorial CD-ROM
◆ **Chapter Review** Interactive questions help students to self-assess their mastery of key chapter concepts.

Student Edition Connection Strategies

◆ **Section 1** Visual Arts Connection, p. 119

◆ **Section 2** Integrating Space Science, pp. 122-126
Integrating Technology, p. 126

◆ **Section 2** Math Toolbox, p. 129
Integrating Chemistry, p. 129
Integrating Technology, p. 131

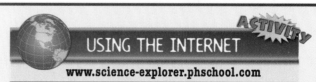

USING THE INTERNET

www.science-explorer.phschool.com

Visit the Science Explorer internet site to find an up-to-date activity for Chapter 4 of *Earth's Waters*.

ACTIVITY	Time (minutes)	Materials Quantities for one work group	Skills
Section 1			
Discover, p. 114	15	**Consumable** water, wooden tongue depressor **Nonconsumable** aluminum baking pan, sand, pebbles, book, metric ruler	Observing
Try This, p. 116	20	**Consumable** water, thread **Nonconsumable** large aquarium tank, several metal washers and corks	Observing
Section 2			
Discover, p. 122	15	**Nonconsumable** calculator	Predicting
Sharpen Your Skills, p. 124	20	**Consumable** graph paper **Nonconsumable** calculator, ruler	Graphing
Section 3			
Discover, p. 127	10	**Consumable** tap water, salt, two uncooked eggs **Nonconsumable** two beakers or jars, teaspoon, stirring rod	Observing
Science at Home, p. 131	home	**Consumable** cardboard milk carton, tape, water **Nonconsumable** awl or punch	Applying Concepts
Skills Lab, pp. 132–133	40	**Consumable** table salt, water, ice **Nonconsumable** thumbtacks, thermometer, metric ruler, unsharpened pencil, sharpened pencil, 100- and 250-mL graduated cylinders, 250-mL beaker, balance, hot plate, spoon	Designing Experiments, Controlling Variables, Measuring, Creating Data Tables, Graphing
Section 4			
Discover, p. 134	10	**Consumable** warm and cold water, food coloring **Nonconsumable** plastic bowl, plastic dropper, cup, stirring rod	Inferring
Sharpen Your Skills, p. 136	5	No special materials are required.	Drawing Conclusions
Real-World Lab, pp. 138–139	40	**Consumable** 3 sticks modeling clay, newspaper, blue and red construction paper, jointed drinking straw, 400 mL light-reflecting rheoscopic fluid or water and food coloring, chalk **Nonconsumable** rectangular baking tray, permanent marker, ruler, hole puncher	Making Models, Observing, Inferring

A list of all materials required for the Student Edition activities can be found beginning on page T14. You can order Materials Kits by calling 1-800-828-7777 or by accessing the Science Explorer Internet site at **www.science-explorer.phschool.com.**

Protecting a Shoreline

When students think of waves at the beach, they may be more likely to think of surfing than erosion. They may not realize how quickly waves can wash away sand and pebbles, wear away rock, and undermine structures built close to the shore.

Purpose In this project, students will make a model shoreline and lighthouse, generate waves in a wave tank they construct, and measure wave erosion. They will also model and assess ways to prevent wave erosion. By doing this project, students will gain a better understanding of how waves cause erosion and how erosion can be controlled.

Skills Focus After completing the Chapter 4 Project, students will be able to
◆ make a model of a beach and lighthouse and generate waves in a wave tank;
◆ observe and measure wave erosion of the beach;
◆ design and test methods to reduce wave erosion of the beach;
◆ demonstrate and explain the best method to the rest of the class.

Project Timeline The entire project will require at least two weeks. Depending on how much class time students can spend working on the project each day, about two days may be required for each of the following phases.
◆ Brainstorm a plan and a list of materials for the wave tank and model beach and lighthouse.
◆ Make a to-scale sketch of the tank and model and finalize the list of materials.
◆ Build the wave tank and model beach and lighthouse.
◆ Generate waves and measure erosion of the beach, modifying the model and method of measuring as needed.
◆ Brainstorm methods and materials to prevent erosion.
◆ Modify the model to introduce erosion-prevention methods and measure how well the methods prevent erosion.
◆ Demonstrate and explain to the class the best method(s) of preventing erosion.

For more detailed information on planning and supervising the chapter

CHAPTER

4 Ocean Motions

WHAT'S AHEAD

Integrating Space Science

SECTION
1 **Wave Action**

Discover How Do Waves Change a Beach?
Try This Wave Motion

SECTION
2 **Tides**

Discover When Is High Tide?
Sharpen Your Skills Graphing

SECTION
3 **Ocean Water Chemistry**

Discover Will the Eggs Sink or Float?
Skills Lab Investigating Changes in Density

project, see Chapter 4 Project Teacher Notes, pages 92–93 in Teaching Resources.

Suggested Shortcuts
◆ You may wish to divide the class into small groups to carry out the project.
◆ You can make this project shorter and less involved by explaining to students how to build a wave tank and model beach and lighthouse and provide them with the necessary materials. You can give students suggestions for measuring and preventing erosion.

◆ For a class project, build one wave tank with model beach and lighthouse, and then let groups take turns testing methods to protect the beach from erosion.

Possible Materials Wave tanks can be constructed from large cardboard box tops or plastic under-bed storage boxes. Cardboard boxes must be lined with plastic. See Chapter 4 Project Worksheet 1, page 96 in Teaching Resources, for more detailed guidelines. A large aluminum baking pan or a paint roller pan can be used for a smaller, simpler wave tank. For

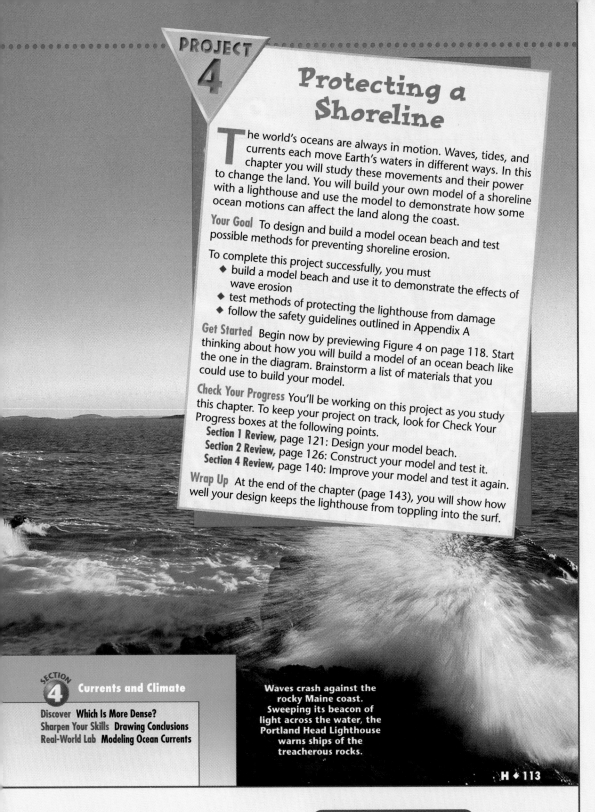

Protecting a Shoreline

The world's oceans are always in motion. Waves, tides, and currents each move Earth's waters in different ways. In this chapter you will study these movements and their power to change the land. You will build your own model of a shoreline with a lighthouse and use the model to demonstrate how some ocean motions can affect the land along the coast.

Your Goal To design and build a model ocean beach and test possible methods for preventing shoreline erosion.

To complete this project successfully, you must
◆ build a model beach and use it to demonstrate the effects of wave erosion
◆ test methods of protecting the lighthouse from damage
◆ follow the safety guidelines outlined in Appendix A

Get Started Begin now by previewing Figure 4 on page 118. Start thinking about how you will build a model of an ocean beach like the one in the diagram. Brainstorm a list of materials that you could use to build your model.

Check Your Progress You'll be working on this project as you study this chapter. To keep your project on track, look for Check Your Progress boxes at the following points.
Section 1 Review, page 121: Design your model beach.
Section 2 Review, page 126: Construct your model and test it.
Section 4 Review, page 140: Improve your model and test it again.

Wrap Up At the end of the chapter (page 143), you will show how well your design keeps the lighthouse from toppling into the surf.

Waves crash against the rocky Maine coast. Sweeping its beacon of light across the water, the Portland Head Lighthouse warns ships of the treacherous rocks.

**SECTION
4 Currents and Climate**

Discover **Which Is More Dense?**
Sharpen Your Skills **Drawing Conclusions**
Real-World Lab **Modeling Ocean Currents**

Program Resources

◆ **Teaching Resources** Chapter 4 Project Teacher Notes, pp. 92–93; Chapter 4 Project Student Materials, pp. 94–97; Chapter 4 Project Scoring Rubric, p. 98

the beach and gradually sloping ocean bottom, students should use a combination of materials, such as fine sand, silt, and small pebbles. The lighthouse may be constructed of small square or rectangular pieces, such as toy blocks, small flat stones, or sugar cubes, held together with modeling clay. Beach protection materials might include larger stones or wooden blocks held together with modeling clay for seawalls, and craft sticks or toy logs placed perpendicular to the beach for groins. To measure erosion, students can use toothpicks stuck into the beach and labeled with masking tape.

Launching the Project Challenge students to think of kinds of structures commonly built along beaches. (*Students might mention lighthouses, high-rise hotels, restaurants, homes, marinas, and amusement parks.*) Ask: **What are some limitations of building near an ocean coast?** (*Students might mention hurricanes, storms, blowing sand, and erosion.*) Emphasize that the shape of a coast is constantly being altered by wave erosion. Therefore, when structures are built on a coast, methods of controlling erosion often must be adopted to protect these structures. Explain to students that in the Chapter 4 Project, they will devise and test methods to protect a model beach and lighthouse from wave erosion. To help students get started, pass out Chapter 4 Project Student Materials, pages 94–97 in Teaching Resources. You may also wish to pass out the Chapter 4 Project Scoring Rubric, page 98, at this time.

Performance Assessment

Use the Chapter 4 Project Scoring Rubric to assess students' work. Students will be assessed on
◆ how well they plan their wave tank and models and the appropriateness of their materials;
◆ the accuracy of the models they build and how well they collect and record data;
◆ how effectively they present their models and explain their results to the class;
◆ if they have worked in groups, how much they contribute to their group's effort.

Objectives

After completing the lesson, students will be able to
◆ describe the characteristics of waves and explain how they form;
◆ describe how waves change near the shore and explain what a tsunami is;
◆ identify the effects of waves on beaches and coastlines.

Key Terms wave, crest, wavelength, frequency, trough, wave height, longshore drift, sandbar, rip current, groin, tsunami

1 Engage/Explore

Activating Prior Knowledge

Encourage students who have been to a beach or wave pool to describe how it feels to stand in the waves. Ask: **What happened to your body when a wave passed by?** *(It bobbed up and down.)* **If you were at the beach, what happened to the sand under your feet as the water flowed back out to sea?** *(It was washed away by the water.)* Ask students to consider how much sand would be washed away after years of wave action.

⋯⋯⋯ DISCOVER ⋯⋯⋯

Skills Focus observing **ACTIVITY**
Materials *aluminum baking pan, sand, pebbles, book, ruler, water, wooden tongue depressor*
Time 15 minutes
Tips To save time, do the activity as a class demonstration. For a more dramatic effect, raise the pan a few more centimeters and then ask: **Why does raising the pan change how the waves affect the beach?** *(It increases how fast the water flows and how much sand it can carry.)*
Expected Outcome Students should observe that as the waves move away from the beach, they carry sand, causing erosion of the beach.
Think It Over The flow of water away from the beach caused the sand to be washed away.

SECTION 1 Wave Action

DISCOVER ⋯⋯⋯⋯⋯⋯⋯⋯⋯⋯⋯⋯⋯ ACTIVITY

How Do Waves Change a Beach?

1. In one end of an aluminum pan, build a "beach" of sand and pebbles. Put a book under that end of the pan to raise it about 5 centimeters.

2. Pour water slowly into the other end of the pan until it covers the edge of the sand, just as water touches the edge of a beach.

3. Place a wooden tongue depressor in the water. Move it back and forth gently in a regular rhythm to make waves in the pan. Continue for about 2 minutes.

4. Once the water has stopped moving, observe what has happened to the beach. Wash your hands when you are finished with this activity.

Think It Over
Observing How has the motion of the water changed the edge of the beach?

GUIDE FOR READING

◆ How does a wave form?
◆ How do waves change near the shore?
◆ How do waves affect beaches and coastlines?

Reading Tip Before you read, preview the diagrams and photographs in the section to see different types of wave action. Make a list of questions you have about wave motion.

Stretched flat on his surfboard, the surfer paddles out into the clear turquoise water. The surfboard bobs up and down as he awaits the perfect surfing wave. After a few minutes, he spots the telltale signs in an approaching wave. At the last possible minute before the wave crashes over him, the surfer jumps into a standing position. He balances skillfully as the energy of the wave sends the surfboard skimming down the smooth front of the curling wave.

If you've ever seen a video of surfers "catching a wave" along a Pacific beach, you know that they make this difficult sport look almost easy. But even experienced surfers can seldom predict when the next good wave will roll into shore. As you will read in this section, many different forces influence the size, shape, and timing of waves.

How Waves Form

When you watch the surfer's wave crash onto the beach, you are seeing the last step in the process of the wave's development. The process begins with wind. Without the energy of wind,

READING STRATEGIES

Concept Mapping Make a concept map on the board for students to copy, beginning with the word *waves*. Below *waves*, draw two boxes; write *causes* in the box on the left and *effects* in the box on the right. From *causes* draw two boxes and leave them blank. From *effects*, draw three boxes and leave them blank. As students read the section, they should fill in these four boxes (*wind* and

earthquakes under causes and *longshore drift*, *sandbars*, and *rip currents* under effects).

Vocabulary Preview the terms with students before they read the section. Give special attention to words that students are probably familiar with, such as *crest*, *frequency*, *trough*, and *groin*, but have different meanings in this context. Use students' familiarity with the words to help them understand the new meanings.

the surface of the ocean would be as smooth as a mirror. **Most waves form when winds blowing across the water's surface transmit their energy to the water.** A **wave** is the movement of energy through a body of water.

Waves start in the open ocean. The size of the wave depends on the strength of the wind and on the length of time it blows. A gentle breeze creates small ripples on the surface of the water. Stronger winds create larger waves.

The size of the wave also depends on the distance over which the wind blows. Winds blowing across longer distances build up bigger waves. In the wide Pacific Ocean, a wave might travel a third of the way around the world before reaching the California coast.

Although waves may appear to carry water toward shore, the water does not actually move forward. If it did, ocean water would eventually pile up on the coasts of every continent! The energy of the wave moves toward shore, but the water itself remains where it was. You can test this for yourself by floating a piece of wood or a cork in a bowl of water. Use a spoon to make a wave in the bowl. As the wave passes, the object lurches forward a little, then bobs backward. It ends up in almost the same spot where it started.

Figure 1 A surfer cruises along the smooth front of this cresting wave. The wave's energy moves along, but the water mostly stays where it is. *Applying Concepts In which direction is the energy of this wave moving?*

2 Facilitate

How Waves Form

Demonstration

To illustrate that it is energy and not water that ACTIVITY moves in a wave, tie one end of a piece of rope to a chair or other stationary object and invite a student volunteer to move the other end up and down to generate waves. Students will see that the waves reach the chair but the rope does not get any closer to it. **learning modality: visual**

Including All Students

Help students who are having difficulty ACTIVITY understanding ocean waves by encouraging them to brainstorm ways that people make waves. *(Possible ways might include stepping into a bathtub, jumping into a pool, blowing on hot soup, sloshing soft drink in a can, rowing a boat, and throwing pebbles into a pond.)* Have a volunteer list the ways of making waves on the board. Lead the class in a discussion of how all the ways are similar. *(All involve energy being transferred to a liquid, followed by a ripple-like movement in the liquid as the energy passes through it.)* Invite students to observe this for themselves by blowing through a straw across the surface of water in a bowl. **learning modality: logical/mathematical**

Program Resources

◆ **Teaching Resources** 4-1 Lesson Plan, p. 99; 4-1 Section Summary, p. 100
◆ **Science Explorer Series** *Weather and Climate*, Chapter 2, can provide more information on wind.

Media and Technology

 Audiotapes English-Spanish Summary 4-1

Answers to Self-Assessment

Caption Question

Figure 1 The energy of the wave is moving toward the shore, or from the right side of the photograph to the left side.

Ongoing Assessment

Drawing Have students draw a labeled diagram showing how the wind creates waves, with arrows to show the direction of the wind and the energy moving through the water in the wave. Students can save their drawing in their portfolio.

How Waves Form, continued

Describing Waves

Including All Students

Materials *spring toy* **Time** 5 minutes

Invite two students to hold the opposite ends of a spring toy and take turns moving their end of the toy up and down, first slowly then faster, to generate waves. Ask: **What happens to the waves when you move your hand faster?** (*The waves move faster and get closer together.*) **As the frequency of the waves increases, what happens to the wavelength?** (*It gets shorter.*) **learning modality: kinesthetic**

Using the Visuals: Figure 2

Ask: **What is the distance between the crest and trough of a wave?** *(wave height)* **What is the distance from the crest of one wave to the crest of the next?** *(wavelength)* **How would you describe the movement of the buoy?** *(Up and down in a circular path)* **How would the buoy move if it wasn't tied to a weight?** *(Mostly up and down, but it might also move over the surface of the water because of the wind.)* **learning modality: visual**

Wave Motion

This activity shows how waves formed at the surface affect deeper water.

1. Fill an aquarium about three-quarters full of water.
2. Tie enough metal washers to a cork so that the cork floats about 3 cm from the bottom of the tank.
3. Repeat Step 2 with more corks so that they float 9 cm from the bottom, 15 cm from the bottom, and so on until the last cork floats on the surface.

4. Make small, steady waves in the tank by moving your hand up and down in the water. Note what happens to each cork.
5. Repeat Step 4, increasing the height of the waves by moving your hand faster.

Observing How does increasing the wave height affect the motion of each cork?

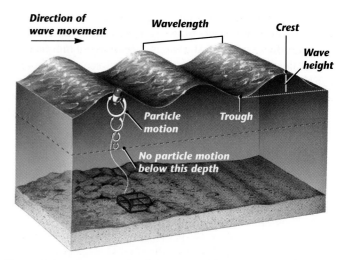

Figure 2 As a wave passes by, the water particles move in a circular motion. The buoy on the surface swings down into the trough of one wave, then back up to the crest of the next wave. Below the surface, the water particles move in smaller circles. At a depth equal to about one half the wavelength, the water particles are not affected by the surface wave.

Figure 2 shows what happens to the water as a wave travels along. As the wave passes, water particles move in a circular path. They swing forward and down with the energy of the wave, then back up to their original position.

Notice that the deeper water particles in Figure 2 move in smaller circles than those near the surface. The wind affects the water at the surface more than the deep water. Below a certain depth, the water does not move at all as the wave passes. If you were inside a submarine in deep water, you would not be able to tell whether the water above you was rough or smooth.

Describing Waves

If you ask a sailor to describe a wave, you might hear some unfamiliar terms. To a sailor, "a following sea" refers to waves traveling in the same direction as the boat. "Combers" are large, cresting waves. And "spindrift" is ocean spray torn by the wind from the surface of the waves.

Scientists have their own vocabulary of terms to describe the size and strength of waves. The name for the highest part of a wave is the **crest**. The horizontal distance between crests is the **wavelength**. Long, rolling waves with lots of space between crests have long wavelengths. Short, choppy waves have shorter wavelengths. Waves are also measured by their **frequency**, the number of waves that pass a point in a certain amount of time.

The name for the lowest part of a wave is the **trough**. The vertical distance from the crest to the trough is the **wave height**. The energy and strength of a wave depend mainly on its wave height. In the open ocean, most waves are between 2 and 5 meters high. During storms, the waves can grow much higher and more powerful.

☑ *Checkpoint* *Do waves that are close together have a longer or shorter wavelength than waves that are far apart?*

How Waves Change Near Shore

In deep water, waves usually travel as long, low waves called swells. As the waves approach the shore, the water becomes shallower. Follow the waves in Figure 3 as they enter the shallow water. The bottoms of the waves begin to touch the sloping ocean floor. Friction between the ocean floor and the water causes the waves to slow down. As the speed of the waves decrease, their shapes change. **Near shore, the wave height increases and the wavelength decreases.** When the wave reaches a certain height, the crest of the wave topples. The wave breaks onto the shore, forming surf.

At first, the energy of the breaking wave, or breaker, causes the water to surge up the beach. But the force of gravity pulling down on the rising water soon causes it to lose its energy. The water that moves up the beach flows back into the sea. Have you ever stood at the water's edge and felt the pull of the water rushing back out to the ocean? This pull, often called an undertow, carries shells, seaweed, and sand away from the beach. A strong undertow can be dangerous to swimmers.

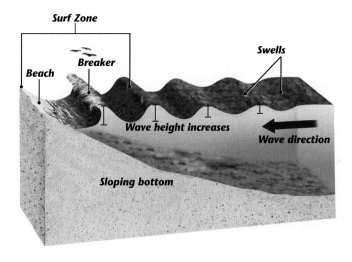

Figure 3 Friction with the ocean floor causes waves to slow down in the shallow water near shore. The wave height increases until the waves break, forming surf. *Interpreting Diagrams What happens to the wavelength as the waves approach shore?*

Using the Visuals: Figure 3

Use the figure to reinforce how a wave changes near shore. Ask: **What happens to the bottoms of waves as the waves near the shore?** *(They touch the ocean floor, causing the waves to slow down.)* **What happens to the tops of waves when the bottoms slow down?** *(They keep moving forward until the waves topple over.)* Encourage students to imagine that they're running and they stop suddenly. Ask: **How does your body react?** *(The top of the body keeps moving forward.)* Point out that in waves when the bottom of one wave slows down, the water in the waves behind it keeps moving forward and piles up, causing the wave height to increase until it breaks. **learning modality: visual**

Demonstration

Materials *manila folder or stiff paper, five marbles*
Time 5 minutes

Open the folder flat on a desk (or crease a piece of stiff paper) and place four marbles in a row down the middle. Place a fifth marble a few cm from the group, and then flick it with your finger so it moves forward and hits the row of marbles. The flicked marble will stop, but its energy will travel through the four marbles, causing the last one to roll away from the others. Ask: **What made the marble on the end roll away?** *(The energy that was transmitted from the flicked marble through the other marbles)* **How is this model like the movement of energy through water as a wave?** *(Energy moves, but particles don't.)* **learning modality: visual**

Answers to Self-Assessment

☑ *Checkpoint*
Waves that are close together have a shorter wavelength than waves that are far apart.

Caption Question
Figure 3 As the waves approach the shore, wavelength decreases.

Ongoing Assessment

Skills Check Point out that much of the damage done by hurricanes is caused by the huge waves they produce. Challenge students to infer why the high winds that occur during hurricanes produce such huge waves.

How Waves Affect the Shore

Using the Visuals: Figure 4

To reinforce longshore drift and rip current, ask: **What does longshore drift move?** *(water and sand)* **Why has the sandbar formed?** *(Because the longshore drift is moving in that direction, and the waves are slowing down, causing sand to be deposited)* **How has the sandbar helped create a rip current?** *(A narrow opening has formed through the sandbar, allowing a rush of water to flow back to the sea.)* **learning modality: visual**

Building Inquiry Skills: Comparing and Contrasting

The term rip current is often confused with the term undertow, which is also called backwash. Make sure students are not confusing the two terms by asking: **How are rip current and undertow similar and how are they different?** *(Both are movements of water away from the beach after waves break on shore. Undertow is the gradual outflow of water from any wave that breaks on shore. Rip current is the rapid outflow of a narrow stream of trapped water through a break in a sandbar.)* Have students make a Venn diagram showing these differences and similarity. **learning modality: verbal**

What happens on shore as waves pound the beach? The diagram in Figure 4 shows some of their effects. Since wave direction at sea is determined by the wind, waves usually roll toward shore at an angle. But as they touch bottom, the shallower water slows the shoreward side of the wave first. The rows of waves gradually turn and become more nearly parallel to the shore.

Longshore Drift As the waves come into shore, water washes up the beach at an angle, carrying sand grains with it. The water and sand then run straight back down the beach. This movement of sand along the beach is called **longshore drift**. As the waves slow down, they deposit the sand they are carrying on the shallow, underwater slope in a long ridge called a **sandbar**.

Rip Currents As a sandbar grows, it can trap the water flowing along the shore. In some places, water breaks through the sandbar and begins to flow back down the sloping ocean bottom. This process creates a **rip current**, a rush of water that flows rapidly back to sea through a narrow opening. Rip currents can carry a swimmer out into deep water. Because rip currents are narrow, a strong swimmer can usually escape by swimming across the current, parallel to the beach.

✓ *Checkpoint* *In what direction does a rip current pull a swimmer?*

Figure 4 Waves approach the shore at an angle. This results in a gradual movement of sand along the beach. *Interpreting Diagrams In which direction is longshore drift moving the sand along this beach?*

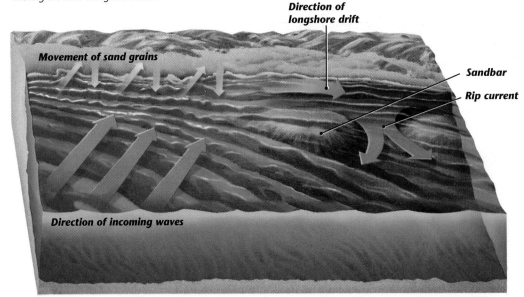

Direction of longshore drift

Movement of sand grains

Sandbar

Rip current

Direction of incoming waves

Background

Facts and Figures The erosion and deposition of sand that change the shape of a beach occur in cycles that correspond to the weather. During fair weather, waves generally tend to be low, often under 1 m high, and have little energy. Under these conditions, more sand is deposited on the beach than is eroded away. During stormy weather, in contrast, wave height and power greatly increase. Under these conditions, more sand is eroded from the beach than is deposited. When the storms end, the waves return to fair-weather size and sand builds up on the beach again.

Figure 5 "The Breaking Wave off Kanagawa" is a wood-block print by the Japanese artist Hokusai.

Waves and Beach Erosion

The boundary between land and ocean is always changing shape. If you walk on the same beach every day, you might not notice that it is changing. From day to day, waves remove sand and bring new sand at about the same rate. But if you visit a beach just once each year, you might be startled by what you see. **Waves shape a beach by eroding the shore in some places and building it up in others.**

As you learned in Chapter 2, erosion is the process of breaking up rock and carrying it away. At first, waves striking a rocky shoreline carve the rocks into tall cliffs and arches. Over many thousands of years, waves break the rocks into pebbles and grains of sand. A wide, sandy beach forms. Then the waves begin to eat away at the exposed beach. The shoreline slowly moves farther inland. Longshore drift carries the sand along the coast and deposits it elsewhere.

Reducing Erosion

Many people like to live near the ocean. But over time, erosion can wear away the beach. This threatens the homes and other buildings. To avoid losing their property, people look for ways to reduce the effect of erosion.

Groins One method of reducing erosion along a stretch of beach is to build a wall of rocks or concrete, called a **groin,** outward from the beach. The sand carried by the water piles up

Visual Arts CONNECTION

The Japanese artist Hokusai (1760–1849) is well known for his land and ocean scenes. His print at the left shows a cresting wave with the snow-capped Mt. Fuji in the background.

As a teenager, Hokusai was apprenticed to a wood-block engraver. A wood-block print is made by engraving a separate block of wood for each color ink used in the picture. How many blocks do you think Hokusai needed for this print?

In Your Journal

Imagine you are writing a catalog for a museum exhibit of ocean scenes. Write a brief description of Hokusai's print for the catalog.

Waves and Beach Erosion

Inquiry Challenge

Materials *large plastic box or aluminum baking pan, sand, pebbles, books, water*
Time 20 minutes

Challenge students to identify factors that affect the rate of beach erosion. Suggest that students first predict what these factors might be, and then decide how they can test these factors. For example, students might predict that one factor is slope of the ocean floor. They can test this factor by varying the slope of a beach model and comparing the erosion caused by waves of similar force. Other factors students might identify are size and energy of waves and beach composition. **learning modality: logical/mathematical**

Visual Arts CONNECTION

Materials: *potatoes, knife, finger paint*
Time: 10 minutes

To help students understand how wood-block prints are made, use a potato to model the process. Cut the potato in half and carve a simple shape on the surface of one half. Explain that the carved surface must be a "negative" of the desired image. Invite students to dip the carved potato in finger paint and use it to make a print on a piece of paper. Point out that each color of a wood-block print is done with a separate block.

In Your Journal Before students write their descriptions, encourage them to think about the process of wood-block printing to evaluate Hokusai's print, especially for color and detail. **learning modality: verbal**

Program Resources

 Science Explorer Series *Earth's Changing Surface,* Chapter 3, provides more information on wave erosion.

Media and Technology

Transparencies "Longshore Drift and Rip Currents," Transparency 13

Answers to Self-Assessment

✓ Checkpoint

A rip current pulls a swimmer out to sea away from shore.

Caption Question

Figure 4 It is moving the sand along the beach from left to right.

Ongoing Assessment

Writing Have students use the following three terms correctly in a short paragraph: *longshore drift, sandbar, rip current.*

Reducing Erosion

Including All Students

Explain that in addition to groins, there are two other types of structures people build to help control shoreline erosion: breakwaters and jetties. A breakwater is a wall made of rock, concrete, timber, or steel built parallel to the shore. Waves lose much of their energy when they strike a breakwater, and therefore cannot do as much damage on shore. A jetty is a pier or wall made of stone, concrete, timber, or steel that is built out from the shore, often from the mouth of a river. A jetty helps control where erosion and deposition occur. Challenge students to draw a breakwater and a jetty, based on your descriptions. They should use labels to show how each helps control erosion.
limited English proficiency

Demonstration

Materials *shallow aluminum baking pan, drinking straw, corn meal, block or pebble*
Time 10 minutes

ACTIVITY

To demonstrate the formation of sand dunes, invite a student volunteer to direct his or her exhaled breath through a straw toward the edge of a thin layer of corn meal in a baking pan that contains an obstacle, such as a toy block or large pebble. Students will observe that the corn meal moves away from the end of the straw in a semicircular pattern and piles up in front of the obstacle. Ask:
Why does the corn meal form a dune in front of the obstacle? *(The obstacle slows down the air movement, causing the air to drop the particles of corn meal. As the pile gets bigger, it contributes to the effect.)*
learning modality: visual

Figure 6 Sand piles up against a series of groins people have built along the North Carolina coast. Building groins to stop longshore drift is one way to reduce beach erosion.

against the groins instead of moving along the shore. Figure 6 shows how groins interrupt the movement of water. However, the groins increase the amount of erosion farther down the beach.

Dunes Some natural landforms protect beaches and reduce erosion, although they can't completely stop the movement of sand. Dunes, hills of wind-blown sand covered with plants, make a beach more stable and protect the shore from erosion. The strong roots of dune plants, such as beach grass and sea oats, hold the sand in place. These plants help to slow erosion by both wind and water. But the dunes and plants can be easily destroyed by cars, bicycles, or even by many people walking over them. Without the plants to hold the sand in place, the dunes can be easily washed away by wave action.

Barrier Beaches Another natural landform that protects shorelines from wave action occurs along low-lying beaches. Long sand deposits called barrier beaches form parallel to the shore. The beaches are separated from the mainland by a shallow lagoon. Waves break against the barrier beach instead of against the land inside. For this reason, people are working to preserve natural barrier beaches like those off Cape Cod, the New Jersey shore, and the Georgia and Carolina coasts.

Figure 7 Sand dunes are a natural form of beach protection. These yellow-flowered sea oats and beach grasses anchor a dune on Cape Cod, Massachusetts.

Background

Facts and Figures Although most sand dunes form on barrier beaches, some of the biggest dunes in the world have formed on the mainland. Dunes on the southern coast of Oregon, for example, extend up to 5 km inland from the coast, and dunes on the southwestern shore of Lake Michigan in Indiana reach a height of more than 100 m.

Tsunamis are the biggest, strongest waves ever recorded. A 1771 tsunami poured over an island near Japan and tossed a block of coral weighing over 700 metric tons 2.5 km inland. An 1883 tsunami crashed onto the islands of Java and Sumatra. It measured over 34 m high, or taller than a 10-story building.

Tsunamis

So far you have been reading about waves that are caused by the wind. Another kind of wave forms far below the ocean surface. This type of wave, called a **tsunami**, is caused by an earthquake on the ocean floor. The abrupt movement of the ocean floor sends pulses of energy through the water above it. When tsunamis reach the coast, they can be as devastating as an earthquake on land, smashing buildings and bridges.

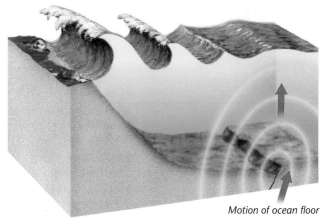
Motion of ocean floor

Despite the tremendous amount of energy a tsunami carries, people on a ship at sea may not even realize a tsunami is passing. How is this possible? A tsunami in deep water may have a wavelength of 200 kilometers or more, but have a wave height of less than a meter. But when the tsunami reaches shallow water near the coast, friction with the ocean floor causes the long wavelength to decrease suddenly. The wave height increases as the water "piles up." The tsunami becomes a towering wall of water. Some tsunamis have reached heights of 20 meters—taller than a five-story building!

Tsunamis are most common in the Pacific Ocean, often striking Alaska, Hawaii, and Japan. In 1998, tsunamis in Papua New Guinea killed more than 2,000 people. Nations are searching for ways to avoid such devastation. Some Japanese cities have built barriers designed to break up the waves. Scientists also monitor the ocean floor for warnings of earthquakes that may produce tsunamis.

Figure 8 At sea, a tsunami travels as a long, low wave. Near shore, the wave height increases suddenly. The wall of water smashes onto the land, tossing ships onto the shore and destroying buildings.
Interpreting Diagrams What is the source of a tsunami's energy?

Section 1 Review

1. Describe how ocean waves form.
2. How do wavelength and wave height change as a wave enters shallow water?
3. How does wave action cause changes in a coastline?
4. How do water particles move within a wave?
5. **Thinking Critically Relating Cause and Effect** Explain how building a groin affects the beach on each side of the groin.

Check Your Progress

CHAPTER PROJECT 4

You are ready to design your model ocean beach. Sketch your design. Be sure to consider what materials you will use for your shoreline and lighthouse. How will you make waves? When your design is finished, you are ready to gather your materials and construct your model. (*Hint:* Design your model, including the lighthouse, to scale.)

Chapter 4 **H ◆ 121**

Program Resources

Science Explorer Series *Inside Earth,* Chapter 2, has more information on earthquakes.
◆ **Teaching Resources** 4-1 Review and Reinforce, p. 101; 4-1 Enrich, p. 102

Media and Technology

Interactive Student Tutorial CD-ROM H-4

Answers to Self-Assessment

Caption Question

Figure 8 The source of a tsunami's energy is an earthquake on the ocean floor.

Tsunamis

Cultural Diversity

Explain that *tsunami* is a Japanese word that means "wave that overflows the land," which aptly describes the effects of these killer waves. Ask: **Why do you think that the word we use to describe these waves is a Japanese word?** (*Tsunamis occur mainly in the Pacific Ocean, and Japan has been hit by these waves repeatedly. As English speakers learned about these waves, they adopted the Japanese name for them.*) **learning modality: verbal**

3 Assess

Section 1 Review Answers

1. Most ocean waves form when winds blowing across the ocean transmit their energy to the water. Tsunamis are caused by an earthquake on the ocean floor.
2. Wavelength decreases and wave height increases.
3. By eroding the coastline in some places and building it up in others
4. In a circular path
5. Sand piles up on the windward side of the groin instead of being carried down the beach, while the other side of the groin shows greater erosion.

Check Your Progress

CHAPTER PROJECT 4

Students should have a firm idea by now how they will construct their wave tank and model beach and lighthouse. If plans or materials seem unworkable, suggest alternatives. Stress the importance of scale in designing the beach. Waves can be generated by moving an object or hand up and down in the water of the wave tank.

Performance Assessment

Oral Presentation Call on students to identify the causes and effects of waves and to explain how each cause produces waves and how waves produce each effect.

121 ◆ H

SECTION 2 Tides

Objectives

After completing the lesson, students will be able to

◆ explain what causes tides and the daily and monthly tide cycles;

◆ describe how people can use the energy of tides.

Key Terms tide, spring tide, neap tide

1 Engage/Explore

Activating Prior Knowledge

Encourage students who have been to the ocean to share their observations of tides. For example, ask: **Did the water come farther up the beach at different times of the day? Were there any signs posted about tides? Was there any other evidence of tides?** (*Perhaps students saw sand castles slowly covered over when the tide came in, wet sand exposed when the tide went out, signs posting the times of tides or warnings about high tides, or lines of seaweed and shells marking the farthest reach of tides.*) **Based on these observations, how do tides differ from waves?** (*Tides occur on a regular schedule, not just when the wind blows, and they are the actual movement of water, not just the movement of energy through water.*) Point out that tides differ from waves in these and other ways because they have a different cause, as students will read in this section.

DISCOVER

Skills Focus predicting
Materials *calculator*
Time 15 minutes
Tips Remind students that when subtracting minutes they cannot "borrow" from the hours column.
Think It Over Answers may vary. Students should observe that high tides get earlier as one goes north. Therefore, high tides in Portland should occur at about 4:00 A.M. and 4:45 P.M.

SECTION 2 Tides

DISCOVER

ACTIVITY

When Is High Tide?

Maine
Bar Harbor
3:41 A.M.
4:26 P.M.
Portland
New Hampshire
Portsmouth
4:15 A.M.
4:59 P.M.
Massachusetts
0 — 50 mi
0 — 50 km

Twice a day, the ocean rises and falls on the New England coast. These daily changes in water level are called tides. The map shows the times of the two high tides in each city on a particular day.

1. Calculate the length of time between the two high tides for each city. Remember to consider both hours and minutes.

2. Look at the times of the high tides in Bar Harbor and in Portsmouth. Is there a pattern in the times of the high tides?

Think It Over
Predicting Notice that the high tides for Portland are not shown. Based on the times of the other high tides on the map, predict when the high tides will occur in Portland.

GUIDE FOR READING

◆ What causes tides?

◆ How are tides a source of energy?

Reading Tip As you read, use the headings to make an outline about tides.

Y ou're standing on a riverbank in the town of Saint John, Canada. In the distance there's a loud roaring sound, like a train approaching. Suddenly a wall of water twice your height thunders past. The surge of water rushes up the river channel so fast that it almost looks as if the river is flowing backward!

This thundering wall of water is an everyday event at Saint John. The town is located where the Saint John River enters the Bay of Fundy, an arm of the Atlantic Ocean. The Bay of Fundy is famous for its dramatic daily tides. When the tide comes in, fishing boats float on the water near the piers. But once the tide goes out, so much water flows back to sea that the boats are stranded on the muddy harbor bottom.

Figure 9 The Bay of Fundy in Canada is noted for its great differences in water level at high and low tide. **A.** Near the mouth of the bay, boats float in the Saint John River at high tide. **B.** At low tide, the boats are grounded.

122 ◆ H

READING STRATEGIES

Reading Tip Students should use the main headings: "What Causes Tides?," "The Daily Tide Cycle," "The Monthly Tide Cycle," and "Energy From Tides." As students read the material under each heading, they should summarize the main points in a few words and add these to their outlines. Suggest that students use their outlines as a study guide and for generating questions they can use to test themselves.

Vocabulary Before students read about spring tides, point out that, in this context, *spring* means "to jump," an indication that spring tides are higher than usual. Stress that spring tides do not occur just in spring but twice a month throughout the year. They are the highest tides each month.

What Causes Tides?

The daily rise and fall of Earth's waters on its coastlines are called **tides.** As the tide comes in, the level of the water on the beach rises gradually. When the water reaches its highest point, it is high tide. Then the tide goes out, flowing back toward the sea. When the water reaches its lowest point, it is low tide. Unlike the surface waves you read about in Section 1, tides happen regularly no matter how the wind blows. Tides occur in all bodies of water, but they are most noticeable in the ocean and large lakes.

Tides are caused by the interaction of Earth, the moon, and the sun. How can distant objects like the moon and sun influence water on Earth? The answer is gravity. Gravity is the force exerted by an object that pulls other objects toward it. Gravity keeps you and everything around you on Earth's surface. As the distance between objects increases, however, gravity's pull grows weaker.

Figure 10 shows the effect of the moon's gravity on the water on Earth's surface. The moon pulls on the water on the side closest to it (point A) more strongly than it pulls on the center of the Earth. This pull creates a bulge of water, called a tidal bulge, on the side of Earth facing the moon. The water at point C is pulled toward the moon less strongly than is Earth as a whole. This water is "left behind," forming a second bulge.

In the places in Figure 10 where there are tidal bulges (points A and C), high tide is occurring along the coastlines. In the places between the bulges (points B and D), low tide is occurring. As Earth rotates, different places on the planet's surface pass through the areas of the tidal bulges and experience the change in water levels.

✓ *Checkpoint* *What force causes the tides to occur on Earth's surface?*

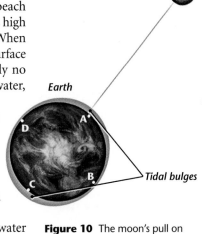

Figure 10 The moon's pull on Earth's water causes tidal bulges to form on the side closest to the moon and the side farthest from the moon. *Comparing and Contrasting Where is the level of the water higher, at point C or point D?*

Chapter 4 **H ◆ 123**

Program Resources

◆ **Teaching Resources** 4-2 Lesson Plan, p. 103; 4-2 Section Summary, p. 104
  Science Explorer Series *Astronomy*, Chapter 1, explains more about the Earth-moon-sun system.

Media and Technology

🎧 **Audiotapes** English-Spanish Summary 4-2

Answers to Self-Assessment

Caption Question

Figure 10 The level of water is higher at Point C.

✓ *Checkpoint*

The force of gravity; the moon and sun's gravity

2 Facilitate

What Causes Tides?

Using the Visuals: Figure 9

Use this figure to reinforce the concept of tides. Ask: **Where has the water gone in the right-hand photo?** (*out to sea*) **What is the force that causes tides to rise and fall?** (*The force of gravity between Earth and the moon and sun*) **How do you think tides in the Bay of Fundy affect people's lives?** (*Boaters and fishing crews have to time their departures and arrivals around the tides.*) **learning modality: visual**

Including All Students

Materials *small water-filled balloon, piece of string about half a meter long*
Time 5 minutes

To illustrate the pull of gravity on water, give a student a small water-filled balloon attached to a string. Have the student carefully swing the balloon around his or her body at the end of the string. (You may want to do this outside.) Ask: **If you are the sun and the balloon is Earth, what is the string?** (*gravity*) **How does the balloon change shape as you swing it?** (*Its surface bulges where the string pulls it.*) **What does this bulge represent?** (*a tidal bulge*) Guide students in seeing how this is similar to the pull of the sun's gravity on Earth's oceans. Point out that the moon's gravity, though weak, has an even greater pull on Earth's oceans because the moon is so close to Earth. **learning modality: kinesthetic**

Ongoing Assessment

Drawing Have students make a simple labeled diagram to show how the moon causes tides on Earth.

123 ◆ H

The Daily Tide Cycle

Building Inquiry Skills: Predicting

Challenge students to solve the following problem: While playing frisbee on the beach in the morning, José lost his sunglasses. At 1:00 P.M., he realized they were missing and went back to the beach to look for them. When he got there, he found the beach under water all the way to the edge of the sand. When should José go back to look for his sunglasses again? *(In about six hours, or around 7:00 P.M., when it is low tide again)* **learning modality: logical/mathematical**

Sharpen your Skills

Graphing

Materials *graph paper, calculator, ruler*

Time 20 minutes
Tips You may need to review graphing negative numbers.
Expected Outcome The high-tide line on the graph should rise steadily while the low-tide line falls, until Day 7 when both trends reverse. Spring tide might be occurring on Day 6 because that is when there is the greatest difference between high and low tides.
Extend Another way to see the relationship between high and low tides is to plot the difference between them. **learning modality: logical/mathematical**

The Monthly Tide Cycle

Including All Students

Use students to model spring tides and neap tides. Have students represent the sun, moon, and Earth and demonstrate the correct positions of each of the bodies at the two spring tides and the two neap tides. Challenge the rest of the class to identify each type of tide as it is demonstrated. **learning modality: kinesthetic**

Graphing

This table lists the highest high tides and lowest low tides at the mouth of the Savannah River at the Atlantic Ocean in Georgia for one week. Use the data to make a graph.

Day	Highest High Tide (m)	Lowest Low Tide (m)
1	1.9	0.2
2	2.1	0.1
3	2.3	0.0
4	2.4	−0.2
5	2.5	−0.2
6	2.6	−0.3
7	1.9	0.3

1. On the horizontal axis, mark the days.
2. On the vertical axis, mark tide heights ranging from 3.0 to −1.0 meters. (*Hint:* Mark the negative numbers below the horizontal axis.)
3. Plot the tide heights for each day on the graph. Connect the high tide points with one line and the low tide points with another line.

How do the high and low tides change during the week? What type of tide might be occurring on Day 6? Explain.

The Daily Tide Cycle

As Earth turns completely around once each day, people on or near the shore observe the rise and fall of the tides as they reach the area of each tidal bulge. The high tides occur about 12 hours and 25 minutes apart in each location. As Earth rotates, eastern-most points pass through the area of the tidal bulge before points farther to the west. Therefore, high tide occurs later the farther west you go along a coastline.

In some places, the two high tides and two low tides are easy to observe each day. But in other places, the range between the water levels is less dramatic. One set of tides may even be so minimal that there appears to be only one high tide and one low tide per day. This situation is common along the coasts of Texas and western Florida, due to the gradual slope of the ocean floor in the Gulf of Mexico.

Several factors affect the height of the tide in any particular location. For example, high tide on a certain day in southern California is not necessarily the same height as high tide farther up the Pacific coast in Oregon. Landforms such as capes, peninsulas, and islands interrupt the water's movements. A basin at the mouth of a river can also increase the range of tides. As you read in Chapter 2, the speed and depth of moving water increases when it flows into a narrower channel. That is what causes the dramatic tides in the mouth of the Saint John River you read about earlier.

☑ *Checkpoint* Describe one factor that affects the height of the tides in a particular area.

The Monthly Tide Cycle

Even though the sun is 150 million kilometers from Earth, it is so massive that its gravity also affects the tides. The sun pulls the water on Earth's surface toward it. In Figure 11 on the facing page, you can follow the positions of the Earth, moon, and sun at different times during a month. Notice that sometimes the moon and sun pull together on Earth's waters. At other times, they pull in different directions. Changes in the positions of Earth, the moon, and the sun affect the height of the tides during a month.

Spring Tides Twice a month, at the new moon and the full moon, the sun and moon are lined up. Their combined gravitational pull produces the greatest range between high and low tide, called a **spring tide.** These tides get their name not because they occur during the season spring, but from an Old English word, *springen*, which means "to jump."

Background

History of Science The idea of using tides for power is far from new. Water wheels turned by ocean waves were in use along the coast of England as early as the 1100s. In this country, a tide mill was used for grinding corn in Massachusetts as early as 1640.

Integrating Science Some animals depend on tides to survive and reproduce. For example, a kind of fish called the grunion lays its eggs on the beach during spring tide. After the tide goes out, the eggs remain safely buried in the sand to hatch into larvae. Two weeks later, just as the larvae are ready to turn into small fish, the next spring tide comes in and carries them out to sea.

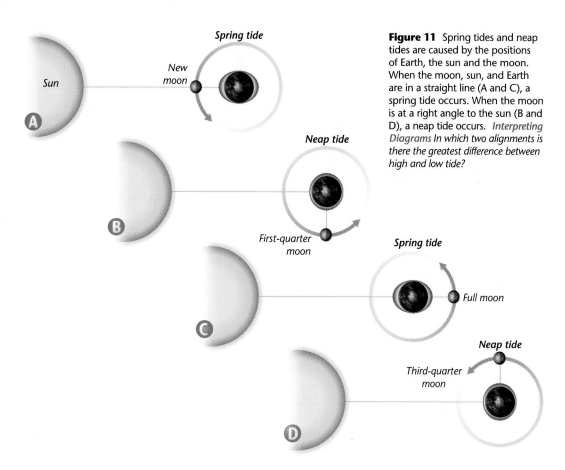

Figure 11 Spring tides and neap tides are caused by the positions of Earth, the sun and the moon. When the moon, sun, and Earth are in a straight line (A and C), a spring tide occurs. When the moon is at a right angle to the sun (B and D), a neap tide occurs. *Interpreting Diagrams In which two alignments is there the greatest difference between high and low tide?*

Neap Tides In between spring tides, at the first and third quarters of the moon, the sun and moon pull at right angles to each other. This line-up produces a **neap tide**, a tide with the least difference between low and high tide. During a neap tide, the sun's gravity pulls some of the water away from the tidal bulge facing the moon. This acts to "even out" the water level over Earth's surface, reducing the difference between high and low tides.

Monthly Tide Tables Despite the complex factors affecting the tides, scientists can predict tides quite accurately for various locations. They combine knowledge of the movements of the moon and Earth with information about the shape of the coastline and other local conditions. If you live near the coast, your local newspaper probably publishes a tide table. Knowing the times and heights of tides is important to sailors, marine scientists, people who fish, and others who live along a coast.

Program Resources

◆ **Interdisciplinary Explorations Series** "Where River Meets Sea," pp. 26–27

Media and Technology

 Transparencies "Spring and Neap Tides," Transparency 14

Answers to Self-Assessment

☑ *Checkpoint*
Answers may vary. Factors include landforms—such as capes, peninsulas, and islands, which interrupt the water's movement—and the change in speed and depth of the water as it moves into a narrower channel, such as a river basin.

Caption Question
Figure 11 In alignments A and C

Using the Visuals: Figure 11
Have students note the alignment of the sun, moon, and Earth in each part of the figure. Then ask: **If the difference between high and low tides in alignment A is 3.0 m and in alignment B is 0.5 m, what would you expect the difference between high and low tides to be in alignment D?** *(The same as in alignment B, or 0.5 m, because this is the other neap tide)* **learning modality: logical/mathematical**

Addressing Naive Conceptions
Because they are sometimes called tidal waves, it is a common misconception that the giant waves called tsunami are caused by tides. Ask students: **What are tidal waves?** *(Students may know tidal waves are unusually large, but not realize they are the same as tsunami.)* Explain that tides have nothing to do with so-called tidal waves, or tsunami. Ask: **What causes a tsunami?** *(Earthquakes on the ocean floor)* **learning modality: verbal**

Ongoing Assessment

Writing Have students write a concise paragraph explaining the difference between daily high and low tides, on the one hand, and spring and neap tides on the other.

 Students can save their paragraph in their portfolio.

Energy From Tides

Integrating Technology

Explain that waves as well as tides can be used to generate power. Ask: **Why would tides provide a more dependable power source than waves?** (*Tides occur regularly at a fairly predictable level, whereas the timing and height of waves depend on the wind, which can vary considerably.*) **learning modality: logical/mathematical**

3 Assess

Section 2 Review Answers

1. Moon's gravity pulls on water on the side of Earth facing it more strongly than it pulls on Earth itself. This creates a bulge of water, called a tidal bulge, on the side of Earth closest to the moon.
2. Water can be trapped at high tide. When it is released, gravity pulls it down through tunnels to power electric generators.
3. The sun, moon, and Earth are positioned in a straight line when spring tides occur.
4. Answers may vary. One answer is to prevent being stranded on the beach at low tide.

Check Your Progress

CHAPTER PROJECT 4

Stress the need for consistency in the size and frequency of waves so their effects on beach erosion can be compared before and after erosion-prevention methods are in place. Suggest that students measure erosion by placing numbered toothpicks at regular intervals along the beach. Students can note which toothpicks have fallen after each wave. This will help them see which part of the beach needs the most protection. Students should refer to the text for methods of controlling erosion.

Performance Assessment

Drawing Have students draw a labeled diagram showing the positions of the sun, moon, and Earth during spring and neap tides.

Figure 12 Pulled by the tide, water rushes through this tidal power plant in France. *Making Generalizations Why are very few locations suitable for building tidal power plants?*

Energy From Tides

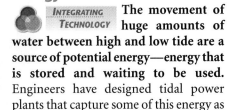 **INTEGRATING TECHNOLOGY** The movement of huge amounts of water between high and low tide are a source of potential energy—energy that is stored and waiting to be used. Engineers have designed tidal power plants that capture some of this energy as the tide moves in and out.

The first large-scale tidal power plant was built in 1967 on the Rance River in northwestern France. As high tide swirls up the river, the plant's gates open so that the water flows into a basin. As the tide retreats, the gates shut to trap the water. Gravity pulls the water back to sea through tunnels. The energy of the water moving through the tunnels powers generators that produce electricity, just as in a hydroelectric dam on a river.

Although tidal energy is a clean, renewable source of energy, it has several limitations. Harnessing tidal power is practical only where there is a large difference between high and low tides—at least 4 or 5 meters. There are very few places in the world where such a large difference occurs. Daily tides also may not occur at the time when there is a demand for electricity. However, tidal power can be a useful part of an overall plan to generate electricity that also includes other power sources between tides.

 ## Section 2 Review

1. Explain how the moon causes a tidal bulge to form on the side of Earth closest to it.
2. How can tides be used to generate electricity?
3. Describe the positions of the sun and the moon in relation to Earth when spring tides occur.
4. **Thinking Critically Applying Concepts** Imagine that you are the captain of a fishing boat. Why would it be helpful to know the times of the tides?

Check Your Progress

CHAPTER PROJECT 4

Now that you have built your model, plan an experiment to observe the effects of wave erosion on the shoreline. How will you measure the amount of wave action needed to topple the lighthouse? Once you have observed how waves cause shoreline erosion, repair the beach and design a way to reduce the erosion. Test your method by sending more waves against the shore. (*Hint:* For both tests, place toothpicks at regular intervals on the beach to measure erosion.)

Answers to Self-Assessment

Caption Question

Figure 12 Very few locations are suitable for building tidal power plants because few places in the world have a great enough range between high and low tides.

Program Resources

◆ **Teaching Resources** 4-2 Review and Reinforce, p. 105; 4-2 Enrich, p. 106
Science Explorer Series *Electricity and Magnetism*, Chapter 3, has more about sources of electric power.

Media and Technology

Interactive Student Tutorial CD-ROM H-4

DISCOVER ···ACTIVITY···

Will the Eggs Sink or Float?

1. Fill two beakers or jars with tap water.
2. Add three teaspoons of salt to one beaker. Stir until it dissolves.
3. Place a whole, uncooked egg in each jar. Handle the eggs gently to avoid breakage. Observe what happens to each egg.
4. Wash your hands when you are finished with this activity.

Think It Over

Observing Compare what happens to the two eggs. What does this tell you about the difference between salt water and fresh water?

I f you've ever been swimming in the ocean and swallowed some water, you know that it is salty. Why? According to an old Swedish legend, it's all because of a magic mill. This mill could grind out anything its owner wanted, such as herring, porridge, or even gold. A greedy sea captain once stole the mill and took it away on his ship, but without finding out how to use it. He asked the mill to grind some salt but then could not stop it. The mill ground more and more salt, until the captain's ship sank from its weight. According to the tale, the mill is still at the bottom of the sea, grinding out salt!

Probably no one ever took this tale seriously, even when it was first told. The scientific explanation for the ocean's saltiness begins with the early stages of Earth's formation, when the ocean covered the entire surface of the planet. Undersea volcanoes erupted, spewing chemicals into the water. Gradually, the lava from these volcanic eruptions built up areas of land. Rain fell on the bare land, washing more chemicals from the rocks into the ocean. Over time, these dissolved substances built up to the levels present in the ocean today.

GUIDE FOR READING

◆ How salty is ocean water?
◆ How do conditions in the ocean change with depth?

Reading Tip Before you read, preview the headings in the section. Then predict some characteristics of ocean water.

The Salty Ocean

Just how salty is the ocean? If you boiled a kilogram of seawater in a pot until the water was all gone, there would be about 35 grams of salts left in the bottom of the pot. **On average, one kilogram of ocean water contains about 35 grams of salts—that is, 35 parts per thousand.** The total amount of dissolved salts in water is called **salinity**.

Chapter 4 **H ◆ 127**

READING STRATEGIES

Reading Tip Before students preview the headings in the section, check that they know which headings are main headings and which are subheadings. After students preview the headings, suggest that they use them to outline the material in the section.

Program Resources

◆ **Teaching Resources** 4-3 Lesson Plan, p.107; 4-3 Section Summary, p. 108

Media and Technology

 Audiotapes English-Spanish Summary 4-3

Objectives

After completing the lesson, students will be able to
◆ identify the salinity, gas content, and temperature of ocean water;
◆ describe how ocean conditions change with depth.

Key Terms salinity, submersible

1 Engage/Explore

Activating Prior Knowledge

Most students will know that the ocean is salty, but they may not have thought about how this makes ocean water different from fresh water. Ask: **Why is salt often put on icy sidewalks and roads?** (*The salt melts the ice.*) **Which do you think freezes at a lower temperature, salt water or fresh water?** (*salt water*) Guide students in concluding that the salt in ocean water interferes with the formation of ice, making ocean water freeze at a lower temperature than fresh water. Point out that this is just one way salty ocean water differs from fresh water, as students will learn in this section.

········ DISCOVER ········

Skills Focus observing
Materials *two beakers or jars, tap water, salt, teaspoon, stirring rod, two uncooked eggs*
Time 10 minutes
Tips The three teaspoons of salt are approximate; students may need to add a little more or less for their egg to float.
Think It Over Students should observe that the egg sinks in fresh water but floats in salt water. Students may infer from their observations that salt water is denser than fresh water.

2 Facilitate

The Salty Ocean

Using the Visuals: Figure 13

Check to see if students understand how the two circle graphs are related by asking: **About what percent of ocean water is chloride?** *(Chloride makes up about half the ions dissolved in ocean water, which in turn make up about 3.5 percent of ocean water. Therefore, chloride is about half of 3.5 percent, or nearly 2 percent, of ocean water.)* Explain that each wedge of the right-hand graph represents an ion. When the salt sodium chloride dissolves, it breaks into sodium and chloride ions.
learning modality: logical/mathematical

Integrating Chemistry

ACTIVITY

Materials *small paper cup, water, stirrer, tablespoon, salt*
Time 10 minutes

When class starts, give students a paper cup one quarter full of water. Half the students should mix a tablespoon of salt into their cup, then all the students should put their cup in a freezer. When class ends, have students compare cups. They should observe that the plain water is frozen but the salty water is not.
learning modality: kinesthetic

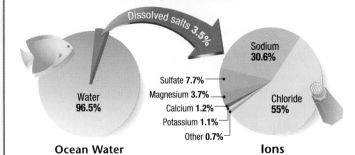

Composition of Ocean Water

Dissolved salts 3.5%

Ocean Water
- Water 96.5%

Ions
- Sodium 30.6%
- Sulfate 7.7%
- Magnesium 3.7%
- Calcium 1.2%
- Potassium 1.1%
- Other 0.7%
- Chloride 55%

Figure 13 Ocean water contains many different dissolved salts. When salts dissolve, they separate into particles called ions. *Interpreting Graphs Which ion is most common in ocean water?*

The substance you know as table salt—sodium chloride—is the salt present in the greatest amount in ocean water. When sodium chloride dissolves in water, it separates into sodium and chloride particles called ions. Other salts, such as magnesium chloride, form ions in water in the same way. Together, chloride and sodium make up almost 86 percent of the ions dissolved in ocean water, as shown in Figure 13. Ocean water also contains smaller amounts of about a dozen other ions, including magnesium and calcium, and other substances that organisms need, such as nitrogen and phosphorus.

Variations in Salinity In most parts of the ocean, the salinity is between 34 and 37 parts per thousand. But near the surface, rain, snow, and melting ice add fresh water to the ocean, lowering the salinity there. Salinity is also lower near the mouths of large rivers such as the Amazon or Mississippi. These rivers empty great amounts of fresh water into the ocean. Evaporation, on the other hand, increases salinity, since the salt is left behind as the water evaporates. For example, in the Red Sea, where the climate is hot and dry, the salinity can be as high as 41 parts per thousand. Salinity can also be higher near the poles. As the surface water freezes into ice, the salt is left behind in the remaining water.

Figure 14 These people are relaxing with the paper while floating in the water! The Dead Sea in Israel is so salty that people float easily on its surface. *Relating Cause and Effect How is Israel's hot, dry climate related to the Dead Sea's high salinity?*

Background

Facts and Figures Consider these salty facts and figures about Earth's waters.
- There are an estimated 4.5 trillion metric tons of salt dissolved in Earth's oceans and seas If all this salt was spread out over Earth's surface, it would bury a 15-story building.
- In one small part of the Red Sea, the salinity was recorded to be 270 parts per thousand, or almost eight times as salty as most ocean water.
- More than 150 km out to sea from the mouth of the Amazon River, the ocean water is still fresh, not salty.
- A few lakes are as salty as, or even saltier than, oceans, including the Great Salt Lake in Utah and the Dead Sea in Israel.

Effects of Salinity

 INTEGRATING CHEMISTRY Salinity affects several properties of ocean water. For instance, ocean water does not freeze until the temperature drops to about −1.9°C. The salt acts as a kind of antifreeze by interfering with the formation of ice crystals. Salt water also has a higher density than fresh water. That means that the mass of one liter of salt water is greater than the mass of one liter of fresh water. Because its density is greater, seawater has greater buoyancy. It lifts, or buoys up, less dense objects floating in it. This is why an egg floats higher in salt water than in fresh water.

Gases in Ocean Water

Just as land organisms use oxygen and other gases in the air, marine organisms use gases dissolved in ocean water. Two gases found in ocean water that are necessary for living things are oxygen and carbon dioxide.

Oxygen in seawater comes from the atmosphere and from algae in the ocean. Algae use sunlight to carry out photosynthesis, releasing oxygen into the water in the process. Oxygen is scarcer in seawater than in air and is most plentiful near the surface. Carbon dioxide, on the other hand, is about 60 times as plentiful in the oceans as in the atmosphere. Algae need carbon dioxide for photosynthesis. Animals such as corals also use carbon dioxide, which provides the carbon to build their hard skeletons.

☑ *Checkpoint* What are two sources of the oxygen in ocean water?

The Temperature of Ocean Water

In New England, the news reports on New Year's Day often feature the shivering members of a "Polar Bear Club" taking a dip in the icy Atlantic Ocean. Yet on the same day, people enjoy the warm waters of a Puerto Rico beach. Like temperatures on land, temperatures at the surface of the ocean vary with location and the seasons.

The broad surface of the ocean absorbs energy from the sun. Because warm water is less dense than cold water, this warm water stays as a layer on the surface. Near the equator, surface temperatures often reach 25°C, about room temperature. The temperature drops as you travel away from the equator.

The temperature of water affects the amount of dissolved oxygen it can hold. The cold waters in the polar regions contain more dissolved oxygen than warm, tropical waters. But there is still enough oxygen in tropical seas to support a variety of organisms, such as those shown in Figure 15.

Calculating Density

To calculate the density of a substance, divide the mass of the substance by its volume.

$$\text{density} = \frac{\text{mass}}{\text{volume}}$$

For example, one liter (L) of ocean water has a mass of 1.03 kilograms (kg). Therefore, its density is

$$\frac{1.03 \text{ kg}}{1.00 \text{ L}} = 1.03 \text{ kg/L}$$

Five liters of one type of crude oil has a mass of 4.10 kg. What is its density?

$$\frac{4.10 \text{ kg}}{5.00 \text{ L}} = 0.82 \text{ kg/L}$$

If this oil spilled on the ocean's surface, would it sink or float? Explain your answer in terms of density.

Figure 15 Both this neon-pink basslet and the lacy green sponge depend on the dissolved gases in ocean water.

H ◆ 129

Media and Technology

💿 **Exploring Physical Science Videodisc** Unit 1, Side 1, "Density"

‖‖‖‖‖‖‖‖‖‖‖
Chapter 1

Answers to Self-Assessment

Caption Question

Figure 13 Chloride
Figure 14 Israel's hot, dry climate increases the Dead Sea's salinity by increasing evaporation.

☑ *Checkpoint*

Oxygen in seawater comes from the atmosphere and from algae in the ocean.

Math TOOLBOX

Time 10 minutes
Tips The oil will float because of its lower density. Clarify that density is how much mass something has for its volume. For example, an empty soda can that is full of air has less mass than one full of soda because air has a lower density. **learning modality: logical/ mathematical**

Gases in Ocean Water

Building Inquiry Skills: Relating Cause and Effect

Point out that the text states oxygen is most plentiful near the surface of the ocean. Ask: **Why is there more oxygen near the surface of the ocean than in deep water?** (*That's where oxygen enters from the atmosphere and where algae, which produce oxygen, live.*) **learning modality: logical/mathematical**

The Temperature of Ocean Water

Including All Students

Ask students: **Why are temperatures warmer at the equator than temperatures farther away from the equator?** (*Some students may know that one reason is the sun's rays strike Earth more directly at the equator.*) **ACTIVITY** Have one student shine a flashlight directly onto a piece of graph paper while another student draws around the lighted area. Repeat this process with the light shining at an angle. Then have students estimate the area of each space. Ask: **In which case would the sun's rays provide more heat and why?** (*Where they shine directly, because they are more concentrated.*) **learning modality: visual**

Ongoing Assessment

Oral Presentation Call on students to describe places in the ocean where salinity is very low or very high.

129 ◆ H

Changes with Depth

EXPLORING
the Water Column

After students have examined the visual essay, have them apply what they learned by describing conditions they would find if they traveled down the water column in a submersible. Divide the class into groups of three and suggest that each group member assume responsibility for determining the brightness, presence or absence of plants, salinity, temperature, and water pressure at one of three depths below the surface: 50 m, 1,500 m, or 4,000 m. Group members should combine their data in a table and then compare their table with those of other groups. Urge groups to resolve any differences in their tables. **cooperative learning**

Including All Students

To help students visualize **ACTIVITY** how deep the ocean is at its very deepest (about 11,000 m), suggest that they make a to-scale drawing of the three zones, using a scale of 500 m to 1 cm. Remind students to label their drawings with the ocean zones and their depths and to give the scale in a key. **learning modality: logical/ mathematical**

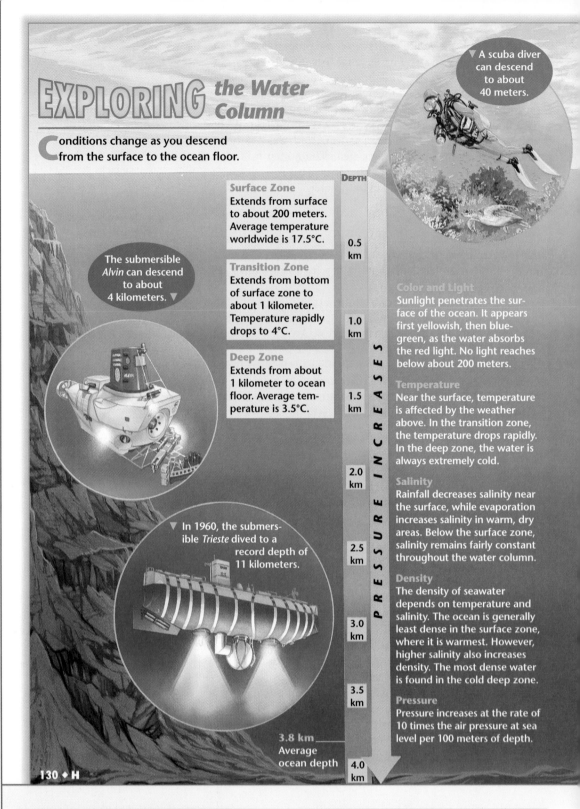

EXPLORING the Water Column

Conditions change as you descend from the surface to the ocean floor.

▼ A scuba diver can descend to about 40 meters.

Surface Zone
Extends from surface to about 200 meters. Average temperature worldwide is 17.5°C.

The submersible *Alvin* can descend to about 4 kilometers. ▼

Transition Zone
Extends from bottom of surface zone to about 1 kilometer. Temperature rapidly drops to 4°C.

Deep Zone
Extends from about 1 kilometer to ocean floor. Average temperature is 3.5°C.

▶ In 1960, the submersible *Trieste* dived to a record depth of 11 kilometers.

DEPTH

0.5 km
1.0 km
1.5 km
2.0 km
2.5 km
3.0 km
3.5 km
4.0 km

3.8 km Average ocean depth

PRESSURE INCREASES

Color and Light
Sunlight penetrates the surface of the ocean. It appears first yellowish, then blue-green, as the water absorbs the red light. No light reaches below about 200 meters.

Temperature
Near the surface, temperature is affected by the weather above. In the transition zone, the temperature drops rapidly. In the deep zone, the water is always extremely cold.

Salinity
Rainfall decreases salinity near the surface, while evaporation increases salinity in warm, dry areas. Below the surface zone, salinity remains fairly constant throughout the water column.

Density
The density of seawater depends on temperature and salinity. The ocean is generally least dense in the surface zone, where it is warmest. However, higher salinity also increases density. The most dense water is found in the cold deep zone.

Pressure
Pressure increases at the rate of 10 times the air pressure at sea level per 100 meters of depth.

130 ♦ H

Background

Integrating Science Air contains both oxygen and nitrogen. Under normal pressure nitrogen is not absorbed by the blood. However, when divers are exposed to very high pressure in deep water, their blood absorbs nitrogen as well as oxygen. If they come back up to the surface too quickly, the pressure drops suddenly and the nitrogen dissolved in their blood comes out of solution. This results in bubbles of nitrogen gas in the blood, a very painful, even life-threatening, condition called decompression illness or, more commonly, the bends. To avoid the bends, divers going deeper than about 40 m must return to surface pressure very slowly in a special decompression chamber.

Changes with Depth

Gazing down into the blue-green water from the deck of a ship, you might think that the vast volume of water beneath you is all the same. But in fact, conditions change dramatically from the surface to the depths. If you could descend from the surface to the ocean floor, you would pass through a vertical section of the ocean referred to as the water column. *Exploring the Water Column* shows some of the changes you would observe.

Temperature Decreases If you took temperature readings at different depths, you would observe a pattern. **Temperature decreases as you descend through the water column.** There are three temperature zones in the water column. The first zone, the surface zone, typically extends from the surface to between 100 and 500 meters. Next is the transition zone, which extends from the bottom of the surface zone to about one kilometer. The temperature drops very quickly in the transition zone, to about 4°C. Below the transition zone is the deep zone. The temperature in the deep zone is a constant 3.5°C or colder in most of the ocean.

Pressure Increases Pressure is the force exerted by the weight of water above pressing down. **Pressure increases continuously from the surface to the deepest part of the ocean.** The average depth of the ocean floor is 3.8 kilometers. There the pressure is about 400 times greater than air pressure at Earth's surface.

INTEGRATING TECHNOLOGY Pressure is one obstacle facing scientists who want to study the ocean. A diver can descend safely only to about 40 meters. To survive in deeper water, scientists must use a submersible. A **submersible** is an underwater vehicle built of strong materials to resist pressure. In a submersible, scientists can directly observe the ocean floor, collect samples, and study deep ocean water chemistry.

Section 3 Review

1. What is the salinity of ocean water?
2. How do temperature and pressure change as you descend from the surface to the ocean floor?
3. Describe one factor that increases the salinity of seawater and one factor that decreases salinity.
4. **Thinking Critically** **Inferring** Would you expect the seawater just below the floating ice in the Arctic Ocean to be higher or lower in salinity than the water in the deep zone there? Explain.

Science at Home

Ask an adult family member to poke two holes in a milk carton as shown. Cover the holes with tape and fill the carton with water. Holding the carton a meter above a bathtub or sink, remove the tape and observe the streams of water. Explain that increased pressure causes the water to flow out of the bottom hole more quickly. How does this model conditions in the ocean?

Chapter 4 **H ◆ 131**

Program Resources

◆ **Teaching Resources** 4-3 Review and Reinforce, p. 109; 4-3 Enrich, p. 110
◆ **Interdisciplinary Explorations Series** "Where River Meets Sea," pp. 15–16, 18–21, 22–23, 24–25
◆ **Integrated Science Laboratory Manual** H-4, "Density and Salinity"

Media and Technology

Transparencies "Exploring the Water Column," Transparency 15

Interactive Student Tutorial CD-ROM H-4

Inquiry Challenge

Challenge students to find a way to demonstrate that water pressure increases with depth. Have students write out their plans, and after your approval, test their plans. A sample answer might be to push an empty plastic bottle with a lid down into a bucket of water until it begins to collapse. **learning modality: logical/mathematical**

3 Assess

Section 3 Review Answers

1. Salinity is the total amount of dissolved salts it contains, on average 35 parts per thousand.
2. Temperature decreases and pressure increases.
3. Factors increasing salinity include evaporation and freezing; factors decreasing salinity include precipitation and rivers.
4. Salinity would be higher just below the ice because when salt water freezes it leaves the salt behind.

Science at Home

Materials *cardboard milk carton, tape, water, awl or punch*

Tips Students may say that water flows out of the bottom hole with greater force because water is under greater pressure at the bottom of the carton, just as water is under greater pressure at the bottom of the ocean.

Performance Assessment

Writing Have students write a paragraph explaining in their own words why it is easier to float in the ocean than in a freshwater lake.

131 ◆ H

Investigating Changes in Density

Preparing for Inquiry

Key Concept The density of water increases as salinity increases or temperature decreases.

Skills Objectives Students will be able to:
- design an experiment to determine how a given factor affects the density of ocean water;
- control the other variables as they measure how their variable affects the density of salt water;
- measure water density using a hydrometer;
- create a data table and use the data to make a graph.

Time 40 minutes

Advance Planning You may wish to have students make the hydrometers and practice using them ahead of time. Hydrometers should be calibrated at about 2 cm for fresh, room-temperature water.

Alternative Materials Large clear plastic soda bottles with the tops cut off can be used instead of graduated cylinders. Lumps of clay can be used instead of tacks.

Guiding Inquiry

Invitation Fill a clear, 1- or 2-L soda bottle with ice-cold water and fill another with very warm water to which food coloring has been added. Invite students to touch the sides of the bottles to feel the difference in temperature. Put a file card over the mouth of the warm-water bottle and carefully invert it over the cold-water bottle, making sure to line up the rims of the two bottles. Then, as students observe, gently slide out the file card. Ask: **Why doesn't water in the top bottle mix with water in the bottom bottle?** *(Because it is warmer, which makes it less dense)* **What would have happened if the positions of the two bottles had been reversed?** *(The colder water from the top bottle would sink down and mix with the warmer water in the bottom bottle.)* Reverse the positions of the bottles to demonstrate. Tell students

---

Investigating Changes in Density

In this lab, you will practice the skill of controlling variables as you learn more about density.

Problem

How do various factors affect the density of ocean water?

Materials

thumbtacks	beaker, 250 mL	water
thermometer	ice	hot plate
table salt	balance	spoon
metric ruler	sharpened pencil	

unsharpened pencil with eraser

graduated cylinders, 100 mL and 250 mL

Procedure

1. Work with your group to brainstorm a list of variables that affect the density of ocean water. Some variables to consider are water temperature and salinity. As a group, choose one variable to test in this investigation.
2. One way to measure density is with a tool called a *hydrometer.* To make a hydrometer, follow the instructions on the facing page.
3. Design an experimental plan to determine how the variable you chose affects density. For example, if you have chosen temperature as your variable, you might choose to start with salt water at 0°C, then heat it to 10°C, 20°C, and 30°C. If salinity is your variable, you might start with 100 mL of tap (fresh) water and add 10 g of salt, then add another 10 g to make 20 g, then add 10 g more to make 30 g. Write out your experimental plan.

DATA TABLE

Manipulated
Variable: _____

Condition Tested	Hydrometer Reading

4. List all the variables you will need to keep constant during your experiment. Revise your experimental plan and add steps to ensure that all other variables remain constant.
5. Review your plan. Make sure it includes the materials you will use and their amounts. Also make sure you have addressed all safety issues. Then check the plan with your teacher.
6. Copy the data table into your notebook.
7. Perform your experiment using the pencil hydrometer.

Analyze and Conclude

1. In your experimental plan, which variable was the manipulated variable, and which was the responding variable? Explain. (Refer to the Skills Handbook if you need more information about these types of variables.)
2. Make a graph of the data you collected in the experiment. Graph the manipulated variable on the horizontal axis. Graph the responding variable on the vertical axis.
3. How do changes in the hydrometer reading relate to density?

---

that in this lab they will learn how to measure the density of water that varies in temperature or salinity.

Helping Design a Plan

- Students should state which variable, such as salinity or temperature, they wish to test. This is the manipulated variable.
- Then students should explain how they will manipulate that variable. For example, ask: **What different temperatures or concentrations of salt will you use?** *(For best results, the temperatures or salinities should*

vary as much as possible.)
- Then ask: **Which variable will you control, and how will you control it?** *(Either salinity or temperature; by using only water of the same salinity while varying temperature or by using only water of the same temperature while varying salinity)*
- Finally ask: **How will you measure the responding variable?** *(By measuring the density of water as the manipulated variable takes on different values)*

Making a Hydrometer

A. Begin with an unsharpened pencil. Starting 1 cm from the unsharpened end, use a second, sharpened pencil to make marks every 0.5 cm along the side of the pencil. Continue making marks until you reach the 4-cm mark.

B. Label each mark, starting at the unsharpened end of the pencil with the label 0.5.

C. Insert 3 thumbtacks as weights into the eraser end of the pencil.
CAUTION: *Be careful not to cut yourself on the sharp points of the thumbtacks.*

D. Fill the 250-mL graduated cylinder with water at room temperature. Place the pencil in the water, eraser down.

E. Add or remove thumbtacks and adjust their placement in the eraser until the pencil floats upright, with about 2 cm sticking up above the surface of the water.

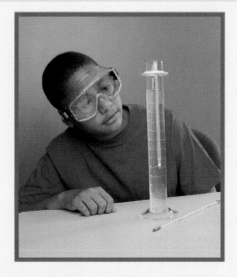

F. In your notebook, record the number next to the mark that is closest to the point where the pencil hydrometer projects from the water. As the density of the water increases, the hydrometer will float above the point you have just marked. If the water becomes less dense, the hydrometer will float below that point.

4. Use the graph to describe the relationship between the manipulated variable you tested and density.

5. Where in Earth's oceans would you find conditions like the ones that you tested?

6. **Think About It** Why is it important to make sure that all conditions other than the manipulated variable are kept constant in an experiment? How well were you able to keep the other variables constant?

More To Explore

In this experiment you observed how manipulating a particular variable affects the density of ocean water. Now conduct a second experiment, this time manipulating a different variable. As you design this experiment, make sure to control all variables except the one you are testing. Be sure to check your experimental plan with your teacher before you begin.

Sample Data Table 1

Manipulated Variable: Salinity

Salinity (g salt/L water)	Hydrometer Reading (cm)
0	2
30	4
60	6

Program Resources

◆ **Teaching Resources** Chapter 4 Skills Lab, pp. 115–117

Safety

Caution students to be careful of the sharp tack points, to use oven mitts or tongs to handle hot items, and to use caution with electricity. Review the safety guidelines in Appendix A.

Sample Data Table 2

Manipulated Variable: Temperature

Temperature (C°)	Hydrometer Reading (cm)
5	4
25	3
45	3

Evaluating Student Plans

Groups should describe their experimental plan in explicit terms.

◆ For example, if temperature is the manipulated variable, they should first specify how they will control salinity.

◆ Then they should state specifically how they will vary temperature.

Troubleshooting the Experiment

◆ Make sure the pencils remain vertical.

◆ Students should stir well so any salt dissolves completely.

Expected Outcome

The more salt that is added to the water, or the colder the water that is used, the greater the density and the higher the pencil in the hydrometer.

Analyze and Conclude

1. Most groups will choose either temperature or salinity for the manipulated variable. The responding variable in either case is density of water, because as temperature or salinity changes, density changes.

2. Groups should graph either temperature or salinity on the horizontal axis and density on the vertical axis.

3. The higher the pencil floats in the water, the higher the hydrometer reading and the greater the density of water.

4. The graphs should show that density rises as temperature decreases or salinity increases.

5. Answers will vary depending on the manipulated variable.

6. It is important to control all the other variables so that any differences in the responding variable can be assumed to be due to the manipulated variable alone. Students may say that it was easy to keep salinity constant but more difficult to control temperature.

Extending the Inquiry

More to Explore Students who used temperature as the manipulated variable can use salinity and vice versa.

Objectives

After completing the lesson, students will be able to
◆ identify the forces that cause surface currents and deep currents;
◆ describe how surface currents affect climate on land.

Key Terms current, Coriolis effect, climate, upwelling, El Niño

1 Engage/Explore

Activating Prior Knowledge

Elicit descriptions from students of how a river flows. Then ask: **How does the movement of water in a river differ from what you've learned about how ocean water moves?** (*Rivers flow in one direction; waves and tides cause water in oceans to move up and down in deep water and into shore and back to sea in shallow water.*) Explain that there have been instances when someone has sealed a message in a bottle, thrown the bottle into the ocean, and after a time the bottle was found by a person far away. Ask: **How do you think the bottle got there?** (*Some students may know that there are currents in the ocean that could carry the bottle.*) Tell students that they will learn about ocean currents in this section.

DISCOVER

Skills Focus inferring
Materials *plastic bowl, warm and cold water, food coloring, plastic dropper, cup, stirring rod*
Time 10 minutes
Tips The greater the difference in temperature between the warm and cold water, the more obvious the effect.
Think It Over Students should observe that the cold water settles to the bottom of the bowl. They should conclude that cold water is denser than warm water.

DISCOVER ······················· ACTIVITY

Which Is More Dense?

1. Fill a plastic container three-quarters full with warm water. Wait for the water to stop moving.
2. Add several drops of food coloring to a cup of ice water and stir.

3. Gently dribble colored water down the inside of the container. Observe.

Think It Over
Inferring Describe what happened to the cold water. Which is more dense, warm water or cold water? Explain.

GUIDE FOR READING

◆ What forces cause surface currents and deep currents?
◆ How do surface currents affect climate on land?

Reading Tip As you read, make a list of the kinds of ocean currents. Write a sentence describing the causes of each.

People strolling along a Washington beach one May day in 1990 could hardly believe their eyes. Hundreds of sneakers, in all colors and sizes, were washing ashore from the Pacific Ocean. Puzzled, people gathered up the soggy shoes and took them home, wondering where the sneakers had come from. Eventually, the sneaker spill was traced to a cargo ship from South Korea. Containers had washed overboard in a storm and broken open, spilling thousands of shoes into the water.

The sneakers were a ready-made experiment for oceanographers, scientists who study the oceans. From the shoes' drifting, oceanographers could infer both the path and the speed of water movements in the Pacific. Using what they already knew about these movements, scientists made a computer model predicting when and where more sneakers would come ashore. Right on schedule, sneakers washed up in Oregon and British Columbia, Canada. The model also predicted that the shoes would turn back westward across the Pacific. Again it was correct, as some sneakers arrived in Hawaii. The shoes that did not sink could have traveled all the way back to South Korea!

READING STRATEGIES

Vocabulary As students read about the Coriolis effect and El Niño, suggest that they look up the terms in a dictionary or encyclopedia to find out about their origins. The Coriolis effect is named for a French engineer who discovered in the early 1800s that Earth's rotation deflects moving objects to the right, or clockwise, in the Northern Hemisphere and to the left, or counterclockwise, in the Southern Hemisphere. The term *El Niño*, which is Spanish for "the child," is applied to the unusual conditions of winds and currents that occur every two to five years in the Pacific because the conditions tend to be most pronounced during the Christmas season when the birth of Jesus is celebrated by Christians.

Earlier in this chapter you learned how the oceans move as a result of wave action and tides. A third type of water movement is currents. A **current** is a large stream of moving water that flows through the oceans. Unlike waves, which do not actually transport water from one place to another, currents carry water great distances. Some currents move water at the surface of the ocean, while other currents move the deep water.

Surface Currents

Figure 16 shows the major surface currents in Earth's oceans. **Surface currents, which affect water to a depth of several hundred meters, are driven mainly by winds.** Following the major wind patterns of the globe, surface currents move in circular patterns in the five major ocean basins. Trace these currents on the map. Notice that most of the currents flow east or west, then double back to complete the circle.

Why do the currents move in these circular patterns? If Earth were standing still, winds and currents would flow in straight lines between the poles and the equator. But as Earth rotates, the paths of the winds and currents curve in relation to Earth's surface. This effect of Earth's rotation on the direction of winds and currents is called the **Coriolis effect** (kawr ee OH lis effect). In the Northern Hemisphere, the Coriolis effect causes the currents to curve to the right. In the Southern Hemisphere, the Coriolis effect causes the currents to curve to the left. You can see the impact of the Coriolis effect by comparing the directions of the currents in the two hemispheres on Figure 16.

Figure 16 Large surface currents generally move in circular patterns in Earth's oceans. *Interpreting Maps Name four currents that flow along the coasts of North America. State whether each current is warm or cold.*

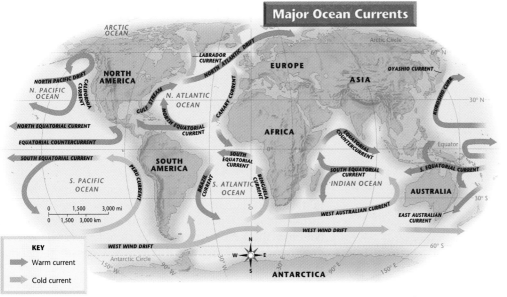
Major Ocean Currents

Chapter 4 **H ◆ 135**

Program Resources

◆ **Teaching Resources** 4-4 Lesson Plan, p. 111; 4-4 Section Summary, p. 112

Media and Technology

 Transparencies "Major Ocean Currents," Transparency 16

 Audiotapes English-Spanish Summary 4-4

Answers to Self-Assessment

Caption Question

Figure 16 The California Current and Labrador Current are cold currents; the North Pacific Drift and Gulf Stream are warm currents.

2 Facilitate

Surface Currents

Demonstration

Materials *large plastic box or aluminum baking pan, water, ground black pepper, hair dryer*

ACTIVITY

Time 10 minutes

Fill the box or pan half full of water and sprinkle some pepper on the water at one end. While students observe, use the hair dryer to blow the pepper across the water to the other end of the pan. Then ask: **Why did the pepper move?** *(Students may say that "wind" from the hair dryer moved the pepper.)* Clarify that the pepper moved on a current of water that was put into motion by the flow of air from the hair dryer. Ask: **How is this similar to surface currents in the ocean?** *(The wind blowing across the ocean puts the surface water into motion as currents.)* **learning modality: visual**

Using the Visuals: Figure 16

Call students' attention to the Gulf Stream and have them trace the direction it flows on the map. Ask: **Is the water carried by Gulf Stream warmer or cooler than the water it flows through? Why?** *(Warmer, because it flows from the warm waters of the equator to the north where the ocean is colder)* **What determines whether a current is cold or warm?** *(It is largely determined by where it originates; warm currents originate near the equator and cold currents originate near the poles.)* **learning modality: visual**

Ongoing Assessment

Skills Check Have students make a table that compares and contrasts waves, tides, and surface currents in terms of their causes and how they move water.

 Students can save their table in their portfolio.

Including All Students

To help students better understand the Coriolis effect, have them cut a construction paper circle about 20 cm in diameter and carefully push the point of a pencil through the center. Then they should place a drop of water on top of the circle near the pencil and, holding the pencil between the palms of their hands, twirl it in a counterclockwise direction. Students will see the water appear to swirl around the paper in a clockwise direction. Ask: **How does this demonstrate the Coriolis effect?** (*The rotating Earth, like the spinning paper, moves faster than the water on the surface, causing currents to move in the opposite, or clockwise, direction.*) **learning modality: kinesthetic**

How Surface Currents Affect Climate

Sharpen your Skills

Drawing Conclusions

Time 5 minutes

Tips Make sure students know that the Benguela Current is a cold-water current.

Expected Outcome Students should conclude that the Benguela Current brings cool, dry weather to the southwestern coast of Africa.

Extend Encourage students to use an encyclopedia or other reference book to find out about the climate of the southwestern coast of Africa. **learning modality: logical/mathematical**

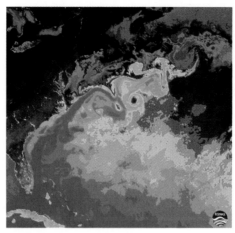

Figure 17 This satellite photograph of the Atlantic Ocean has been enhanced with colors that show water temperature. Red and orange indicate warmer water, while green and blue indicate colder water. The warm Gulf Stream flows around Florida as you can see in the lower left corner of the photograph.

Drawing Conclusions

Locate the Benguela Current on Figure 16 on the previous page. Near the southern tip of Africa, the winds blow from west to east. Using what you have learned about surface currents and climate, what can you conclude about the impact of this current on the climate of the southwestern coast of Africa?

The largest and most powerful surface current in the North Atlantic Ocean, the Gulf Stream, is caused by strong winds from the west. The Gulf Stream resembles a fast-moving, deep-blue river within the ocean. It is more than 30 kilometers wide and 300 meters deep, and it carries a volume of water 100 times greater than the Mississippi River. The Gulf Stream carries warm water from the Gulf of Mexico to the Caribbean Sea, then northward along the coast of the United States. Near Cape Hatteras, North Carolina, it curves eastward across the Atlantic, as a result of the Coriolis effect.

Checkpoint **Why doesn't the Gulf Stream travel in a straight line?**

How Surface Currents Affect Climate

The Gulf Stream and North Atlantic Drift are very important to people in the city of Trondheim, Norway. Trondheim is located along Norway's western coast. Although it is very close to the Arctic Circle, winter there is fairly mild. Snow melts soon after it falls. And fortunately for the fishing boats, the local harbors are free of ice most of the winter. The two warm currents bring this area of Norway its mild climate. **Climate** is the pattern of temperature and precipitation typical of an area over a long period of time.

Currents affect climate by moving cold and warm water around the globe. In general, currents carry warm water from the tropics toward the poles and bring cold water back toward the equator. **A surface current warms or cools the air above it, influencing the climate of the land near the coast.**

Winds pick up moisture as they blow across warm-water currents. For example, the warm Kuroshio Current brings mild, rainy weather to the southern islands of Japan. In contrast, cold-water currents cool the air above them. Since cold air holds less moisture than warm air, these currents tend to bring cool, dry weather to the land areas in their path.

Deep Currents

So far you have been reading about currents that move the water in the top few hundred meters of the ocean. Deeper below the surface, another type of current causes the chilly waters at the bottom of the ocean to creep slowly across the ocean floor. **These deep currents are caused by differences in density rather than surface winds.**

As you read in Section 3, the density of water depends on its temperature and its salinity. When a warm-water surface current moves from the equator toward the poles, its water gradually cools off. As ice forms near the poles, the salinity of the water increases from the salt left behind during freezing. As its temperature decreases and salinity increases, the water becomes denser and sinks. Then, the cold water flows back along the ocean floor as a deep current. Deep currents follow the hills and valleys of the ocean floor. Deep ocean currents are also affected by the Coriolis effect, which causes them to curve.

Deep ocean currents move and mix water around the world. They carry cold water from the poles back toward the equator. Deep ocean currents flow much more slowly than surface currents. They may take as long as 1,000 years to make the round trip from the pole to the equator and back again!

Upwelling

In most parts of the ocean, the surface waters do not usually mix with the deep ocean waters. However, some mixing does occur in the polar regions when the surface waters cool, sink, and form deep currents. Mixing also occurs when winds cause upwelling. **Upwelling** is the upward movement of cold water from the ocean depths. As winds blow away the warm surface water, cold water rises to replace it, as shown in Figure 18.

Upwelling brings up tiny ocean organisms, minerals, and other nutrients from the deeper layers of the water. Without this

Figure 18 As cold water rises from the deep ocean, it brings a new supply of nutrients to the surface. The nutrients feed enormous schools of fish such as these anchovies. *Relating Cause and Effect What causes cold water to rise during upwelling?*

Wind

Warm surface water

Upwelling

Building Inquiry Skills: Applying Concepts

Ask students: **Are deep currents cold-water currents or warm-water currents?** *(Deep currents are always cold-water currents)* **Why do cold-water currents mainly flow along the ocean floor?** *(Because cold water is denser than warm water, and this causes it to sink to the bottom)* **learning modality: logical/mathematical**

Building Inquiry Skills: Comparing and Contrasting

Challenge each pair of students to make a table that compares and contrasts surface and deep currents. First, students should decide what headings to use for their table, that is, which aspects of currents to compare and contrast. Then, each partner should be responsible for filling in the cells of the table for one type of current. Urge pairs to share and compare their completed tables. **cooperative learning**

Upwelling

Using the Visuals: Figure 18

Have students use this figure to create a flow chart of the process of upwelling and its effects. Students should infer that events must happen in a certain order for upwelling to occur: first strong winds from the land blow over the ocean, the winds blow away warm surface water, cold water carrying organisms and nutrients rises to take the warm water's place, the nutrients supply food for fish, fishing crews catch the fish. **learning modality: visual**

Answers to Self-Assessment

☑ Checkpoint

The Gulf Stream doesn't travel in a straight line because the Coriolis effect causes it to curve to the right.

Caption Question

Figure 18 Cold water rises to take the place of warm surface water that is blown away.

Ongoing Assessment

Writing In a short paragraph, have students explain in their own words why deep currents originate mainly near the poles.

137 ◆ H

Modeling Ocean Currents

Preparing for Inquiry

Key Concept Winds blowing across the ocean create surface currents that affect the climate along coasts.

Skills Objectives Students will be able to

◆ make a model of the Atlantic Ocean and surrounding land masses;

◆ observe currents flowing around their model ocean;

◆ infer how currents affect climate on nearby land masses.

Time 40 minutes

Advance Planning Rheoscopic fluid is a liquid that contains light-reflecting particles. It can be ordered from Novo Star Designs, Inc., 317 South Main Street, Burlington, NC 27216–1328. The movement of rheoscopic fluid will be easier to see if the pans are spray-painted with flat black enamel paint. Spray-paint pans with flat white paint if colored water is used instead of rheoscopic fluid. Paint the pans at least one day ahead so the paint will be thoroughly dry. You may wish to make the paper punches yourself before class to save time.

Alternative Materials Cafeteria trays can be used instead of baking trays for this lab. If so, use dark trays for rheoscopic fluid and light trays for colored water. Be sure students build the clay up high enough on the trays to prevent the water from overflowing. You can use water tinted with food coloring instead of rheoscopic fluid.

Guiding Inquiry

Invitation Help students focus on the key concept by asking: **What causes surface currents?** (*Winds blowing across the ocean*) **What determines the direction in which a surface current flows?** (*The direction in which a major wind pattern blows*) **What determines whether a surface current has warm water or cold water?** (*The area from which it originates; currents that start near the equator are warm and currents that start near the poles*

are cold.) **How do surface currents affect climate along coasts?** (*They warm or cool the air above them, which influences the climate on nearby land.*)

Introducing the Procedure

◆ **What is the purpose of the paper punches?** (*They can be used to help track the current.*)

◆ Give students time to read through the whole procedure, and then ask: **Why does it matter in which direction you blow on the surface of the water to simulate currents?** (*Students*

motion, the surface waters of the open ocean would be very scarce in nutrients. Because of the increased supply of nutrients, zones of upwelling are usually home to enormous schools of fish.

One major area of upwelling lies in the Pacific Ocean off the west coast of South America. Here, upwelling occurs when strong winds from the Andes Mountains sweep across the ocean. Huge schools of silvery anchovies thrive on the nutrients that are brought to the surface. This rich fishing area is important to millions of people who depend on it for food and jobs.

Modeling Ocean Currents

Why is the climate in Dublin, Ireland, so different from the climate in St. John's in Newfoundland, Canada? Since both cities are located at the same latitude, you might expect similar climate conditions in the two locations. But when it's 8°C in Dublin in January, it's usually below 0°C in St. John's. This investigation will help you understand why.

Problem

How can you model the movement of ocean water due to surface currents?

Skills Focus

making models, observing, inferring

Materials

rectangular baking tray   chalk
modeling clay, 3 sticks   ruler
permanent marker   hole puncher
newspaper
construction paper, blue and red
jointed drinking straws, one per student
light-reflecting rheoscopic fluid, 400 mL (or
   water and food coloring)

Procedure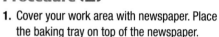

1. Cover your work area with newspaper. Place the baking tray on top of the newspaper.

2. Using the map on the facing page as a guide, draw a chalk outline of the eastern coast of North and South America on the left side of the tray. Draw the outline of the west coast of Europe and Africa on the right side of the tray.

3. Use modeling clay to create the continents, roughly following the chalk outlines you have drawn. Build the continents to a depth of about 3 cm. Press the clay tightly to the pan to form a watertight seal.

4. Fill the ocean area of your model with rheoscopic fluid (or water and food coloring) to a depth of 1 cm.

5. Place 10 blue paper punches in the ocean area marked with a blue X on the map. Place 10 red paper punches in the area marked with a red X.

6. Select a drinking straw and bend it at the joint. Write your initials on the short end of the straw with the marker.

are modeling specific winds, because winds almost always blow in a certain direction over a given part of the ocean)

Troubleshooting the Experiment

◆ Check students' models of the continents before they add water so they can modify the shapes as necessary.

◆ Make sure students are blowing in the right direction to create a circular current.

El Niño

Changes in winds and currents can greatly impact the oceans and the neighboring land. One example is **El Niño,** an abnormal climate event that occurs every 2 to 7 years in the Pacific Ocean. El Niño begins when an unusual pattern of winds forms over the western Pacific. This causes a vast sheet of warm water to move eastward toward the South American coast. El Niño conditions can last for one to two years before the usual winds and currents return.

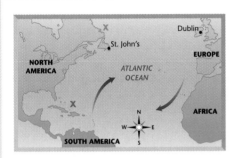

7. With a partner, simulate the pattern of winds that blow in this region of the world. One partner should position his or her straw across the westernmost bulge of Africa and blow toward the west (see arrow on map). The other partner should position his or her straw across the northern end of South America and blow toward the northeast (see arrow on map). Make sure that the straws are bent and that the short ends are parallel to the ocean surface. Both partners should begin blowing gently through the straws at the same time. Try to blow as continuously as possible for one to two minutes.

8. Observe the motion of the fluid and paper punches over the surface of the ocean. Notice what happens when the fluid and punches flow around landmasses.

Analyze and Conclude

1. Draw a map that shows the pattern of ocean currents that was produced in your model. Use red arrows to show the flow of warm water moving north from the equator. Use blue arrows to show the flow of cold water southward from the polar regions.

2. Use Figure 16 to add names to the currents you drew on your map. Which currents are warm-water currents? Which are cold-water currents?

3. Use your model to describe the relationship between winds and surface currents in the ocean.

4. Use your knowledge of ocean currents to explain why the climate in St. John's is different than the climate in Dublin.

5. Apply Suppose you wanted to sail to Europe from the east coast of the United States. What two natural factors could help speed up your trip? Explain your answer.

More to Explore

Use your model to simulate an upwelling off the coast of Africa. What conditions cause upwellings to occur? What are the results?

Expected Outcome

Students should observe that the paper punches travel roughly clockwise around the model of the ocean.

Analyze and Conclude

1. Students' maps should show that the water current moved in a circular pattern around the Atlantic north of the equator. Red arrows should show that warm water flowed northeast from the Gulf of Mexico toward the northern Atlantic. Blue arrows should show that cold water flowed southwest from the northern Atlantic toward the Caribbean.

2. Warm-water currents include the Gulf Stream, North Atlantic Drift, and North Equatorial Current. Cold-water currents include the Canary Current and the Labrador Current.

3. When students blew through their straws to model winds, they also created surface currents on their model ocean. The surface currents flowed in the same direction as the winds blew.

4. Even though both cities are at the same latitude, the warm waters of the Gulf Stream bring a warm climate to Dublin, Ireland, whereas the cold waters of the Labrador Current bring a cool climate to St. John's, Canada.

5. To sail to Europe from the east coast of the United States, the Gulf Stream and the winds that drive it (the prevailing southwesterlies) could help speed up your trip because both travel from southwest to northeast across the Atlantic Ocean.

Extending the Inquiry

More to Explore Students can simulate an upwelling by modeling a wind blowing off the coast of Africa onto the ocean surface. Upwellings occur when the wind blows away warm surface water. This results in cold water from the bottom of the ocean rising to replace the warm water at the surface.

Program Resources

◆ **Teaching Resources** Chapter 4 Real-World Lab, pp. 118–119

El Niño

Real-Life Learning

Divide the class into groups and give each group precipitation records for 1980 through the present for a west-coast city (available in *Statistical Abstracts of the United States*). Each group should graph its data and then, based on the level of precipitation, try to identify the years in which the two worst El Niños occurred (1982–1983 and 1997–1998). **learning modality: logical/mathematical**

3 Assess

Section 4 Review Answers

1. They are driven mainly by winds and follow global wind patterns, moving in circular patterns in ocean basins.
2. The water warms the air above it, and winds blow the warmed air over the land.
3. They form when dense ocean water near the poles sinks and flows slowly along the ocean floor toward the equator.
4. Currents in both hemispheres move in the same direction as the major wind patterns, but they move in opposite directions from each other because of the Coriolis effect: clockwise in the North and counterclockwise in the South.

Check Your Progress

CHAPTER PROJECT 4

Suggest that students consider using more than one method of erosion control. They might try natural methods, such as sand dunes. To determine how much additional wave action their lighthouse can withstand, they should note how many waves it takes and how high the waves must be to topple the lighthouse.

Performance Assessment

Writing Have students imagine that a shipload of rubber ducks spilled off the southern coast of Florida. Challenge them to write a story describing the trip these ducks might take and where they could end up.

Figure 19 Heavy rains caused by El Niño washed out this road in La Honda, California, forcing homes to be evacuated. El Niño can result in severe weather all around the world.

El Niño's Impact El Niño can have disastrous consequences. For example, the arrival of El Niño's warm surface water prevents upwelling off the western coast of South America. Without the nutrients brought by upwelling, fish die or go elsewhere to find food, ruining the fishing catch that season. Seabirds, with no fish to eat, also must leave the area or starve.

El Niño has serious effects on land, too. It causes shifts in weather patterns around the world, bringing unusual and often severe conditions to different areas. For example, El Niño of 1997 and 1998 caused an unusually warm winter in the northeastern United States. However, it was also responsible for heavy rains, flooding, and mudslides in California, as well as a string of deadly tornadoes in Florida.

Forecasting El Niño Although scientists do not fully understand the conditions that create El Niño, they have been able to predict its occurrence using computer models of world climate. Knowing when El Niño will occur can reduce its impact. Scientists and public officials can plan emergency procedures and make changes to protect people and wildlife.

Section 4 Review

1. Describe how surface currents form and travel in the ocean.
2. How is heat transferred from Earth's oceans to land areas?
3. Explain how deep currents form and move in the ocean.
4. **Thinking Critically** **Comparing and Contrasting** Describe the similarities and differences in the movement of surface currents in the Northern Hemisphere and Southern Hemisphere.

Check Your Progress

CHAPTER PROJECT 4

This is the time to make final changes to your method of shoreline protection to further decrease erosion. Test your improved method. How much additional wave action does the lighthouse withstand? (*Hint:* Try using a combination of methods to protect the shoreline and lighthouse.)

Background

Facts and Figures One of the largest El Niños on record occurred during the years 1997 to 1998. Although the massive warm-water current was already shrinking by January of 1998, even then it was still 1.5 times the size of the continental United States. Because it was so large, the 1997–1998 El Niño also brought some of the worst—and most unusual—weather that many parts of the world had ever seen. Many places had unusually wet or dry conditions. There were torrential downpours in parts of eastern and central Africa that are usually arid, and drought conditions in northeastern Brazil, Indonesia, and Australia, where it is usually wet. In the United States, El Niño was responsible for unusually wet weather on the West Coast and in the Southeast, and unusually warm weather in the North.

SECTION 1 Wave Action

Key Ideas

◆ Most waves are caused by winds blowing across the surface of the water.

◆ When waves enter shallow water, the wavelength shortens and wave height increases. The wave becomes unstable and breaks on the shore.

◆ Waves erode shorelines, carving cliffs and breaking up rocks into pebbles and sand.

◆ An earthquake on the ocean floor can cause a very powerful wave called a tsunami.

Key Terms

wave	crest	wavelength
frequency	trough	wave height
longshore drift	sandbar	rip current
groin	tsunami	

SECTION 2 Tides

INTEGRATING SPACE SCIENCE

Key Ideas

◆ Tides are caused by the interaction of Earth, the moon, and the sun.

◆ There are two high tides and two low tides each day in most places.

◆ The height of tides during a month varies with changes in the positions of Earth, the moon, and the sun.

Key Terms

tide	spring tide	neap tide

SECTION 3 Ocean Water Chemistry

Key Ideas

◆ Chloride and sodium are the most abundant ions in ocean water.

◆ Salinity varies throughout the ocean, depending on the amount of evaporation or freezing, as well as the addition of fresh water from rivers or precipitation.

◆ Below the ocean surface, the water is divided into layers by temperature, with uniformly cold temperatures in deep water.

◆ Pressure increases greatly with increasing depth in the ocean.

Key Terms

salinity	submersible

SECTION 4 Currents and Climate

Key Ideas

◆ Currents are formed by Earth's rotation, winds, and differences in water temperature.

◆ The movement of warm-water and cold-water surface currents carries water around the world and influences coastal climates.

◆ Density differences between warm and cold water cause many deep-water currents in the ocean.

◆ El Niño changes the pattern of winds and currents and affects Earth's weather.

Key Terms

current	Coriolis effect	climate
upwelling	El Niño	

USING THE INTERNET

www.science-explorer.phschool.com

CHAPTER 4 REVIEW

Program Resources

◆ **Teaching Resources** 4-4 Review and Reinforce, p. 113; 4-4 Enrich, p. 114

◆ **Teaching Resources** Chapter 4 Project Scoring Rubric, p. 98; Chapter 4 Performance Assessment, pp. 181–183; Chapter 4 Test, pp. 184–187

Media and Technology

 Interactive Student Tutorial CD-ROM H-4

 Computer Test Bank Test H-4

Reviewing Content: Multiple Choice

1. b **2.** b **3.** c **4.** d **5.** a

Reviewing Content: True or False

6. longshore drift **7.** chloride **8.** true **9.** increases **10.** true

Checking Concepts

11. A rip current forms when water trapped behind a sandbar rushes out from the shore through a narrow opening.

12. A tsunami forms when an earthquake on the ocean floor sends pulses of energy through the water above. It travels through the ocean until it reaches a coast. Tsunamis are destructive because when they reach the coast, their wavelengths suddenly decrease. Their wave heights increase dramatically, and they become a towering wall of water.

13. There are two high tides a day in most places because, as Earth rotates on its axis once every 24 hours, each place on Earth twice passes through a tidal bulge.

14. Warm-water currents tend to make the climate milder and wetter on the coasts they pass by because air blowing inland is warmed and moistened by the current.

15. Upwelling occurs when winds blow away the warm surface water, allowing cold water to rise up to replace it. Upwelling brings up tiny ocean organisms, minerals, and nutrients from the deeper layers of the water, and this attracts large numbers of fish.

16. Answers will vary. Students should show that they understand how waves change the shape of the shoreline through erosion and deposition of sand by correctly using terms such as longshore drift, sandbar, and sand dune.

Thinking Visually

17. The correct sequence of the five steps is: **a.** wind creates ripple on ocean surface; **b.** wave travels as low swell; **c.** wave touches bottom in shallow water; **d.** wavelength decreases and wave height increases; **e.** wave breaks on shore. Sample title: Life of a Wave

---

CHAPTER 4 REVIEW

Reviewing Content

For more review of key concepts, see the Interactive Student Tutorial CD-ROM.

Multiple Choice
Choose the letter of the best answer.

1. Rolling waves with a large distance between crests have a long
   a. wave height. b. wavelength.
   c. frequency. d. trough.
2. Groins are built to reduce the effect of
   a. tsunamis.
   b. longshore drift.
   c. rip currents.
   d. deep currents.
3. At the full moon, the combined gravitational pulls of the sun and moon produce the biggest difference between low and high tide, called a
   a. surface current. b. neap tide.
   c. spring tide. d. rip current.
4. Ocean water is more dense than fresh water at the same temperature because of
   a. pressure.
   b. the Coriolis effect.
   c. upwelling.
   d. salinity.
5. Winds and currents move in curved paths because of
   a. the Coriolis effect.
   b. longshore drift.
   c. wave height.
   d. tides.

True or False
If the statement is true, write true. If it is false, change the underlined word or words to make the statement true.

6. Sand is gradually carried down the beach by <u>upwelling</u>.
7. The most common ions dissolved in ocean water are sodium and <u>potassium</u>.
8. Two gases dissolved in ocean water that are important to living things are oxygen and <u>carbon dioxide</u>.
9. As you descend deeper into the ocean, the water gets colder and pressure <u>decreases</u>.
10. <u>Currents</u> carry cold and warm ocean water around the world.

Checking Concepts

11. Explain how a rip current forms.
12. Explain how a tsunami forms and moves. Why are tsunamis so destructive?
13. Why are there two high tides a day in most places?
14. How do warm-water currents affect climate?
15. Describe the causes and result of upwelling.
16. **Writing to Learn** Imagine a beach or seashore that you have visited or would like to visit. Using what you know about wave action, write a description of the shape of the beach, sand drift, cliffs, dunes, and other features.

Thinking Visually

17. **Flowchart** Copy the flowchart about the movement of a wave onto a sheet of paper. Complete the flowchart by putting the following five steps in the correct sequence: *wave travels as low swell; wind creates ripple on ocean surface; wave breaks on shore; wavelength decreases and wave height increases; wave touches bottom in shallow water.* Add a title. (For more on flowcharts, see the Skills Handbook.)

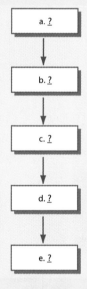

a. ?
b. ?
c. ?
d. ?
e. ?

Applying Skills

18. Students' graphs should be properly labeled with depth on the x-axis and temperature on the y-axis. The curve should be highest at 0 meters, fall quickly to the right as depth increases, and then level out at about 1,200 meters.

19. The transition zone occurs between about 500 meters and 1,200 meters. Between these depths, the temperature drops from about 18°C to 9°C.

20. Answers may vary. Students may predict that temperature at the surface fluctuates from season to season because the water is warmed by the sun more in the summer than winter. Students should say that temperature at 1,400 meters will not change with the seasons because this is too deep for sunlight to penetrate.

Thinking Critically

21. Movements of water caused at least in part by winds include waves, surface currents, and upwelling. Movements of water not caused by winds include tsunamis, tides, and deep currents.

Applying Skills

The temperature readings in the table were obtained in the Atlantic Ocean near Bermuda. Use the data to answer Questions 18–20.

Depth (m)	Temp. (°C)	Depth (m)	Temp. (°C)
0	19	1,000	9
200	18	1,200	5
400	18	1,400	5
600	16	1,600	4
800	12	1,800	4

18. **Graphing** Construct a line graph using the data in the table. Plot depth readings on the horizontal axis and temperature readings on the vertical axis.

19. **Drawing Conclusions** Use your graph to identify the temperature range in the transition zone.

20. **Predicting** Predict how the ocean temperature at depths of 0 meters and at 1,400 meters would change with the seasons in this location. Explain your reasoning.

Thinking Critically

21. **Classifying** Classify these different movements of ocean water by whether each is caused by winds or not caused by winds: waves, tsunamis, tides, surface currents, deep currents, upwelling.

22. **Applying Concepts** Would you expect salinity to be high or low in a rainy ocean region near the mouth of a river? Why?

23. **Comparing and Contrasting** In what ways is the ocean at 1,000 meters deep different from the ocean at the surface in the same location?

24. **Relating Cause and Effect** How does the movement of ocean currents explain the fact that much of western Europe has a mild, wet climate?

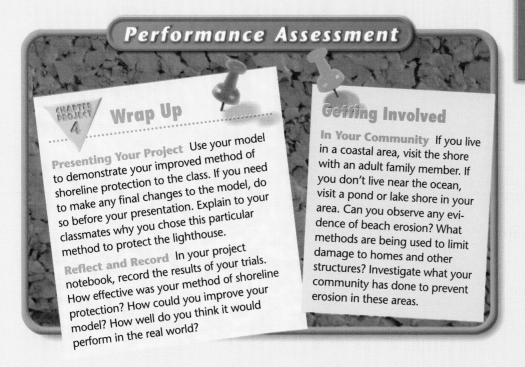

Performance Assessment

Wrap Up

Presenting Your Project Use your model to demonstrate your improved method of shoreline protection to the class. If you need to make any final changes to the model, do so before your presentation. Explain to your classmates why you chose this particular method to protect the lighthouse.

Reflect and Record In your project notebook, record the results of your trials. How effective was your method of shoreline protection? How could you improve your model? How well do you think it would perform in the real world?

Getting Involved

In Your Community If you live in a coastal area, visit the shore with an adult family member. If you don't live near the ocean, visit a pond or lake shore in your area. Can you observe any evidence of beach erosion? What methods are being used to limit damage to homes and other structures? Investigate what your community has done to prevent erosion in these areas.

Performance Assessment

Wrap Up

Presenting Your Project
As each student or group demonstrates the method of erosion control that works best, assess how well the method prevents beach erosion and protects the lighthouse. Students should explain what other methods they tried and why they were less successful.

Reflect and Record In assessing the effectiveness of their method, students should compare it with other students' methods. If the methods differ, they should reflect whether differences in how they constructed their models or generated waves might have affected the results. In judging how well their method would perform in the real world, students should consider ways their models and waves differ from real beaches, structures, and waves. For example, their model lighthouse may not have been held together with strong enough mortar, or the waves they generated may not have been as high as real waves might be along some parts of the shore.

Getting Involved

In Your Community Before students go to the shore, challenge the class to brainstorm evidence of beach erosion, such as sandbars. List correct ideas on the board. Also review and list ways to prevent beach erosion and protect structures on the shore, such as groins and seawalls. Students should copy the lists and take them when they visit the shore. Students can learn more about what the community has done to prevent erosion by contacting the state or local conservation department, which may have a website on the internet.

---

22. You would expect salinity to be low because rain and river water are both fresh, so they dilute ocean water and make it less salty.

23. Compared to the surface, ocean water at 1,000 meters is colder, darker, denser, and at higher pressure. Water at 1,000 meters may also be more or less salty than water at the surface, depending on factors such as precipitation, temperature, and proximity to the mouths of large rivers.

24. Much of western Europe has a mild, wet climate because the Gulf Stream brings warm water from the Gulf of Mexico northeast across the Atlantic to the coast of Europe. Winds blowing inland across this warm current make the climate warmer and wetter on the mainland.

Program Resources

◆ **Inquiry Skills Activity Book** Provides teaching and review of all inquiry skills

Sections	Time	Student Edition Activities	Other Activities	
CHAPTER PROJECT 5 **At Home in the Sea** p. 145	Ongoing (3 weeks)	Check Your Progress, p. 161 Check Your Progress, p. 168 Wrap Up, p. 179		
1 **Exploring the Ocean** pp. 146–155 ◆ Describe the exploration of the ocean and its floor and identify factors that make ocean-floor research difficult. ◆ Describe features of the ocean floor and the processes that have shaped the ocean floor.	4–5 periods/ 2–3 blocks	**Discover** What Can You Learn Without Seeing?, p. 146 **Sharpen Your Skills** Interpreting Data, p. 152 **Science at Home**, p. 154 **Skills Lab: Interpreting Data** The Shape of the Ocean Floor, p. 155	TE TE TE TE TE	Including All Students, p. 149 Building Inquiry Skills: Making Models, p. 149 Building Inquiry Skills: Graphing, p. 151 Demonstration, p. 152 Inquiry Challenge, p. 153 Building Inquiry Skills: Relating Cause and Effect, p. 153
2 *INTEGRATING LIFE SCIENCE* **Life at the Ocean's Edge** pp. 156–161 ◆ Describe the factors that affect where ocean organisms live. ◆ Identify the conditions that organisms in the rocky intertidal zone must overcome. ◆ Name and describe the major types of coastal wetlands.	2–3 periods/ 1–2 blocks	**Discover** Can Your Animal Hold On?, p. 156	TE TE TE ISLM IES	Addressing Naive Conceptions, p. 157 Inquiry Challenge, p. 159 Real-Life Learning, p. 160 H-5, "Microscopic Water Life" "Where River Meets Sea," pp. 6–8, 9–10, 11–12
3 *INTEGRATING LIFE SCIENCE* **The Neritic Zone and Open Ocean** pp. 162–168 ◆ Describe conditions in the neritic zone that support organisms and two neritic zone habitats—kelp forests and coral reefs. ◆ Describe conditions and identify where algae live in the open ocean. ◆ Explain how hydrothermal vents support organisms.	2–3 periods/ 1–2 blocks	**Discover** How Deep Can You See?, p. 162 **Sharpen Your Skills** Inferring, p. 166	TE TE IES	Inquiry Challenge, p. 164 Building Inquiry Skills: Making Models, p. 167 "Where River Meets Sea," pp. 33–34
4 **Resources From the Ocean** pp. 169–176 ◆ Explain how the supply of fish in a fishery changes from year to year and list sources of water pollution. ◆ Identify the ocean's living and nonliving resources and explain how they can be protected.	3–4 periods/ 2–3 blocks	**Discover** Is It From the Ocean?, p. 169 **Try This** Seaweed Candy, p. 171 **Sharpen Your Skills** Observing, p. 172 **Science at Home**, p. 174 **Real-World Lab: You and Your Environment** Cleaning Up an Oil Spill, p. 176	TE TE IES	Real-Life Learning, p. 170 Inquiry Challenge, p. 172 "Where River Meets Sea," pp. 35–37, 38, 39–42
Study Guide/Chapter Review pp. 177–179	1 period/ $\frac{1}{2}$ block		ISAB	Provides teaching and review of all inquiry skills

For Standard or Block Schedule The Resource Pro® CD-ROM gives you maximum flexibility for planning your instruction for any type of schedule. Resource Pro® contains Planning Express®, an advanced scheduling program, as well as the entire contents of the Teaching Resources and the Computer Test Bank.

CHAPTER PLANNING GUIDE

Program Resources	Assessment Strategies	Media and Technology
TR Chapter 5 Project Teacher Notes, pp. 120–121 TR Chapter 5 Project Student Materials, pp. 122–125 TR Chapter 5 Project Scoring Rubric, p. 126 SES Book B, *Animals,* Chapters 1–4	SE Performance Assessment: Chapter 5 Project Wrap Up, p. 179 TE Check Your Progress, pp. 161, 168 TR Chapter 5 Project Scoring Rubric, p. 126	Science Explorer Internet Site
TR 5-1 Lesson Plan, p. 127 TR 5-1 Section Summary, p. 128 TR 5-1 Review and Reinforce, p. 129 TR 5-1 Enrich, p. 130 TR Chapter 5 Skills Lab, pp. 143–144 SES Book F, *Earth's Interior,* Chapter 1	SE Section 1 Review, p. 154 SE Analyze and Conclude, p. 155 TE Ongoing Assessment, pp. 147, 149, 151, 153 TE Performance Assessment, p. 154 TR 5-1 Review and Reinforce, p. 129	Exploring Physical Science Videodisc, Unit 6 Side 2, "Blind As a Bat" Exploring Earth Science Videodisc, Unit 3 Side 1, "Journey to the Bottom of the Sea" Audiotapes, English-Spanish Summary 5-1 Transparencies 17, "Exploring the Ocean Floor" and 18, "Converging and Diverging Plates" Interactive Student Tutorial CD-ROM, H-5
TR 5-2 Lesson Plan, p. 131 TR 5-2 Section Summary, p. 132 TR 5-2 Review and Reinforce, p. 133 TR 5-2 Enrich, p. 134	SE Section 2 Review, p. 161 TE Ongoing Assessment, pp. 157, 159 TE Performance Assessment, p. 161 TR 5-2 Review and Reinforce, p. 133	Exploring Life Science Videodisc, Unit 3 Side 1, "Travelin' Along" Audiotapes, English-Spanish Summary 5-2 Interactive Student Tutorial CD-ROM, H-5
TR 5-3 Lesson Plan, p. 135 TR 5-3 Section Summary, p. 136 TR 5-3 Review and Reinforce, p. 137 TR 5-3 Enrich, p. 138	SE Section 3 Review, p. 168 TE Ongoing Assessment, pp. 163, 165, 167 TE Performance Assessment, p. 168 TR 5-3 Review and Reinforce, p. 137	Audiotapes, English-Spanish Summary 5-3 Transparency 19, "Ocean Zones" Transparency 20, "An Arctic Food Web" Interactive Student Tutorial CD-ROM, H-5
TR 5-4 Lesson Plan, p. 139 TR 5-4 Section Summary, p. 140 TR 5-4 Review and Reinforce, p. 141 TR 5-4 Enrich, p. 142 TR Chapter 5 Real-World Lab, pp. 145–147	SE Section 4 Review, p. 174 SE Analyze and Conclude, p. 176 TE Ongoing Assessment, pp. 171, 173 TE Performance Assessment, p. 174 TR 5-4 Review and Reinforce, p. 141	Audiotapes, English-Spanish Summary 5-4 Interactive Student Tutorial CD-ROM, H-5
TR Chapter 5 Performance Assessment, pp. 188–190 TR Chapter 5 Test, pp. 191–194	SE Chapter 5 Review, pp. 177–179 TR Chapter 5 Performance Assessment, pp. 188–190 TR Chapter 5 Test, p. 191–194 CTB Test H-5	Interactive Student Tutorial CD-ROM, H-5 Computer Test Bank, Test H-5 Got It! Video Quizzes

Key: **SE** Student Edition   **TE** Teacher's Edition   **TR** Teaching Resources
    CTB Computer Test Bank   **SES** Science Explorer Series Text   **ISLM** Integrated Science Laboratory Manual
    ISAB Inquiry Skills Activity Book   **PTA** Product Testing Activities by *Consumer Reports*   **IES** Interdisciplinary Explorations Series

Meeting the National Science Education Standards and AAAS Benchmarks

National Science Education Standards	Benchmarks for Science Literacy	Unifying Themes
Science As Inquiry (Content Standard A) ◆ **Use appropriate tools and techniques to gather, analyze, and interpret data** Students graph data to determine the shape of the ocean floor. *(Skills Lab)* ◆ **Develop descriptions, explanations, predictions, and models using evidence** Students create a marine habitat model. Students model oil-spill cleanup. *(Chapter Project; Real-World Lab)* **Life Science** (Content Standard C) ◆ **Populations and ecosystems** The ocean is divided into zones, each characterized by different conditions and organisms. *(Chapter Project; Sections 2 and 3)* **Earth and Space Science** (Content Standard D) ◆ **Structure of the Earth System** The interaction of Earth's plates forms many sea-floor features. *(Section 1)* **Science and Technology** (Content Standard E) ◆ **Understanding about science and technology** Technology has helped in ocean study and in obtaining ocean resources. *(Sections 1 and 4; Science & History)* **Science in Personal and Social Perspectives** (Content Standard F) ◆ **Populations, resources, and environments** Human activities can harm marine environments. *(Section 4; Science and Society)*	**1B Scientific Inquiry** Students explore ways to clean up an oil spill. *(Real-World Lab)* **3A Technology and Science** Technology has helped scientists study the ocean and is used to obtain ocean resources. *(Sections 1 and 4; Science & History)* **3C Issues in Technology** Human activities can harm marine environments. *(Section 4; Science and Society)* **4C Processes That Shape the Earth** The interaction of Earth's plates forms many sea-floor features. *(Section 1)* **5A Diversity of Life** Different organisms have adapted to living in different parts of the ocean. *(Chapter Project; Sections 2 and 3)* **5D Interdependence of Life** Ocean organisms are connected through complex feeding relationships. *(Sections 2 and 3)* **7D Social Trade-Offs** Students weigh the pros and cons of shrimp farming. *(Science and Society)* **9B Symbolic Relationships** Students graph data to determine the shape of the ocean floor. *(Skills Lab)* **11B Models** Students create a marine habitat model. Students model oil-spill cleanup. *(Chapter Project; Real-World Lab)*	◆ **Scale and Structure** Earth consists of several layers, and the outer layer, the crust, is made up of moving plates. The ocean is divided into zones, each with different habitats. Students graph data to determine the shape of the ocean floor. *(Sections 1, 2, and 3; Chapter Project; Skills Lab)* ◆ **Systems and Interactions** The interaction of Earth's plates forms many sea-floor features. Physical factors determine where marine organisms can live. Human activities can harm marine environments. *(Sections 1, 2, 3, and 4; Science and Society)* ◆ **Energy** The feeding relationships in a habitat make up a food web. Hydrothermal vents supply chemical nutrients that support a unique group of organisms. Oil and natural gas are found in deposits in the ocean floor. *(Sections 2, 3, and 4)* ◆ **Modeling** Students create models of marine habitats and organisms. Students model oil-spill cleanup. *(Chapter Project; Real-World Lab)* ◆ **Unity and Diversity** The ocean floor has features similar to those found on continents. Physical conditions vary between ocean zones. Coastal wetlands include salt marshes and mangrove forests. The neritic zone includes kelp forest and coral reef habitats. The open-ocean zone is divided into the surface zone and the deep zone. *(Sections 1, 2, and 3)*

Media and Technology

Exploring Physical Science Videodiscs
◆ **Section 1** "Blind As a Bat" tells about sonar.

Exploring Earth Science Videodiscs
◆ **Section 1** "Journey to the Bottom of the Sea" illustrates sea-floor structures and how they are formed.

Exploring Life Science Videodiscs
◆ **Section 2** "Travelin' Along" shows sea turtle migration.

Interactive Student Tutorial CD-ROM
◆ **Chapter Review** Interactive questions help students to self-assess their mastery of key chapter concepts.

Student Edition Connection Strategies

◆ **Section 1** Integrating Technology, pp. 147–148
Science & History, pp. 148–149

◆ **Section 2** Integrating Life Science, pp. 156–161
Language Arts Connection, p. 158

◆ **Section 3** Integrating Life Science, pp. 162–168

◆ **Section 4** Integrating Technology, p. 171
Science and Society, p. 175

USING THE INTERNET

www.science-explorer.phschool.com

Visit the Science Explorer internet site to find an up-to-date activity for Chapter 5 of *Earth's Waters*.

ACTIVITY	Time (minutes)	Materials Quantities for one work group	Skills
Section 1			
Discover, p. 146	15	**Consumable** 10 plastic drinking straws **Nonconsumable** box with mystery object	Inferring
Sharpen Your Skills, p. 152	10	No special materials are required.	Interpreting Data
Science at Home, p. 154	home	**Consumable** graph paper **Nonconsumable** carpenter's measuring tape	Graphing
Skills Lab, p. 155	30	**Consumable** graph paper **Nonconsumable** pencil	Graphing, Inferring
Section 2			
Discover, p. 156	15	**Consumable** common materials (such as tape), water **Nonconsumable** ping-pong ball, rock, common materials (such as suction cups), sink or deep pan	Inferring
Section 3			
Discover, p. 162	15	**Consumable** white plastic lid, string, paper clip, tape, water, flour **Nonconsumable** permanent marker, scissors, meterstick, bucket	Observing
Sharpen Your Skills, p. 166	10	No special materials are required.	Inferring
Section 4			
Discover, p. 169	15	**Consumable** labels from common household products such as thickeners used in cooking, foods, abrasives, polishes, shampoos, and spice mixes containing sea salts	Classifying
Try This, p. 171	20, 5	**Consumable** 2 blocks agar, 1 cup sugar, 4 cups guava or other fruit juice, food coloring, water **Nonconsumable** saucepan, shallow pan, knife	Inferring
Sharpen Your Skills, p. 172	10	No special materials are required.	Observing
Science at Home, p. 174	home	**Consumable** rubber band	Making Models
Real-World Lab, p. 176	40	**Consumable** water, feather, paper towels, paper cup, cotton balls, vegetable oil, wooden sticks **Nonconsumable** graduated cylinder (100 mL), shallow pan, plastic dropper, marking pen	Making Models, Forming Operational Definitions

A list of all materials required for the Student Edition activities can be found beginning on page T14. You can order Materials Kits by calling 1-800-828-7777 or by accessing the Science Explorer Internet site at **www.science-explorer.phschool.com.**

At Home in the Sea

Most students do not often have the opportunity to observe marine organisms in their natural habitats. This project will enable students to demonstrate their understanding of marine habitats and organisms in visual form.

Purpose This project is designed to enhance students' knowledge of specific marine habitats and the organisms commonly found there. Students will research and model the habitats' physical features and typical inhabitants and will communicate that knowledge in a class presentation.

Skills Focus Students will be able to
◆ create three-dimensional models of marine habitats and their typical inhabitants;
◆ identify adaptations that enable organisms to survive in their habitats;
◆ represent interactions between organisms and their physical environment.

Project Timeline This project requires about three weeks to complete. During the first week, each group should measure the space available for the habitat model, choose a habitat, research and list its physical features, sketch the planned model for your review, and choose materials for building the model. During the second week, each group should begin building its model habitat. Each group member should choose one organism to model, research its characteristics, and present a plan for your review. During the third week, group members should complete their model organisms, place them in the habitat, and prepare the presentation. See Chapter 5 Project Teacher Notes on pages 120–121 in Teaching Resources for more detailed guidelines on carrying out the project.

Suggested Shortcuts To save time and materials, you could have students create ocean organisms that are smaller than life-size for dioramas, or you could simply have students make a mural rather than three-dimensional models.

Possible Materials Provide a wide variety of materials from which students can choose. Some possibilities are listed

CHAPTER

5 Ocean Zones

WHAT'S AHEAD

SECTION 1 Exploring the Ocean

Discover What Can You Learn Without Seeing?
Sharpen Your Skills Interpreting Data
Skills Lab The Shape of the Ocean Floor

Integrating Life Science
SECTION 2 Life at the Ocean's Edge

Discover Can Your Animal Hold On?

Integrating Life Science
SECTION 3 The Neritic Zone and Open Ocean

Discover How Deep Can You See?
Sharpen Your Skills Inferring

144 ◆ H

below. Encourage students to suggest and use other materials as well.
◆ *To form the habitat enclosure:* cardboard box, sheets of cardboard or posterboard, chicken wire
◆ *To shape and form the ocean floor:* brown paper, modeling clay, salt dough or papier mâché, plaster of paris, glue and sand to add texture
◆ *To make the organism models:* fabric, rolls of brown or white paper, cotton batting or tissue paper for stuffing, construction paper,

foam rubber, styrofoam, household sponges, paints or colored markers, pipe cleaners, toothpicks
◆ *To represent water:* acetate or cellophane
◆ *To show a food web:* colored yarn to connect organisms

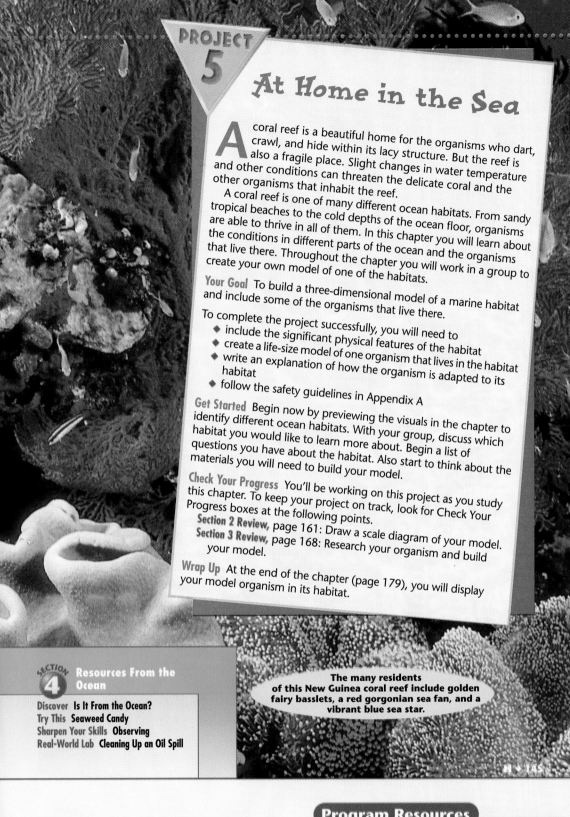

PROJECT 5

At Home in the Sea

A coral reef is a beautiful home for the organisms who dart, crawl, and hide within its lacy structure. But the reef is also a fragile place. Slight changes in water temperature and other conditions can threaten the delicate coral and the other organisms that inhabit the reef.

A coral reef is one of many different ocean habitats. From sandy tropical beaches to the cold depths of the ocean floor, organisms are able to thrive in all of them. In this chapter you will learn about the conditions in different parts of the ocean and the organisms that live there. Throughout the chapter you will work in a group to create your own model of one of the habitats.

Your Goal To build a three-dimensional model of a marine habitat and include some of the organisms that live there.

To complete the project successfully, you will need to
◆ include the significant physical features of the habitat
◆ create a life-size model of one organism that lives in the habitat
◆ write an explanation of how the organism is adapted to its habitat
◆ follow the safety guidelines in Appendix A

Get Started Begin now by previewing the visuals in the chapter to identify different ocean habitats. With your group, discuss which habitat you would like to learn more about. Begin a list of questions you have about the habitat. Also start to think about the materials you will need to build your model.

Check Your Progress You'll be working on this project as you study this chapter. To keep your project on track, look for Check Your Progress boxes at the following points.
Section 2 Review, page 161: Draw a scale diagram of your model.
Section 3 Review, page 168: Research your organism and build your model.

Wrap Up At the end of the chapter (page 179), you will display your model organism in its habitat.

The many residents of this New Guinea coral reef include golden fairy basslets, a red gorgonian sea fan, and a vibrant blue sea star.

SECTION 4 Resources From the Ocean

Discover Is It From the Ocean?
Try This Seaweed Candy
Sharpen Your Skills Observing
Real-World Lab Cleaning Up an Oil Spill

Program Resources

Science Explorer Series *Animals*, Chapters 1–4, can provide background on marine animals.
◆ **Teaching Resources** Chapter 5 Project Teacher Notes, pp. 120–121; Chapter 5 Project Student Materials, pp. 122–125; Chapter 5 Project Scoring Rubric, p. 126

Launching the Project To introduce the project and motivate student interest, show the class photographs—or a video or CD-ROM—of different marine habitats with their typical organisms. Encourage students to ask questions and offer comments about the environments and organisms they see, but do not attempt to preteach chapter content.

Allow time for students to read the description of the project in their text and the Chapter 5 Project Overview on pages 122–123 in Teaching Resources. Then encourage discussion of the various habitats and organisms that could be modeled, materials that could be used, and any initial questions students may have. Pass out copies of the Chapter 5 Project Worksheets on pages 124–125 in Teaching Resources for students to review.

Have students work in small groups as a cooperative learning task. To ensure that every student will have ample opportunity to participate in planning and building a model habitat, each group should consist of no more than four students. Also emphasize that each student is to build his or her own model organism for the group's habitat.

Performance Assessment

The Chapter 5 Project Scoring Rubric on page 126 in Teaching Resources will help you evaluate how well students complete the Chapter 5 Project. You may wish to share the scoring rubric with your students so they are clear about what will be expected of them. Students will be assessed on
◆ planning their models, including the completeness and accurateness of their final habitat sketches and the thoroughness of their research on their marine organism model;
◆ how accurately and neatly they make their models;
◆ how well they present their models to the class;
◆ how well they work together in their groups.

145 ◆ H

Objectives

After completing the lesson, students will be able to
◆ describe the exploration of the ocean and its floor and identify factors that make ocean-floor research difficult;
◆ describe features of the ocean floor and the processes that have shaped it.

Key Terms sonar, continental shelf, continental slope, seamount, abyssal plain, mid-ocean ridge, trench, magma, plates, sea-floor spreading

1 Engage/Explore

Activating Prior Knowledge

Ask students: **What does the ocean floor look like?** Encourage them to share what they have seen in books, on television, and in movies. Lead students to understand that the ocean floor has a varied surface, similar to the land's surface.

DISCOVER

Skills Focus inferring
Materials *10 plastic drinking straws, box with mystery object*
Time 15 minutes
Advance Preparation Obtain as many small cardboard boxes with lids as there will be groups doing the activity. In the bottom of each box, glue or tape an object whose identity could be inferred by determining its contours, such as a ball, small toy, spool, or spoon. Use a different object in each box, making sure each object clears the lid by at least 2 cm. With a sharp pencil or awl, poke 10–15 holes in the lid at various locations.
Tips Students should use the straws as probes, inserting them straight down into the holes and observing how far they stick up.
Expected Outcome Students may not be able to determine the object's identity with certainty, but they should be able to suggest reasonable possibilities.
Think It Over The depths of the straws indicated the object's location, size, and

SECTION 1 Exploring the Ocean

DISCOVER · ACTIVITY

What Can You Learn Without Seeing?

1. Your teacher will provide your group with ten plastic drinking straws and a covered box containing a mystery object. The top of the box has several holes punched in it. Using the straws as probes, try to determine the size, shape, and location of the object inside the box.

2. Based on the information you gathered, describe your object. What can you say about its length, shape, and position? Write down your hypothesis about the identity of the object.

3. Remove the box top to reveal the object.

Think It Over
Inferring Explain how you used the method of indirect observation in this activity to learn about the object.

GUIDE FOR READING

◆ What factors make ocean-floor research difficult?
◆ What processes have shaped the ocean floor?

Reading Tip As you read, make a list of features found on the ocean floor. Write one sentence about each feature.

Figure 1 This engraving shows HMS *Challenger* in the Indian Ocean in 1874, two years into its journey around the world.

Imagine going on a voyage around the world lasting three and a half years. Your assignment: to investigate "everything about the sea." Your vessel: a former warship, powered by sails and a steam engine. Its guns have been removed to make room for scientific gear. On board there are thermometers for measuring the temperature of ocean water and hundreds of kilometers of cable for lowering dredges to the bottom of the ocean. With the dredges, you scrape sand, muck, and rock from the ocean floor. You drag trawl nets behind the ship to collect ocean organisms.

The crew of a British ship, HMS *Challenger*, began such a voyage in 1872. By the end of the journey, the scientists had gathered enough data to fill 50 volumes and had collected more than 4,000 new organisms! It took 23 years to publish all the information they learned about oceanwater chemistry, currents, ocean life, and the shape of the ocean floor. The voyage of the *Challenger* was so successful that it became the model for many later ocean expeditions.

READING STRATEGIES

Reading Tip Seven ocean-floor features are identified in this section: continental shelf, continental slope, trenches, abyssal plain, mid-ocean ridge, seamounts, and volcanic islands. Suggest that students scan the section first to find and list the names of these features, leaving room after each term to write the sentences later. Encourage students to describe the features in their own words.

Vocabulary The terms *diverging* and *converging* may present difficulty for some students. To help them remember the terms and their meanings, explain that the root *verge* comes from a Latin word meaning "bend or turn." Ask what the prefixes *di-* and *con-* mean. (*Di-, from* dis-, *means "apart, away"*; con-, *from* com-, *means "together."*) If students do not know these meanings, have them look up the words in a dictionary.

Voyages of Discovery

For thousands of years before the *Challenger* expedition, people explored the ocean. Knowledge of the ocean has always been important to the people living along its coasts. The ocean has provided food and served as a route for trade and travel to new settlements.

The Phoenicians, who lived along the Mediterranean Sea, were one of the earliest cultures to explore the oceans. By 1200 B.C., they had established sea routes for trade with the other nations around the Mediterranean. After the Phoenicians, people of many European, African, and Asian cultures sailed along the coasts to trade with distant lands.

In the Pacific Ocean around 2,000 years ago, the Polynesians left the safety of the coastline and boldly sailed into the open ocean. Their knowledge of winds and currents enabled the Polynesians to settle the scattered islands of Hawaii, Tahiti, and New Zealand.

As modern science developed and trade increased, ocean exploration changed. Nations needed accurate maps of the oceans and lands bordering them. Governments also wanted their countries to be known for new scientific discoveries. For example, in the late 1700s, the British government hired Captain James Cook to lead three voyages of exploration. Cook's crew included scientists who studied the stars and collected new species of plants and animals.

Within a century of Cook's voyages, almost all of Earth's coastlines had been mapped. Scientists then turned to the study of the ocean's waters and invented methods to explore its unknown depths. The *Challenger* expedition marked the beginning of the modern science of oceanography.

☑ *Checkpoint* **What are two reasons why people have explored the oceans?**

Exploring the Ocean Floor

 INTEGRATING TECHNOLOGY Following the *Challenger's* example, governments and universities sponsored many other major ocean research expeditions. Until recently, however, the ocean floor was unexplored, and much of the life in the oceans was unknown. Why did it take so long to reach this part of the ocean? Studying the ocean floor is difficult because the

Figure 2 Polynesian sailors used stick charts to navigate the Pacific Ocean. The curved sticks represent currents and winds. The pieces of coral might represent rocks or small islands. *Interpreting Maps Use the map to explain why navigation tools were important to the Polynesians.*

Program Resources

◆ **Teaching Resources** 5-1 Lesson Plan, p. 127; 5-1 Section Summary, p. 128

Media and Technology

 Audiotapes English-Spanish Summary 5-1

Answers to Self-Assessment

Caption Question

Figure 2 They needed to know the locations of and distances between islands so they could travel among them safely.

☑ *Checkpoint*

Any two: To gain scientific information, obtain food, conduct trade, establish new settlements, and gain fame

2 Facilitate

Voyages of Discovery

Cultural Diversity

To further students' understanding of the peoples and regions discussed in the text, display a map showing the Pacific Ocean and the coastal areas of the surrounding continents. Explain that Polynesia is a huge area lying within a triangle formed by the Hawaiian Islands (roughly midway between Southeast Asia and Mexico), Easter Island (in the South Pacific, west of Chile), and New Zealand (southeast of Australia). Have volunteers find these three areas on the map and stretch string between them to form a triangle. Ask: **Where do you think the first settlers of Polynesia came from?** *(Some students might infer that the first settlers must have come from Asia.)* Explain that there are still many Asian influences in the cultures of these islands. **learning modality: visual**

Exploring the Ocean Floor

Integrating Technology

Before students read the rest of this section on the next page, ask them to suggest answers to the question at the bottom of this page: **Why did it take so long to reach the ocean floor?** *(Accept all answers without comment.)* Discuss the difficulties of studying the ocean floor after students read the next page. **learning modality: logical/mathematical**

Ongoing Assessment

Oral Presentation Have students identify some early ocean explorers and describe their voyages.

147 ◆ H

Exploring the Ocean Floor, continued

 **SCIENCE & History**

Guide students through the sequence of technological developments shown and described on the time line. Then ask: **What is an advantage of having people dive rather than sending a RUM?** (*People can observe things directly rather than just viewing photographs or videotapes.*) **What is an advantage of using a submersible?** (*It can carry people to greater depths than unprotected divers can go.*) **What is a disadvantage of submersibles?** (*The people inside have a limited view and cannot touch underwater objects.*) **Why do you think it is helpful to have a map of the ocean floor that is accurate to within a few centimeters, such as the one created using gravity mapping?** (*Students might suggest that it is important for development of the ocean floor, for defense, to gain a better understanding of Earth processes, or for various other reasons.*)

In Your Journal Students should be able to find out more about the technologies featured on the time line in books on oceanography and ocean exploration. Suggest that they also look in magazines, such as *National Geographic*. In addition to the six technologies shown on these pages, students could research the diving equipment that was used before scuba was invented (including the diving bell and diving helmet) and specific submersibles, such as *Johnson Sea-Link, Deep Rover, Shinkai 6,500, Alvin,* and *Trieste.* Other interesting topics are the atmospheric diving suit known as JIM (see Background) and the deep-diving robot, *Kaiko.* **learning modality: verbal**

ocean is so deep—3.8 kilometers deep on average, more than twice as deep as the Grand Canyon. As you learned in Chapter 4, conditions are very harsh at such depths. First, because sunlight does not penetrate far below the surface, the deep ocean is in total darkness. Second, the water is very cold—only a few degrees above freezing. Finally, there is tremendous pressure due to the mass of water pushing down from above.

Because of the darkness, cold, and extreme pressure, scientists have had to develop technology to enable them to study the deep ocean floor. Since humans cannot survive these conditions, many of the inventions have involved indirect methods of gathering information. One of the simplest methods, used by the *Challenger's* crew, was to lower a weight on a long line into the water until the weight touched the bottom. The length of line

SCIENCE & History

Technology and Ocean Exploration

The time line includes several inventions that have helped scientists overcome the challenges of studying the ocean world.

1943 SCUBA

Jacques Cousteau and Emile Gagnan invented SCUBA, which stands for "**s**elf-**c**ontained **u**nderwater **b**reathing **a**pparatus." A tank containing compressed air is strapped to the diver's back and connected by a tube to a mouthpiece. SCUBA enables divers to explore to a depth of 40 meters.

| 1915 | 1930 | 1945 | 1960 |

1925 Sonar

Scientists aboard the German ship *Meteor* used sonar to map the ocean floor. They used a device called an echo sounder to produce pulses of sound. The ship's crew then timed the return of the echoes.

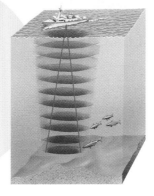

1960 Submersibles

Vehicles with very thick metal hulls protect explorers from extreme pressure and temperature, while enabling them to directly observe the ocean depths.

148 ◆ H

Background

History of Science A significant development in deep-sea diving is the JIM suit, named for Jim Jarratt, its inventor. This diving suit has joints that allow divers to bend their arms and legs. The JIM suit can protect a diver at depths of up to 450 m. Some JIM suits have thrusters that enable the diver to hover in the water. Most importantly, the suit maintains atmospheric pressure so the diver does not need to undergo decompression when resurfacing.

Originally used for work on oil rigs, the JIM suit was first used for scientific research by Sylvia Earle, a marine biologist who has earned international recognition for her deep-sea explorations. Earle's experiences are described in *Window on the Deep* by Andrea Conley (New York: Franklin Watts, 1991).

that got wet was approximately equal to the water's depth at that location. This method was slow and often inaccurate, as the line would descend at an angle. Nevertheless, these depth readings produced the first rough maps of the floor of the North Atlantic.

A major advance in ocean-floor mapping was sonar, a technology invented during World War I to detect submarines. **Sonar**, which stands for **so**und **na**vigation and **r**anging, is a system that uses sound waves to calculate the distance to an object. The sonar equipment on a ship sends out pulses of sound that bounce off the ocean floor. The equipment then measures how quickly the sound waves return to the ship. Sound waves return quickly if the ocean floor is close. Sound waves take longer to return if the ocean floor is farther away.

☑ *Checkpoint* **How is sonar an indirect way of gathering data?**

In Your Journal

Each of the inventions shown on these two pages helped solve a problem of ocean exploration. Find out more about one of these inventions. Write a short newspaper article telling the story of its development. Include details about the people who invented it and how it added to people's knowledge of the oceans.

1986
Remote Underwater Manipulator

The Remote Underwater Manipulator, or RUM III, is about the size of a small car. It is controlled by a computer aboard a ship at the surface. Without a crew, the RUM III can collect samples, take photographs, and map the ocean floor.

1975	1990	2005	2020

1978 Satellites

Seasat A was the first satellite in Earth's orbit to study the oceans. Since satellites make millions of observations a day, they provide data on rapidly changing and widespread ocean conditions. Such data include temperatures, algae growth patterns, and even the movement of large schools of fish.

1995
Gravity Mapping

The United States Navy used advanced satellite data to create a new map of the ocean floor. The satellite detected slight changes in gravity related to the shape of the ocean floor, providing accurate measurements within a few centimeters.

Chapter 5 **H ◆ 149**

Answers to Self-Assessment

☑ *Checkpoint*

Depths are not measured directly but are calculated based on the timing of echoes.

Including All Students

Have students do this activity to reinforce the concept of water pressure increasing with depth and to help them understand the problems this causes in underwater exploration. Students should submerge a small, empty plastic soda bottle with the lid on tightly in a tank or deep sink of water. As they move the bottle lower in the water, they should notice it start to collapse. Ask: **Why is the bottle collapsing?** (*Water pressure is pushing in on all sides of the bottle.*) Point out that at 3.8 km below the ocean's surface, pressure is 400 times greater than it is at sea level. Ask: **What would this kind of pressure do to most hollow objects?** (*It would crush them.*) Help students relate this to the construction of submersibles.
learning modality: kinesthetic

Building Inquiry Skills: Making Models

Explain that the process of using sound waves to determine distance is known as *echolocation*. Let students do the following activity so they can gain a basic understanding of how the process works. Divide the class into pairs, and have the two students in each pair stand facing each other about 1 m apart. One student should hold up a large sheet of cardboard at face level. The other student should close his or her eyes, then walk *slowly* toward the first student while vocalizing sounds (for example, saying "Ah!" repeatedly). Have the partners switch places and repeat. Then ask: **What did you hear as you walked toward the cardboard?** (*Students will hear echoes of their own voices, with the sound changing as they get closer to the cardboard.*)
learning modality: kinesthetic

Ongoing Assessment

Oral Presentation Have students explain what problems have to be overcome for people to explore the ocean floor.

Features of the Ocean Floor

EXPLORING
the Ocean Floor

Point out that the visual essay shows all the features described in the text about a journey from one continent to another. To help students relate the text and essay descriptions, you could have a different volunteer read each text paragraph aloud, pausing at each boldfaced term to let another volunteer read aloud the related essay caption.

Students may be able to relate the ocean-floor features to features found on land. For example, students might relate the continental shelf and continental slope on the left in the essay with the foothills of the Rocky Mountains in the western United States, the abyssal plain with the Great Plains, and the continental slope and shelf on the right with the foothills of the Appalachian Mountains in the eastern United States. Students might suggest that the Grand Canyon is like an ocean-floor trench. **learning modality: visual**

Including All Students

Encourage students to imagine what Earth would look like if the oceans dried up and all the features of the ocean floor were visible. Then show them an illustration showing a "dry Earth" from space. (An excellent example can be found in Rand McNally's *Atlas of the Oceans,* ©1994, pages 118–119.) As an alternative for visually impaired students, use a relief map of the ocean floor. Have students locate and name each continent shown. Then have them trace the journey from one continent to another on the illustration, naming each feature as they reach it—much like the journey described in the text and shown in the visual essay. **learning modality: visual**

Features of the Ocean Floor

Once scientists were able to map the ocean floor, they discovered something surprising. The bottom of the ocean was not a flat, sandy plain stretching between the continents, as many people had thought. In fact, the ocean floor was rocky and dramatically uneven. The deep waters hid mountain ranges bigger than any on Earth's surface, as well as deep canyons reaching into Earth's interior.

If you could take a submarine voyage along the ocean floor, what would you see? Trace your journey from the edge of one continent to another in *Exploring the Ocean Floor.*

As you leave the harbor, your submarine first passes over the **continental shelf**, a gently sloping, shallow area of the ocean floor that extends outward from the edge of a continent. At a depth of about 130 meters, the ocean floor suddenly plunges steeply below you. This steep incline at the edge of the continental shelf is called the **continental slope**. The continental slope marks the true edge of a continent, where the rock that makes up the continent stops and the rock of the ocean floor begins.

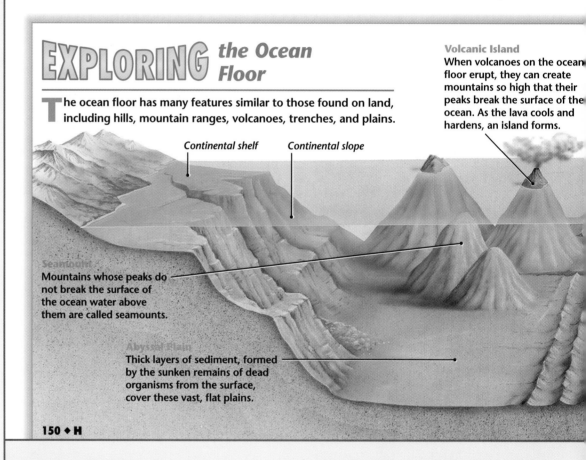

EXPLORING the Ocean Floor

The ocean floor has many features similar to those found on land, including hills, mountain ranges, volcanoes, trenches, and plains.

Continental shelf

Continental slope

Volcanic Island
When volcanoes on the ocean floor erupt, they can create mountains so high that their peaks break the surface of the ocean. As the lava cools and hardens, an island forms.

Seamount
Mountains whose peaks do not break the surface of the ocean water above them are called seamounts.

Abyssal Plain
Thick layers of sediment, formed by the sunken remains of dead organisms from the surface, cover these vast, flat plains.

150 ◆ H

Background

Facts and Figures Sediments on the ocean floor are of two types. One type forms from the remains of organisms that once lived in the ocean's surface waters. The other type forms from material that is eroded from the land.

Very little eroded material reaches the deep ocean basins. Most is deposited on the continental shelves and at the foot of continental slopes. Near the mouth of a large silt-carrying river, the material builds up in a fan-shaped area similar to a delta. Many parts of the deep ocean floor are covered with a sediment ooze made up of organic remains. Sediment thickness varies throughout the ocean. Near the mid-ocean ridge, the newly formed crust has little or no sediment covering it. Moving away from the ridge, the depth increases to hundreds of meters thick.

Your submarine descends more gradually now, following the ocean floor as it slopes toward the deep ocean. After some distance, you encounter a group of mountains. Some are tall enough to break the ocean's surface, forming islands. Others, called **seamounts**, are mountains that are completely underwater. Some seamounts have flat tops because their peaks have eroded away.

Next you cross a broad area covered with thick layers of mud and silt. This smooth, nearly flat region of the ocean floor is called the **abyssal plain** (uh BIHS uhl plain). After gliding over the abyssal plain for many kilometers, you need to steer the submarine sharply upward to avoid a mountain range ahead. The **mid-ocean ridge** is a continuous range of mountains that winds around Earth, much as the line of stitches winds around a baseball. The mid-ocean ridge passes through all of Earth's oceans. Nearly 80,000 kilometers long, it is the longest mountain range on Earth.

At the top of the mid-ocean ridge, your submarine is about two kilometers above the abyssal plain, but you are still at least one kilometer below the surface. From this vantage you can see

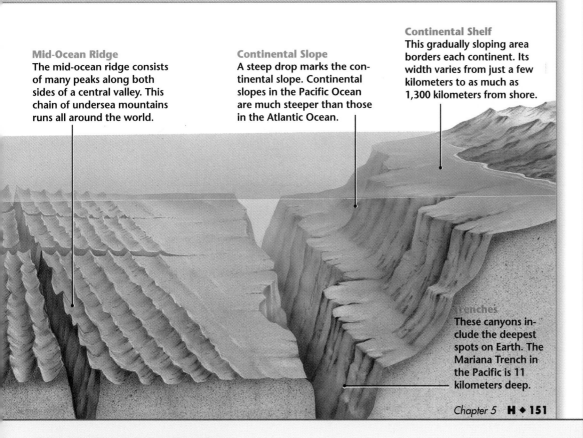

Mid-Ocean Ridge
The mid-ocean ridge consists of many peaks along both sides of a central valley. This chain of undersea mountains runs all around the world.

Continental Slope
A steep drop marks the continental slope. Continental slopes in the Pacific Ocean are much steeper than those in the Atlantic Ocean.

Continental Shelf
This gradually sloping area borders each continent. Its width varies from just a few kilometers to as much as 1,300 kilometers from shore.

Trenches
These canyons include the deepest spots on Earth. The Mariana Trench in the Pacific is 11 kilometers deep.

Chapter 5 **H ◆ 151**

Building Inquiry Skills: Graphing

ACTIVITY

Draw students' attention to the statement in *Exploring the Ocean Floor* that the Mariana Trench is about 11 km deep. To help students appreciate the great depth of this trench, ask: **Which is bigger, Mt. Everest or the Mariana Trench?** *(the Mariana Trench)* Then give each student a copy of the table below and ask: **How many Mt. Everests would fit into the Mariana Trench?** *(about 1.2)* **How many Grand Canyons would fit into it?** *(almost 7)* Finally, suggest that students use the information in the table to make a bar graph comparing the sizes of the objects listed. Make sure students label the vertical axis *Depth or Height (km)* and the horizontal axis with the names of the objects. **learning modality: logical/mathematical**

Object	Depth/Height
Mariana Trench (Pacific)	11.0 km
Mt. Everest (Tibet)	9.0 km
Mt. McKinley (Alaska)	6.0 km
Grand Canyon (Arizona)	1.6 km
Sears Tower (Chicago)	0.5 km
Tallest tree (California)	0.1 km

Including All Students

Urge curious students to consult dictionaries to learn the origin of the word *abyss*. (*From the Latin* abyssus, *derived from the Greek* abussos, *meaning "bottomless"*) Ask: **Why is abyssal plain a good name for that part of the ocean floor?** *(It is flat like a plain on land and, except for the bottom of trenches, is the deepest area of the ocean.)* **limited English proficiency**

Ongoing Assessment

Drawing Have each student draw a cross-sectional view of the ocean floor from one continent to another and label at least four different features without referring to *Exploring the Ocean Floor*.

 Students can save their drawings in their portfolios.

Sharpen your Skills

Interpreting Data

Time 10 minutes

Tips Tell students that the diagram should compare the two mountains' total heights from base to summit.

Expected Outcome Mauna Kea (13,800 m) is larger than Mt. Everest (8,850 m).

Extend Suggest that students compare Mauna Kea's total height with the depth of the Mariana Trench (about 11 km, or 11,000 m). **learning modality: logical/mathematical**

Movements of the Ocean Floor

Demonstration

To help students visualize the layers inside Earth, show them a hard-boiled egg. Ask: **If this were Earth, what would the shell represent?** *(the crust)* Peel the egg and cut it in half. Ask: **What is the white? the yolk?** *(the mantle, the core)* **Where does magma form?** *(in the mantle)* **learning modality: visual**

Using the Visuals: Figure 4

Point out the arrows on the map showing the direction of plate movement. Ask: **Which plates are moving toward the Pacific Plate?** *(Eurasian, Indo-Australian, North American)* **Which are moving away from the Pacific Plate?** *(Philippine, Nazca, Antarctic)* **What kind of ocean-floor feature would you expect to find along the boundary between the Pacific Plate and the Eurasian Plate? Explain your answer.** *(A trench, because the plates are converging)* **What feature would you expect to find between the Pacific Plate and the Antarctic Plate? Explain your answer.** *(A mid-ocean ridge, because the plates are diverging)* **learning modality: logical/mathematical**

Sharpen your Skills

Interpreting Data

What is Earth's largest mountain? Use the following data to answer the question. Mauna Kea projects about 4,200 meters above sea level. Its base is on the floor of the Pacific Ocean, approximately 9,600 meters deep. Mt. Everest rises 8,850 meters from base to summit. Its base is located 100 meters above sea level. (*Hint:* Drawing a diagram may be helpful. Start with a line that represents sea level.)

Figure 3 When an undersea volcano reaches above the surface of the water, it forms an island. This peak is Mauna Kea in Hawaii.

that the mid-ocean ridge actually consists of two parallel chains of mountains separated by a central valley.

You descend from the mid-ocean ridge to another abyssal plain. Soon your submarine's lights reveal a dark gash in the ocean floor ahead of you. As you pass over it, you look down into a steep-sided canyon in the ocean floor called a **trench**. The trench is so deep you cannot see the bottom.

Your journey is nearly over as your submarine slowly climbs the continental slope. Finally you cross the continental shelf and maneuver the submarine into harbor.

✓ *Checkpoint* *Which ocean floor feature makes up the deepest parts of the ocean?*

Movements of the Ocean Floor

As oceanographers mapped the ocean floor, their measurements told them about the features you saw on your imaginary journey between the continents. To learn more about the floor of the deep ocean, scientists aboard a drilling ship named *Glomar Challenger*, in honor of the original *Challenger*, collected samples of the rock. They drilled the rock samples from both sides of the mid-ocean ridge in the Atlantic Ocean. Tests on the samples showed that the rock closest to the ridge had formed much more recently than the rock farther away from the ridge. This information helped explain how the ocean floor formed. To understand how, you first need to know something about Earth's structure.

Background

History of Science In 1915 the German geophysicist and meteorologist Alfred Wegener first published his hypothesis of continental drift. He argued that the continents were once joined together in a single supercontinent, Pangaea, that broke apart 200–180 million years ago. The continents then drifted to their present locations. As evidence to support his theory, Wegener cited similar types of fossils and ages of geological formations on now-separate continents.

Wegener's theory was not widely accepted until the 1950s and 1960s, when scientists found evidence of Earth's alternating magnetic poles in bands of rock along the mid-ocean ridge. Interpreting this evidence, geologist H.H. Hess proposed that new ocean floor is created at the ridge through the process of sea-floor spreading.

Layers Inside Earth Earth consists of layers that cover the planet's center, or core. The thin, rocky, outer layer of Earth is called the crust. The thick layer between the crust and the core is the mantle. The high temperature and pressure inside Earth cause some of the material in the mantle to form a hot liquid called **magma.** Magma flows very slowly. It can escape upward through cracks in the crust and erupting volcanoes. Magma that reaches the surface is called lava. As hot lava cools, it forms new crust.

A Cracked Crust Earth's crust is not solid. Instead, the crust is broken into irregularly shaped pieces like the shell of a cracked, hard-boiled egg. The pieces of Earth's crust, called **plates,** move on the liquid of the mantle. About 14 major plates make up Earth's crust, as shown in Figure 4. They lie beneath the continents as well as the oceans. The plates move at an average speed of several centimeters per year—barely faster than your fingernails grow! Where two plates come together or spread apart, they create different landforms. Plate movements have shaped many of the most dramatic features of the Earth, both on land and under the ocean. **The mountain ranges of the mid-ocean ridge, trenches, and underwater volcanoes are all formed by the interactions of Earth's plates.**

Diverging Plates The mid-ocean ridge is located along the boundaries between plates that are diverging, or moving apart. Along the ridge, magma squeezes up through the cracks between

Figure 4 Earth's crust is divided into 14 major plates. *Interpreting Maps Name the plates that lie beneath parts of the continent of North America.*

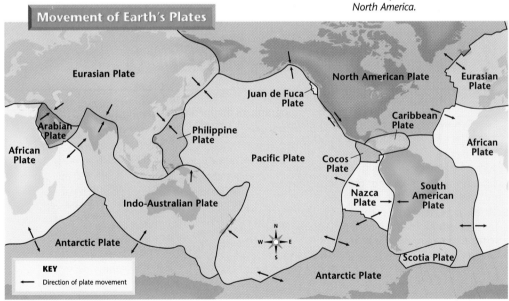

Movement of Earth's Plates

Eurasian Plate
North American Plate
Eurasian Plate
Juan de Fuca Plate
Caribbean Plate
Arabian Plate
Philippine Plate
African Plate
African Plate
Pacific Plate
Cocos Plate
Indo-Australian Plate
Nazca Plate
South American Plate
Antarctic Plate
Scotia Plate
Antarctic Plate

KEY
→ Direction of plate movement

Program Resources

 Science Explorer Series *Earth's Interior,* Chapter 1, covers the topic of plate tectonics.

Media and Technology

Transparencies "Converging and Diverging Plates," Transparency 18

Answers to Self-Assessment

☑ Checkpoint

Trenches are the deepest parts of the ocean floor.

Caption Question

Figure 4 The North American, Juan de Fuca, Caribbean, and Pacific plates

---

Inquiry Challenge

Challenge small groups to devise a model that demonstrates the process of plate divergence. Tell students they can use any materials that are readily available in the classroom or at home so long as they follow the safety guidelines in Appendix A. Allow class time for each group to present and explain its model. *(Possible model: Place two sheets of waxed paper side by side with their edges above the crack between two desks that have been pushed together. Hold a tube of toothpaste below the crack, and slowly squeeze it to force the paste upward through the crack and onto the waxed paper. The sheets will move in opposite directions away from the crack as the paste flows. For another possible model, see 5-1 Enrich in Teaching Resources, page 130.)*
cooperative learning

Building Inquiry Skills: Relating Cause and Effect

Materials *Paper towels, water*
Time 5 minutes

After students have read about converging plates, explain that at some places where plates push against each other, new landforms are created. To help students understand this process, have each student dampen two paper towels, lay them side by side, and slowly push them toward each other. Ask: **What happened to the towels?** *(They crumpled up.)* **What features on the ocean floor do the wrinkles represent?** *(seamounts)*
learning modality: kinesthetic

Ongoing Assessment

Writing Have each student write a paragraph describing the types of movement of Earth's plates and their results.

 Students can save their paragraphs in their portfolios.

3 Assess

Section 1 Review Answers

1. Darkness, cold, and extreme pressure
2. A mid-ocean ridge forms as magma squeezes up between diverging plates, adding new rock to the ocean floor. Trenches form along the boundaries of converging plates when one plate sinks under the other.
3. Answers may vary. Students could describe the voyage of HMS *Challenger*, Captain Cook's voyages, any of the techniques or equipment presented in *Science & History*, or the tests conducted by scientists aboard the *Glomar Challenger*.
4. Where plates converge, one plate sinks under the other. Old rock sinks into these trenches and back into Earth's interior.
5. Students should infer that the upwelling magma contains minerals from Earth's mantle.

Science at Home

Materials *carpenter's measuring tape, graph paper*

Tips To ensure that students understand the procedure and can explain it to their family members at home, have volunteers demonstrate the measurement process in the classroom with your guidance. Ask students what kind of graph they should make *(a line graph)* and what they think the graph will look like. *(Distances from the ceiling should be plotted on the vertical axis and distance from the "start" wall on the horizontal axis. The points will show the locations and heights of furniture and other objects in the room.)* You may want to start a graph on the board, using the classroom measurements to show students how to plot the data. Remind students not to climb on furniture when taking measurements.

Performance Assessment

Drawing Have each student draw and label a simple sketch, showing plate divergence at a mid-ocean ridge and plate convergence at a trench.

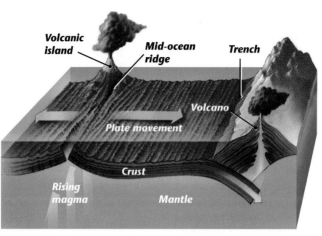

Figure 5 Where two plates diverge, magma from Earth's mantle rises up through the crack. Where two plates converge at a trench, one plate sinks under the other. *Interpreting Diagrams What happens when magma rises to Earth's surface?*

the diverging plates. As the magma hardens along the ridge, it adds a new strip of rock to the ocean floor. Each new eruption along the ridge gradually pushes the older rock away from the center of the ridge. Over many millions of years, this process, called **sea-floor spreading**, produced the ocean floor. The rock samples collected by the *Glomar Challenger* helped confirm the theory of sea-floor spreading by showing that the rocks closer to the ridge had been produced more recently than those farther away.

Converging Plates When the new ocean floor grows along the mid-ocean ridge, where does the old ocean floor farther away from the ridge go? Why doesn't Earth keep getting bigger? The answers to these questions lie in the deep ocean trenches you read about earlier. Where plates come together, or converge, one plate sinks under the other. As new rock is added at the edges of the plates along the mid-ocean ridge, old rock farther away from the mid-ocean ridge sinks into the trenches and back into Earth's interior. This process allows the ocean floor to spread while Earth itself remains the same size.

Section 1 Review

1. List three factors that make exploring the deep ocean difficult.
2. Explain how the movement of Earth's plates forms the mid-ocean ridges and trenches.
3. Describe one technique or expedition that has added to people's knowledge of the oceans.
4. Explain why Earth does not grow in size as new material is added to the ocean floor.
5. **Thinking Critically** **Inferring** Newly formed volcanic islands have a rich supply of minerals. Explain why this is so.

Science at Home

With a family member, choose a room in your house and make a "room-floor" map based on depth readings. Imagine that the ceiling is the ocean surface and the floor is the bottom of the ocean. Follow a straight path across the middle of the room from one wall to another. At regular intervals, use a carpenter's measuring tape to take a depth reading from the ceiling to the floor or to the top of any furniture in that spot. Plot the depths on a graph. Then challenge another family member to identify the room by looking at the graph.

Answers to Self-Assessment

Caption Question

Figure 5 The magma hardens, forming new strips of rock on either side of the boundary, or erupting as lava from a volcano.

Program Resources

◆ **Teaching Resources** 5-1 Review and Reinforce, p. 129; 5-1 Enrich, p. 130

Media and Technology

 Interactive Student Tutorial CD-ROM H-5

THE SHAPE OF THE OCEAN FLOOR

Imagine you are an oceanographer traveling across the Atlantic along the 45° N latitude line marked on the map. You and your crew are using sonar to gather data on the depth of the ocean between Nova Scotia, Canada, and the town of Soulac on the coast of France. In this lab, you will interpret the data to create a profile of the ocean floor.

Halifax, Canada   Soulac, France
45°

Problem

How can you use data about ocean depths to determine the shape of the ocean floor?

Materials

pencil   graph paper

Procedure

1. Draw the axes of a graph. Label the horizontal axis Longitude. Mark from 65° W to 0° from left to right. Label the vertical axis Ocean Depth. Mark 0 meters at the top of the vertical axis to represent sea level. Mark −5000 meters at the bottom to represent the depth of 5000 meters below sea level. Mark depths at equal intervals along the vertical axis.

2. Examine the data in the table. The numbers in the Longitude column give the ship's location at 19 points in the Atlantic Ocean. Location 1 is Nova Scotia, and Location 19 is Soulac. The numbers in the Ocean Depth column give the depth measurements recorded at each location. Plot each measurement on your graph. Remember that the depths are represented on your graph as numbers below 0, or sea level.

3. Connect the points you have plotted with a line to create a profile of the ocean floor.

Analyze and Conclude

1. On your graph, identify and label the continental shelf and continental slope.
2. Label the abyssal plain on your graph. How would you expect the ocean floor to look there?
3. Label the mid-ocean ridge on your graph. Describe the process that is occurring there.
4. What might the feature at 10° W be? Explain.
5. **Think About It** How is it helpful to organize data into a data table or graph?

More to Explore

Use the depth measurements in the table to calculate the average depth of the Atlantic Ocean between Nova Scotia and France.

Ocean Depth Sonar Data	
Longitude	Ocean Depth (m)
1. 64° W	0
2. 60° W	91
3. 55° W	132
4. 50° W	73
5. 48° W	3512
6. 45° W	4024
7. 40° W	3805
8. 35° W	4171
9. 33° W	3439
10. 30° W	3073
11. 28° W	1756
12. 27° W	2195
13. 25° W	3146
14. 20° W	4244
15. 15° W	4610
16. 10° W	4976
17. 05° W	4317
18. 04° W	146
19. 01° W	0

The Shape of the Ocean Floor

Preparing for Inquiry

Key Concept A profile of the ocean floor can be created by plotting depths on a graph.

Skills Objectives Students will be able to
◆ graph depth data presented in a table;
◆ infer the identity of ocean-floor features.
Time 30 minutes

Guiding Inquiry

Introducing the Procedure

◆ Point out that the voyage from Nova Scotia to Soulac would pass over an ocean-floor landscape similar to the one in *Exploring the Ocean Floor.*

◆ Show students a large globe or world map and ask: **Which are the longitude lines?** *(The lines running vertically from pole to pole)* Point out that these lines show distances east and west of the Prime Meridian, which passes through Greenwich, England.

◆ Discuss the graphing procedure. Emphasize that the longitudes listed in the table should be plotted on the graph's horizontal axis and the depths on the vertical axis. Ask: **What would be good intervals to mark on the horizontal axis?** *(Every 5° or 10° from 65°W to 0°W)* What would be good intervals for the vertical axis? *(Every 250 m or 500 m from 0 to −5,000)*

Troubleshooting the Experiment

◆ The graph works best if students tape two $8\frac{1}{2} \times 11$-inch pieces of graph paper together along the $8\frac{1}{2}$-inch sides so they can spread out the horizontal axis.

◆ Make sure students label the two axes appropriately. Remind them that they should *not* label the table's exact depths or any "in-between" longitudes on the axes.

Expected Outcome

Students' graphs may vary slightly; see sample at lower right.

Analyze and Conclude

1. Continental shelf: Locations 1–4 and 18–19; continental slope: Locations 4–5 and 17–18
2. Abyssal plain: Locations 5–9. The ocean floor would look smooth and nearly flat except for seamounts.
3. Mid-ocean ridge: Locations 9–13. Seafloor spreading; magma squeezes up between two plates, hardens, and adds new rock to the ocean floor.

4. The bottom of a trench; trenches are the deepest parts of the ocean floor.
5. It makes the data easier to understand, compare, and interpret.

Extending the Inquiry

More to Explore 2511 m

Program Resources

◆ **Teaching Resources** Chapter 5 Skills Lab, pp. 143–144

SECTION 2 Life at the Ocean's Edge

Objectives

After completing the lesson, students will be able to
- describe the factors that affect where ocean organisms live;
- identify the conditions that organisms in the rocky intertidal zone must overcome;
- name and describe the major types of coastal wetlands.

Key Terms plankton, nekton, benthos, food web, intertidal zone, estuary, brackish

1 Engage/Explore

Activating Prior Knowledge

Encourage students to describe saltwater beaches they have observed either directly or in movies and TV shows. Ask questions such as: **What did the beach look like? What kinds of living things did you see there? What nonliving things had washed up?**

DISCOVER

Skills Focus inferring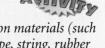
Materials *ping-pong ball, rock, box of common materials (such as suction cups, glue, tape, string, rubber bands, plastic wrap, hooks, clay), sink or deep pan, water*
Time 15 minutes
Tips Let each student or group decide whether the animal will cling to the rock permanently (like a sea anemone or sponge) or temporarily (like an octopus). Encourage students to use realistic, animallike structures rather than simply wrapping wire or tape around the ball and rock to hold them together.
Expected Outcome Students' solutions will vary.
Think It Over If the animal could not hold onto the rock, waves or tides would wash it onto the beach or out to sea.

SECTION 2 Life at the Ocean's Edge

DISCOVER — ACTIVITY

Can Your Animal Hold On?

1. Your teacher will give you a ping-pong ball, a rock, and a box containing some materials. The ping-pong ball represents an ocean animal. Use some of the materials to design a way for the animal to cling to the rock.

2. Attach the ping-pong ball to the rock.

3. Place the rock in a sink or deep pan. Run water over the rock from a faucet or pitcher. Observe how well your animal stays in place on the rock.

Think About It
Inferring How might the ability to "hold on" be important to an animal that lives on the shore?

GUIDE FOR READING

- What factors affect where ocean organisms live?
- What conditions must organisms in the rocky intertidal zone overcome?
- What are the major types of coastal wetlands?

Reading Tip As you read, make a list of the habitats described in this section. Write a sentence or two describing each habitat.

156 ◆ H

At first glance, a sandy ocean beach may seem lifeless. As you walk along the water's edge in the soft, wet sand, you may notice some dark, tangled seaweed that has washed up on the shore. A crab scuttles away from the pile as you walk by. Seagulls screech and swoop overhead. But for the most part, the beach appears deserted.

If you look more closely at the wet sand, you will see evidence of living things right beneath your feet. Tiny, round holes are signs of burrowing clams. These clams dig down into the sand for protection and to prevent being washed away in the waves. If you wade into the water, you may be able to spot a sand crab taking advantage of the surf to feed. The bottom half of its body buried in the sand, the crab waits for the waves to carry in a fresh supply of food for its next meal.

The organisms on this beach are well suited to the conditions there. In this section, you will learn how marine organisms have adapted to other areas where the land and ocean meet.

Living Conditions

A sandy beach is one type of marine, or ocean, habitat. Remember that an organism's habitat provides the things the organism needs to survive. An organism also must be suited to the physical conditions of the environment it lives in. **Some physical factors that determine where marine organisms can live include salinity, water temperature, light, dissolved gases, nutrients, and wave action.**

As you learned in Chapter 4, these conditions vary in different parts of the ocean. For example, salinity is lower where rivers flow into the ocean, bringing a stream of fresh

---

READING STRATEGIES

Reading Tip Three major types of habitats are described in this section: a sandy beach, a rocky shore (which includes tide pools), and coastal wetlands (salt marshes and mangrove forests). Make sure students do not include estuaries as a habitat. Point out that estuaries are a *physical feature*, a "meeting place" of salt and fresh water, and that it is the coastal wetlands found in and around estuaries that are the habitats.

Concept Mapping To clarify the above information, guide students through the creation of a concept map, with the top circle labeled *Ocean Habitats*, the three major types of habitats in the next level of circles, *salt marshes* and *mangrove forests* below *coastal wetlands,* and specific characteristics of each habitat in the lowest level of circles.

water. Salinity is higher in shallow, warm seas, where more evaporation takes place. Because cold water holds more dissolved gas than warm water, cold ocean waters contain more oxygen than tropical waters. Different organisms are suited to live in these different conditions. As a result, the same organisms do not live in every part of the ocean.

On land, most organisms live on or near the surface. The ocean, on the other hand, is a three-dimensional environment. It is inhabited by organisms at every depth. Scientists classify marine organisms according to where they live and how they move.

Plankton are tiny algae and animals that float in the water and are carried by waves and currents. Algae plankton include geometrically-shaped diatoms like those shown in Figure 6. Animal plankton include microscopic crustaceans and fish larvae. **Nekton** are free-swimming animals that can move throughout the water column. Octopus and squid, most fishes, and marine mammals such as whales and dolphins are nekton. **Benthos** are organisms that inhabit the ocean floor. Some benthos, like crabs, sea stars, and lobsters, move from place to place. Others, like sponges and sea anemones, stay in one location.

Plankton, nekton, and benthos are all found in most marine habitats. Many plankton and benthos are algae which, like plants, use sunlight to produce their own food through photosynthesis. Other plankton and benthos, as well as all nekton, are consumers. They eat either the algae or other consumers. Finally, some organisms, including many benthos, are decomposers. They break down wastes and remains of other organisms. These feeding relationships in a habitat make up a **food web**.

Figure 6 Marine organisms can be classified as plankton, nekton, or benthos. **A.** Intricate diatoms, one type of algae plankton, float on the ocean surface. **B.** These microscopic crustaceans, called copepods, are animal plankton. **C.** Free-swimming animals, such as this school of sweetlip fish, are nekton. **D.** Benthos live on the ocean floor. The sea stars and sea anemones in this colorful array are benthos.

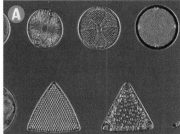

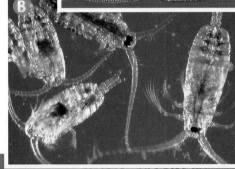

H ◆ 157

Language Arts
CONNECTION

Students can verify that this poem fits the haiku format by counting the syllables on their fingers as they recite the poem quietly or by marking the syllables on a copy of the poem they have made. Emphasize that a haiku is an "in-a-nutshell" description of something, with unnecessary words left out. In this haiku, for example, *is* has been omitted from the last line.

In Your Journal If some students need additional support in writing their own haiku, suggest that they try describing the image in a sentence, then look for alternative words to make the syllable count work.

Portfolio Students can save their haiku in their portfolios. **learning modality: verbal**

Rocky Shores

Building Inquiry Skills: Predicting

Before students read "Along the Rocks" and "In Tide Pools," ask: **What kinds of body structures would help animals survive in an area that is sometimes underwater and sometimes exposed to sun and air?** *(Shells or other protective coverings, or structures that enable them to hide among rocks or bury themselves in sand when exposed)* Encourage students to keep these ideas in mind as they think about the habitats and organisms they will model for the chapter project. **learning modality: logical/ mathematical**

Language Arts
CONNECTION

About 350 years ago, a form of poetry called *haiku* grew popular in Japan. Here is an example of a haiku about a beach.

Shining air bubbles
pushing up the hardpacked sand:
a shy clam revealed.

This poem may appear simple, but it follows a strict structure. A haiku is a 17-syllable poem written in 3 lines. There are 5 syllables in the first line, 7 syllables in the second line, and 5 syllables in the third line. A haiku should capture a moment in nature and suggest a mood or feeling.

In Your Journal

Prepare to write your own haiku about the edge of the ocean. Work with a partner to think of what you might see, hear, and feel. Review the habitats in this section for ideas. Then choose one simple, specific subject to write about. Write a draft and exchange it with your partner. After making revisions, illustrate your poem.

The first group of ocean habitats you will learn about are those found at the very edge of the ocean. The sandy beach you read about earlier is one example. Two habitats with a richer variety of life are rocky shores and salt marshes. As you read, think about how conditions in these habitats are similar, and how they are different.

☑ *Checkpoint* *Are sharks plankton, nekton, or benthos? Why?*

Rocky Shores

Imagine if your home had no walls or roof. Twice a day, a huge storm passes through, bringing a drenching downpour and winds so strong you can hardly keep your balance. At other times, the hot sun beats down, leaving you parched and dry. This is what life is like for organisms that live on rocky shores in the intertidal zone. The **intertidal zone** stretches from the highest high-tide line on land out to the point on the continental shelf exposed by the lowest low tide.

Organisms that live in the rocky intertidal zone must be able to tolerate the pounding of the waves and changes in salinity and temperature. They must also withstand periods of being underwater and periods of being exposed to the air. They must avoid drying out, hide from predators, and find food in this harsh setting. How are organisms able to survive?

Along the Rocks Rocky shores are found along much of both coasts of the United States. Figure 7 shows some of the colorful organisms that typically live along the rocky California coast.

The highest rocks, above the highest high-tide line, make up the spray zone. The spray zone is never completely covered with water, but it gets wet as the waves break against the rocks. A stripe of black algae indicates the highest high-tide line. The rocks below this level are encrusted with barnacles. Barnacles can close up their hard shells, trapping a drop of water inside to carry

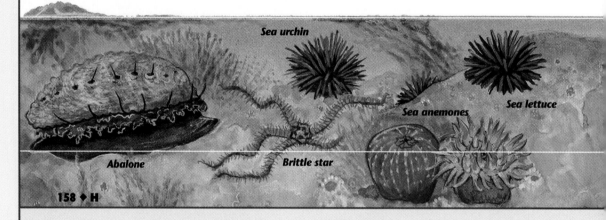

Sea urchin
Sea anemones
Sea lettuce
Abalone
Brittle star

Background

Integrating Science With its regular exposure to waves, air, sunlight, and changes in temperature, the intertidal zone is a stressful habitat for the organisms found there. As noted in the student text, organisms that live along a rocky shore typically have some way of sealing in moisture—a slimy coating, for example, or a shell or case that can be closed.

Unlike the organisms that inhabit a rocky shore, organisms that live on a sandy beach generally do not have adaptations to protect them against drying out. Because the sand is constantly shifting and provides little protection against wave action, most animals living there are active and continuous burrowers. Rather than anchoring themselves in place, many of these animals follow the changing tide line up and down the beach.

them through the dry period until the next high tide. Lower down, clumps of blue and black mussels stick out amidst the algae. The mussels produce sticky threads that harden on contact with the water, attaching the mussels to the rock. The threads are so strong that scientists are studying them as a model for new glues. The rocks are also home to flat mollusks called limpets. Limpets have a large, muscular foot to hold on tightly. They secrete drops of mucus around the edges of their shells to form a tight seal.

Algae that live in the intertidal zone are also adapted to withstand the physical conditions. Rootlike structures anchor the strands of algae firmly to the rocks. Some algae are covered with a thick layer of slime. The slime keeps the algae from drying out during low tide.

In Tide Pools When the tide goes out, some water remains in depressions among the rocks called tide pools. As the water in a tide pool is warmed by the sun, it begins to evaporate. The remaining water becomes saltier. If it rains, however, the salinity quickly decreases. Organisms in the tide pool must be able to withstand these changes in temperature and salinity, as well as the force of the waves when the tide comes in again.

Sea stars cling to the rocks with rows of tiny suction cups on their undersides. Spiny purple sea urchins crawl slowly along the bottom of the tide pool. If the bottom is sandy, sea urchins can use their spines to dig a hole in which to bury themselves during heavy surf. Under shady rock ledges, sponges and sea anemones wait for the incoming tide to bring a fresh supply of plankton and other food particles. A sea anemone may look delicate, but some can survive out of water for over two weeks. When out of the water, the anemone pulls its tentacles inside. It folds up into a round blob, resembling a rolled-up sock.

Figure 7 The constantly changing water level in the intertidal zone creates different habitats along a rocky coast. *Comparing and Contrasting How are conditions different for organisms near the top of the rocks compared to organisms at the bottom?*

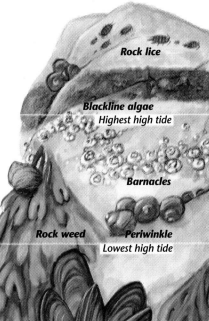

Rock lice

Blackline algae
Highest high tide

Barnacles

Rock weed
Periwinkle
Lowest high tide

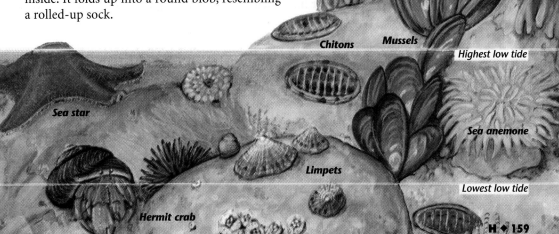

Chitons
Mussels
Highest low tide

Sea star

Limpets
Sea anemone

Lowest low tide

Hermit crab

H ◆ 159

Using the Visuals: Figure 7

Ask students: **Which organisms in this picture live in the spray zone?** *(The rock louse and blackline algae)* **Why do different organisms live in different levels of the intertidal zone?** *(They are adapted for different conditions—greater or lesser wave intensity, more or less exposure to sun and air, and changes in temperature and salinity.)* Have students review the text, this time looking specifically for information about those adaptations, including how organisms hold on to rocks. *(Limpets: large, muscular foot and mucus; mussels: sticky threads; algae: rootlike structures; sea stars: tiny suction cups)* Prompt students to recall the methods and materials they used to attach the ping-pong ball to the rock if they did the Discover activity, and ask: **Were the techniques you used similar to the adaptations of any of these organisms? Which ones?** *(Answers will vary.)* Encourage students to keep the adaptations described on these pages in mind as they plan and build model organisms for the chapter project.
learning modality: visual

Inquiry Challenge

Challenge students to design an experiment that tests how the salinity of a saltwater solution changes as the water evaporates. Students will most likely design tests that involve leaving a saltwater solution in a warm or sunlit place to evaporate.
learning modality: logical/ mathematical

Answers to Self-Assessment

☑ *Checkpoint*

Sharks are nekton; they can swim freely throughout the water column.

Caption Question

Figure 7 Organisms near the top are never completely covered with water, whereas those at the bottom are always covered with water, though its temperature and salinity may vary widely.

Ongoing Assessment

Oral Presentation Have students identify the physical conditions to which intertidal organisms must be adapted.

159 ◆ H

Where River Meets Ocean

Using the Visuals: Figure 8

Have students turn back to pages 60–61 in Chapter 2 to compare the photographs of freshwater wetlands with the two pictures of coastal wetlands on this page. Ask: **What is the major difference between the wetlands shown on pages 60–61 and the wetlands shown here?** *(Bogs, marshes, and swamps have fresh water, whereas salt marshes and mangrove forests have a mixture of salty and fresh water.)* **learning modality: logical/ mathematical**

Real-Life Learning

ACTIVITY

If students live in a coastal state, give them copies of their state's map to examine for estuaries. If they do not live in a coastal state, provide maps of Delaware or Maryland. Ask: **What kinds of estuaries are found in this area? What cities are located near the estuaries?** *(Answers will vary, depending on the area.)* **learning modality: visual**

Including All Students

Encourage students who need additional challenges to find out more about the health of the Chesapeake Bay. Much scientific research has been carried out in this area, and there are numerous books and articles that discuss the causes and effects of pollution in the Chesapeake Bay and the results of cleanup efforts. Students can share what they learn with a written report or oral presentation. **learning modality: verbal**

Other important environments along the ocean's edge are estuaries. **Estuaries** are coastal inlets or bays where fresh water from rivers mixes with the salty ocean water. Water that is partly salty and partly fresh is **brackish.**

Coastal wetlands are habitats found in and around estuaries. **Along the United States coasts, most coastal wetlands are either salt marshes or mangrove forests.** Salt marshes are especially abundant along the east coast from Massachusetts to Florida. Mangrove forests are found in the tropical waters along the southern coast of Florida and the Gulf of Mexico.

Salt Marshes A salt marsh oozes with smelly mud. Mosquitoes swarm over the water as it flows slowly through the tall, green grasses. The fresh water and tides contribute sediments, animal and plant matter, and other nutrients to the salt marsh, forming a soft, rich mud bottom.

A single plant, cord grass, dominates the marsh. Unlike most plants, cord grass can survive in salt water. The plant releases salt through small openings in its long, narrow leaves. The cord grass that is not eaten by animals breaks down and is decomposed by bacteria and fungi in the water. The decomposed material supplies nutrients to organisms in the marsh.

Tidal channels run through the cord grass. Waves break up as they enter the channels, so that organisms in the marsh are protected from the surf. Within the shelter of the marsh, fish, crabs, shrimp, and oysters hatch and feed before entering the harsher ocean environment offshore. As the tide retreats, mud flats are exposed. Hordes of crabs search for food in the rich mud. Herons, stilts, and egrets stalk across the mud to prey on the crabs and other benthos exposed by the low tide.

Mangrove Forests Mangroves—short, gnarled trees that grow well in brackish water—fringe the coastline of southern Florida. The mangroves'

Figure 8 Salt marshes and mangrove forests are two types of coastal wetlands. **A.** Salt water flows through tidal channels in a salt marsh. **B.** Arching prop roots anchor these black mangrove trees firmly in the soft, sandy soil around Florida Bay. *Making Generalizations How does the plant life in each of these habitats provide shelter for marine organisms?*

Background

Facts and Figures Estuaries are extremely productive ecosystems. Productivity is a measurement of how quickly carbon and other nutrients are cycled through an ecosystem.

Several factors contribute to the high productivity of estuaries. As rivers flow into estuaries, they carry nutrients washed from the land. The ocean tides help circulate the nutrients and also help remove waste products. The numerous plants that grow in the fertile mud of the estuaries provide shelter and a source of organic matter for other organisms in the estuaries.

prop roots anchor the trees to the land. Mangroves can withstand all but the strongest hurricane winds. Without the mangroves to break the action of winds and waves, the coastline would change dramatically each hurricane season. The prop roots also trap sediment from the land. They create a protected nursery rich in nutrients for many young animals.

Protecting Estuaries The rivers that flow into estuaries can carry harmful substances as well as nutrients. When pollutants such as pesticides, sewage, and industrial waste get into the river water, they end up in the estuary. The pollutants change the water quality in the estuary. In turn, organisms that live in the estuary are affected. It can take many years for ocean tides to flush a heavy load of pollutants out of an estuary.

For example, Chesapeake Bay is a huge estuary located on the mid-Atlantic coast. It has been a rich source of oysters, clams, and blue crabs. However, pollutants from inland sources accumulated in the bay for many years. Their effect was to greatly reduce the number and kinds of organisms in the Chesapeake. When people realized the threat to the estuary, they took action. The water quality of rivers that empty into Chesapeake Bay is now regulated by law. Cleanup efforts have reduced much of the pollution in the bay. Today, organisms like the blue crab are making a comeback.

Figure 9 A crabber in Chesapeake Bay pulls up the last trap of the day. As the health of the estuary improves, the blue crab population is growing again.

Section 2 Review

1. Name five physical factors that affect organisms in marine habitats.
2. Describe conditions in the rocky intertidal zone.
3. List two ways that salt marshes and mangrove forests are alike and two ways they are different.
4. **Thinking Critically Making Judgments** A builder has proposed filling in a salt marsh to create a seaside resort. What positive and negative impacts might this proposal have on wildlife, local residents, and tourists? Would you support the proposal? Why or why not?

Check Your Progress CHAPTER PROJECT 5

Your group should now select the marine environment you will create. Measure the space where you will build your model. Make a list of the physical features you will need to represent. Draw a scale diagram of your model and show it to your teacher. Label the different features and note the materials you will use. (*Hint:* Draw your sketch on graph paper to plan its size to fit the space.)

Answers to Self-Assessment

Caption Question

Figure 8 Thick cord grass in salt marshes and tree roots in mangrove forests break up ocean waves and provide sheltered places for organisms to hide, feed, and breed.

---

3 Assess

Section 2 Review Answers

1. Any five: Salinity, water temperature, light, dissolved gases, nutrients, wave action, exposure to air
2. Answers should include pounding waves, changes in salinity and water temperature, and exposure to sunlight and air.
3. *Similarities:* Brackish water, shallow water, rich in nutrients, plants break up waves and shelter organisms. *Differences:* Salt marshes have cord grass and a muddy bottom; mangrove forests have mangrove trees and sandy soil and are located further south.
4. Accept a variety of responses so long as students support their viewpoints with specific details. *Sample answer:* Filling in the salt marsh would destroy natural habitats and thus eliminate most wildlife. A resort would help people because it would employ local residents and attract tourists who would support other local businesses.

Check Your Progress CHAPTER PROJECT 5

Hold a class meeting in the area that will be transformed into a marine environment. Discuss the possible habitats that could be built. Monitor students' choices to avoid repetition and encourage variety. Ask students for their ideas about arranging the habitats in a logical order around the area—for example, from the highest part of the intertidal zone at one end to the deep zone at the other end. Assign a specific amount of space to each group, and let students take measurements.

Performance Assessment

Organizing Information Have each student make a two-column table to summarize and compare the characteristics of the intertidal zone and an estuary.

161 ◆ H

SECTION 3 The Neritic Zone and Open Ocean

Objectives

After completing the lesson, students will be able to

◆ describe conditions in the neritic zone that support organisms and two neritic zone habitats—kelp forests and coral reefs;

◆ describe conditions and identify where algae live in the open ocean;

◆ explain how hydrothermal vents support organisms.

Key Terms neritic zone, open-ocean zone, holdfast, atoll, bioluminescence, hydrothermal vent

1 Engage/Explore

Activating Prior Knowledge

Unlike coastal areas, the neritic zone and open ocean are not directly observable by most students. Question students to elicit what they do know about these areas—for example: **What kinds of animals live in the deep ocean? What do those animals feed on? How deep is the water out beyond the continental slope?** *(Accept all responses without comment.)*

DISCOVER

Skills Focus observing **ACTIVITY**
Materials *permanent marker, white plastic lid, scissors, string, paper clip, tape, meterstick, bucket, tap water, flour*
Time 15 minutes
Tips You may want to construct one device yourself beforehand so students can use it as a model. Suggest that they record their observations at each depth.
Expected Outcome At some depth, the flour particles suspended in the water will begin to obscure the lid.
Think It Over Students should infer that visibility decreases as water depth increases.

SECTION 3 The Neritic Zone and Open Ocean

DISCOVER · ACTIVITY · · ·

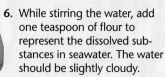

How Deep Can You See?

1. With a permanent marker, divide a white plastic lid into four quarters. Shade in two quarters as shown.

2. ✂ Use a pair of scissors to carefully poke a small hole in the center of the lid.

3. Tie a piece of string to a paper clip. Place the clip underneath the lid and thread the string up through the hole.

4. Tape the string tightly to a meterstick so that the lid presses against the bottom of the meterstick.

5. Fill a large, deep bucket with tap water.

6. While stirring the water, add one teaspoon of flour to represent the dissolved substances in seawater. The water should be slightly cloudy.

7. Lower the lid into the water so that it is 5 cm below the surface. Note whether the lid is still visible in the water.

8. Lower the lid 10 cm below the surface, then 15 cm, and so on until the lid is no longer visible.

Think It Over

Observing At what depth could you no longer see the lid? Based on your results, how do you think visibility changes with depth in the ocean?

GUIDE FOR READING

◆ What conditions in the neritic zone support organisms?

◆ Where do algae live in the open ocean?

◆ How do hydrothermal vents support organisms?

Reading Tip Before you read, preview Figure 10 on the facing page. Predict how the neritic zone and open ocean are similar and how they are different.

Floating mats of golden-brown, leaflike fronds on the ocean surface mark the location of a kelp forest. Diving below the surface, you find yourself surrounded by tall, swaying stalks of giant kelp. Sunlight filters through the water, producing a greenish light. As you pull yourself hand over hand down one of the kelp strands, you notice small bulbs at the base of each frond. You pinch one of the bulbs, and a bubble of gas escapes. These bulbs keep the heavy kelp fronds upright in the water.

The kelp forest is full of life. Bright-orange sheephead fish dart past you. Young sea lions chase each other around the kelp stalks. A sea otter, surrounded by a stream of bubbles, dives past you, down to the rocky bottom. When it rises, the otter is clutching a sea star between its paws. On the surface again, you watch the sea otter as it rolls onto its back among the kelp. The otter deftly uses its paws to scoop out the meat from the soft underside of the sea star.

◀ Sea otter eating a sea star

READING STRATEGIES

Reading Tip Suggest that students set up a two-column table for recording their predictions, with the headings *Similarities* and *Differences* at the top of the table and *Neritic Zone* and *Open Ocean* in the left column (or vice versa). As they read the section, students can cross out any predictions they discover to be incorrect and add other similarities and differences.

Vocabulary *Bioluminescence* is a key term that might be difficult for some students. Point out that *bio-* is from a Greek word meaning living, *lumin* is from Latin and means light, and *-escence* is also from Latin and means to become. When the word parts are combined, students should understand that *bioluminescence* means "a living thing that becomes light." Have them compare this definition with the definition in the text.

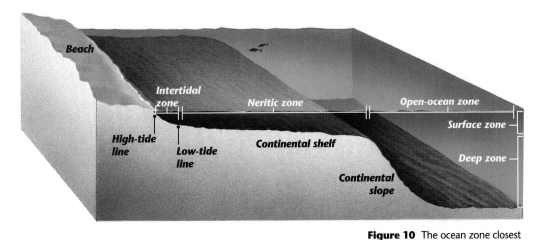

Beach

Intertidal zone

Neritic zone

Open-ocean zone

Surface zone

High-tide line

Low-tide line

Continental shelf

Deep zone

Continental slope

A kelp forest is one habitat found in the neritic zone. The **neritic zone** is the part of the ocean that extends from the low-tide line out to the edge of the continental shelf. Beyond the edge of the continental shelf lies the **open-ocean zone.** Locate the neritic and open-ocean zones in Figure 10. In this section you will learn how organisms are adapted to the conditions in these zones, from the sunlit surface waters to the coldest depths.

Figure 10 The ocean zone closest to land is the intertidal zone, which is bounded by the high-tide and low-tide lines. Next is the neritic zone, followed by the open-ocean zone, which makes up most of the world's oceans. The open ocean is divided by depth into the surface zone and the deep zone. *Interpreting Diagrams* Which zones lie over the continental shelf?

Conditions in the Neritic Zone

A huge variety of organisms are found in the neritic zone, more than in any other area of the ocean. Most of the world's major fishing grounds are found in this zone. What makes the neritic zone home to so many living things? The answer has to do with its location over the continental shelf. **The shallow water over the continental shelf receives sunlight and a steady supply of nutrients washed from the land into the ocean.** The light and nutrients enable large plantlike algae, such as the giant kelp, to grow. These algae serve as a food source and shelter for other organisms.

In many parts of the neritic zone, upwelling currents bring additional nutrients from the bottom to the surface. These nutrients support large numbers of plankton, which form the base of ocean food webs. Schools of fish such as sardines and anchovies feed on the plankton. Major fisheries in upwelling areas include Monterey Canyon off the California coast, Newfoundland's Grand Banks, and Georges Bank off the New England coast.

Two diverse habitats typically found within the neritic zone are kelp forests and coral reefs. As you read about each, think about how they are similar and how they are different.

Checkpoint What are two ways that nutrients may be supplied to the neritic zone?

Program Resources

◆ **Teaching Resources** 5-3 Lesson Plan, p. 135; 5-3 Section Summary, p. 136

Media and Technology

 Audiotapes English-Spanish Summary 5-3

 Transparencies "Ocean Zones," Transparency 19

Answers to Self-Assessment

Caption Question

Figure 10 The intertidal and neritic zones

Checkpoint

Nutrients may be washed into the ocean from the land or brought from the bottom to its surface by upwelling currents.

Conditions in the Neritic Zone

Using the Visuals: Figure 10

Focus students' attention on the intertidal and neritic zones in the illustration. Point out that this figure is not to scale—the deep zone is relatively much deeper than shown here. Then ask: **What is the major difference between these two zones in terms of their water levels?** (*The water level varies at different points in the intertidal zone, while the neritic zone is always underwater.*) **Where does the neritic zone end and the open ocean begin?** (*At the edge of the continental shelf*) **learning modality: visual**

Real-Life Learning

To emphasize the importance of the neritic zone to the nation's economy, urge volunteers to research the types and amounts of fish taken from the neritic zone off U.S. shores by commercial fisheries and the dollar value of those catches each year. Suggest that students begin by looking in *Statistical Abstract of the United States* or *Agricultural Statistics* from the U.S. Department of Agriculture. Let students present their findings in brief oral reports, posters, or illustrated bar graphs. **learning modality: verbal**

Ongoing Assessment

Drawing Have each student draw and label a simple diagram showing the intertidal, neritic, and open-ocean zones, without referring to Figure 10. Students can save their diagrams in their portfolios.

Life in a Kelp Forest

Figure 11 Light streams through a forest of giant kelp and shadowy rockfish near Monterey, California. The closeup shows the gas-filled bulbs that keep the kelp upright in the water.

Life in a Kelp Forest

Kelp forests grow in cold neritic waters, such as those along the Pacific coast from Alaska to Mexico. These large, heavy algae require a solid, rocky bottom to anchor their stalks. A bundle of rootlike strands called a **holdfast** attaches the algae to the rocks. A stalk of giant kelp can grow to 30 meters in length. The gas-filled bulbs shown in the closeup to the left keep the heavy kelp stalk upright in the water.

The kelp use the sunlight and dissolved gases in the neritic zone to produce their own food. The kelp also provide a habitat for many other organisms. The curtains of kelp hide young gray whales from predators while their mothers are feeding. Sea slugs and snails live amid the tangle of the holdfasts.

Sea otters play a particularly important role in the kelp forest. In addition to eating abalone, sea otters feed on sea urchins, which eat the kelp. In areas where sea otters have disappeared, armies of sea urchins have devoured the kelp. The once-thriving forest has become a barren rocky zone.

Coral Reefs

Although a coral reef may look as if it is made of rock, it is actually made of living things. Coral reefs are created by colonies of tiny coral animals, each of which is not much larger than a pencil eraser. The coral animals produce a hard structure that surrounds their soft bodies. After the coral dies, the empty structure remains. New coral animals attach and grow on top of it. Over many years, a reef is built. Most of the coral reefs that exist today were begun about 5,000 to 10,000 years ago.

Microscopic algae live within the bodies of the coral animals and provide food for them. Because the algae require warm temperatures and sunlight, coral reefs can only form in shallow, tropical ocean waters. The reefs grow above continental shelves or around volcanic islands, where the water is shallow.

In areas where the seafloor is sinking, a reef may develop over time into an atoll. An **atoll** is a ring-shaped reef surrounding a shallow lagoon. Figure 12 shows the development of an atoll. It begins as a fringing reef that closely surrounds the edges of the island. As the reef grows upward, the island sinks, and a barrier reef forms. Water separates the top of the barrier reef from the land. The island continues to sink until it is eventually underwater, forming the atoll.

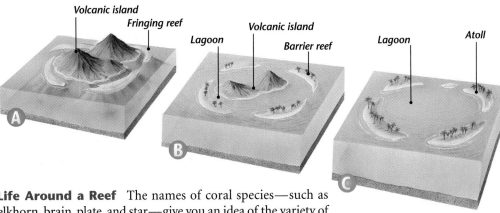

Volcanic island
Fringing reef
Lagoon
Volcanic island
Barrier reef
Lagoon
Atoll

A B C

Life Around a Reef The names of coral species—such as elkhorn, brain, plate, and star—give you an idea of the variety of shapes coral can form. Many animals live in and around the crevices of the reef, including octopuses, spiny lobsters, shrimp, toothy moray eels, and fish in all colors and sizes. Parrotfish like the one in Figure 13 scrape coral off the reef to eat. The parrotfish grind up the broken coral inside their bodies, producing the fine, soft sand commonly found around the reef.

Coral Reefs and Humans Coral reefs are natural aquarium exhibits, displaying a colorful diversity of life to be enjoyed and studied. Reefs also protect coastlines during violent storms. The reefs break up the surf, preventing waves from severely eroding the land. However, human activities can harm the fragile reefs. Boat anchors dragging across a reef can damage it. Divers can accidentally break off pieces of the reef. Even brushing against the reef can harm some of the coral animals. Because coral only grows a few millimeters a year, a reef cannot quickly recover.

Changes in water temperature and clarity also affect coral reefs. For example, if the water becomes too warm, the corals release the algae that live inside them. Cloudy water endangers the algae by reducing the amount of light that reaches them. If sediments produced by storms or human activities bury a reef, the algae in the living coral cannot survive. Without the algae, the coral animals do not grow well and eventually die.

Today many people understand the importance of coral reefs and try to protect them. Many reef areas have been designated as marine sanctuaries, which limits the amount of diving and other activity allowed near the reef. Scientists worldwide are also studying the effects of temperature change and pollution on the reefs to better protect them.

☑ *Checkpoint* *How can human activities impact a coral reef?*

Figure 12 An atoll develops in stages. **A.** A fringing reef closely surrounds an island. **B.** As the island sinks, a lagoon forms inside the barrier reef. **C.** Finally, the island sinks below the surface, leaving a ring-shaped atoll. *Interpreting Diagrams In which stage is the reef the youngest?*

Figure 13 A parrotfish delicately nibbles away at a coral reef in the Red Sea. Reefs provide a habitat for many fish and other marine organisms.

H ◆ 165

Using the Visuals: Figure 12

Encourage students to refer to this illustration as they review the stages of atoll development in the last paragraph on page 164. Then ask: **How do you think conditions in the lagoon might be different from conditions outside the reef or atoll?** *(The water in the lagoon is warmer because it is shallower; the lagoon is also protected from ocean waves and currents.)* **How might these differences affect the types of organisms that live in the lagoon?** *(Organisms that could not survive in the deep, dark, cold water of the ocean depths would be able to survive in a lagoon.)* **learning modality: logical/mathematical**

Real-Life Learning

The United States government has designated a number of sites as national marine sanctuaries (NMSs). These include Stellwagen Bank, Monitor, and Gray's Reef in the Atlantic Ocean; Florida Keys and Flower Garden Banks in the Gulf of Mexico; and Olympic Coast, Cordell Bank, Gulf of the Farallones, Monterey Bay, Channel Islands, Humpback Whale, and Fagatele Bay in the Pacific Ocean. Encourage interested students to choose and find out about one or more of these sanctuaries, especially their role in protecting marine environments. Invite students to share what they learn in a class bulletin board display on marine sanctuaries. **learning modality: verbal**

Program Resources

● **Science Explorer Series** *From Bacteria to Plants*, Chapter 3, has more information on algae.
◆ **Interdisciplinary Explorations Series** "Where River Meets Sea," pp. 33–34

Answers to Self-Assessment

Caption Question

Figure 12 A fringing reef is the youngest.

☑ *Checkpoint*

Any one: Boat anchors can drag across a reef. Divers may break off pieces accidentally or injure the coral animals by brushing against them. Human activities can make the water cloudy, reducing the amount of sunlight. Chemicals can pollute the water.

Ongoing Assessment

Writing Have each student write a paragraph explaining why coral reefs are fragile.

Students can save their paragraphs in their portfolios.

Conditions in the Open Ocean

Sharpen your Skills

Inferring

Time 10 minutes

Tips Make sure students note the three major clues needed to solve the problem: (1) more friction is needed to stay afloat in warm water, (2) more streamlined shapes create less friction, and (3) copepod B is more streamlined than copepod A.

Expected Outcome Based on the text and illustration clues, students can infer that copepod A is found in warm, tropical waters and copepod B in cold, polar waters.

Extend Challenge students to devise a model to demonstrate this relationship between friction and water temperature.
learning modality: logical/ mathematical

Building Inquiry Skills: Applying Concepts

Draw students' attention to the statement that if the water is cloudy, sunlight does not reach as deep. Ask: **Have you ever observed something like this?** (*Students may cite their personal experiences. If necessary, remind them of their observations in the Discover activity at the beginning of this section.*) **In the Discover, why couldn't you see the lid when it was deeper in the water?** (*Students may say that the flour particles blocked the view.*) Explain that when light rays enter clear water and strike a submerged object, they bounce back up and enter our eyes so we see the object. In the cloudy water, however, the light rays bounced off the flour particles and scattered in all directions, so we could not see the submerged lid when it got too deep. **learning modality: verbal**

Sharpen your Skills

Inferring

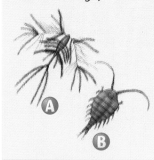

To keep from sinking, many plankton rely on the friction between their bodies and the surrounding water. More friction is needed to stay afloat in warm water than in denser cold water. One of the copepods below is found in tropical ocean waters, while the other is found near the poles. Which do you think is which? Explain your reasoning. (*Hint:* More streamlined shapes create less friction with their surroundings.)

A

B

Conditions in the Open Ocean

The open ocean begins where the neritic zone ends, at the edge of the continental shelf. Diving into the open ocean is like descending a long staircase with a light only at the very top. Light from the sun only penetrates a short distance into the water, typically to a depth of less than 200 meters. If the water is cloudy with sediment, sunlight does not reach as deep. In clear tropical waters, on the other hand, some light may reach as deep as a few hundred meters.

The fact that only a small portion of the open ocean receives sunlight is one way it differs from the neritic zone. Another difference is the amount of dissolved nutrients in the water. While the neritic zone receives a constant supply of nutrients from shore, dissolved nutrients are less abundant in the open ocean. As a result, the open ocean zone supports fewer organisms.

The Surface Zone The surface zone extends as far as sunlight reaches below the surface. **The surface zone is the only part of the open ocean that receives enough sunlight to support the growth of algae.** These microscopic algae are the base of open-ocean food webs. Animal plankton that feed on algae include tiny crustaceans called copepods, shrimp-like krill, and the young of many ocean animals such as crabs, mollusks, and fishes.

Figure 15 on the facing page shows an Arctic food web. Each organism in this food web depends either directly or indirectly on the plankton. Throughout the ocean, plankton are a source of food for other organisms of all sizes. If you think of sharks as sharp-toothed, meat-eating hunters, you might be surprised to learn that the biggest sharks of all feed entirely on tiny plankton! Whale sharks, which can grow to more than 10 meters long, strain plankton from the water. Many whales feed only on plankton as well, including Earth's largest animal, the blue whale.

The Deep Zone When you explored the water column in Chapter 4, you observed that the ocean became darker and colder as you descended. Because of its harsh conditions, the deep ocean is often compared to a desert. Compared to other land and ocean environments, few organisms live in the deep zone. But unlike a desert baking under the bright sun, the deep ocean is cold, dark, and wet.

Figure 14 How would you like to come face to face with this fish? The monstrous-looking anglerfish is an efficient deep-sea hunter. The bioluminescent lure on its forehead attracts prey for the anglerfish to eat.

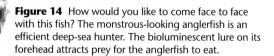

Background

Facts and Figures The deep zone represents more than 90 percent of the water column in most parts of the ocean. This zone is also called the *aphotic zone,* meaning "without light." Most deep-ocean species are dark in color and have few stripes or other markings. Many organisms in the deeper areas have only small, poorly developed eyes or may be completely blind.

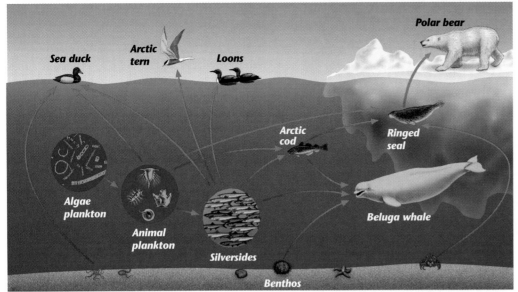

Polar bear

Sea duck

Arctic tern

Loons

Arctic cod

Ringed seal

Algae plankton

Animal plankton

Silversides

Benthos

Beluga whale

Figure 15 This marine food web includes typical organisms found in the Arctic Ocean. The arrows indicate what each organism eats. *Interpreting Diagrams Which organisms feed directly on the Arctic cod? Which organisms depend indirectly on the cod?*

Finding food in the darkness is a challenge. Many deep-sea fishes produce their own light. The production of light by living things is called **bioluminescence.** Some fishes use chemical reactions to produce their own light, like fireflies on land. Other fishes have colonies of bioluminescent bacteria living in pockets on their bodies. Still others have light-producing organs. The anglerfish, for example, has a light organ on its head. The fish lurks in the shadows below the pool of light. Shrimp and fishes that are attracted to the light become the anglerfish's prey.

Because the food supply in most of the deep ocean is much more limited than in shallower water, animals in this zone must be good hunters to survive. The gaping mouths of many deep-sea fishes are filled with fang-like teeth. Rows of sharp teeth stick out at angles, ensuring that any animal it bites cannot escape.

☑ *Checkpoint Why do very few organisms live in the deep zone?*

Hydrothermal Vents

As the submersible *Alvin* descended to a depth of 2,500 meters into the Galápagos Rift in the Pacific Ocean one day in 1977, the scientists aboard could hardly believe their eyes. Outside the submersible, the headlights revealed a bizarre scene. Clouds of black water billowed up from chimney-shaped structures on the ocean floor. Meter-long tubes with gaping, lipstick-red ends swayed in the water. White crabs scuttled over the rocks, crawling around clams as big as dinner plates.

Point out that in a diagram of a food web, each arrow points *from* the organism being eaten *to* the organism doing the eating. To make sure students understand this, ask: **Which organisms are eaten by the ringed seal?** *(animal plankton, cod, benthos)* **Which organisms eat the seal?** *(polar bear)* Next, have students recall the definition of *food web* from Section 2. *(The pattern of feeding relationships in a habitat)* Explain that a food web is made up of many separate food chains. A food chain is one series of feeding relationships—one organism being eaten by another, that organism in turn being eaten by another organism, and so on up the "chain." You may want to add that a food-chain diagram shows how energy is transferred in an ecosystem. Ask: **What is one food chain in this web?** *(Example: algae plankton → animal plankton → small fish → arctic cod → beluga whale)* Have students identify other chains in the web. **learning modality: visual**

Building Inquiry Skills: Making Models

Assign each student one of the organisms or groups (such as algae plankton or benthos) shown in Figure 15, making sure there are more lower-level organisms than top-level consumers. Have students stand and stretch colored yarn between themselves to indicate the feeding relationships shown in the diagram. For greater challenge, repeat the activity using another habitat, such as a tide pool, and let students figure out the feeding relationships on their own. **learning modality: kinesthetic**

ACTIVITY

Answers to Self-Assessment

Caption Question

Figure 15 The beluga whale and seal feed directly on the cod. The polar bear depends indirectly on the cod because it eats seals.

☑ *Checkpoint*

Conditions in the deep zone are harsh, with very cold water and no light. Food supplies are very limited.

Ongoing Assessment

Organizing Information Have each student create a two-column table to compare and contrast the characteristics of the surface zone and deep zone.

 Students can save their tables in their portfolios.

Hydrothermal Vents

Including All Students

Tell students that hydrothermal vents were first discovered in the late 1970s. Ask: **Why do you think the vents were not discovered before then?** (*Scientists did not have the technology for diving to the deepest parts of the ocean floor.*) If students have difficulty making this association, have them review Science & History on pages 148–149. **learning modality: logical/mathematical**

3 Assess

Section 3 Review Answers

1. Shallow water, sunlight, steady supply of nutrients
2. The depth to which sunlight penetrates
3. The heated water coming from the vent carries gases and minerals from Earth's interior.
4. The light that the fish produce attracts prey animals in the darkness.
5. Eroded soil could wash into the ocean and bury the reef or make the water cloudy. Sunlight would not reach the algae living in the coral, and the algae and coral animals would die.

Check Your Progress   CHAPTER PROJECT 5

At this point, each group should have completed its plan for the habitat model and chosen the materials to use. Review each group's design to make sure the physical features and organisms to be included are appropriate for that habitat. Encourage each student to draw a sketch of the organism he or she has chosen to model. As students build their models, meet with them regularly to discuss their progress and any problems they may be encountering.

Performance Assessment

Oral Presentation Have each student describe the major characteristics of the neritic zone, surface zone, or deep zone.

Figure 16 Giant tube worms cluster around a hydrothermal vent on the deep ocean floor.

The scientists were surprised not only by the strange appearance of these deep-sea creatures, but also by the fact that they were so abundant. In the deepest parts of the ocean, organisms tend to be very small and slow-moving because food is so rare. The number, size, and variety of organisms were unusually large for such a deep part of the ocean. What could these organisms find to eat so far from sunlight?

The strange community the scientists in *Alvin* observed was located around a hydrothermal vent. A **hydrothermal vent** is an area where ocean water sinks through cracks in the ocean floor, is heated by the underlying magma, and rises again through the cracks. These vents are located along ocean ridges, where the plates are moving apart and new ocean floor is forming.

The heated water coming from a vent carries gases and minerals from Earth's interior. **The chemical nutrients in the heated water support the unique group of organisms that are found around hydrothermal vents.** Bacteria feed directly on the chemical nutrients that are spewed out of the vents. Like the algae in the surface zone that use sunlight to produce food, these bacteria use the chemicals to produce food. They form the base of the food web at a hydrothermal vent.

Other organisms, like the giant clams, feed on the bacteria. The red-tipped tube worms are supplied with food by bacteria living within their tissues. Meanwhile, the scuttling crabs feed on the remains of the other inhabitants in their unusual habitat.

 ## Section 3 Review

1. Describe the physical conditions in the neritic zone.
2. What factor limits where algae are found in the open ocean?
3. What is the source of nutrients for organisms around a hydrothermal vent?
4. Explain how bioluminescence is important to some fish that live in the deep ocean.
5. **Thinking Critically Relating Cause and Effect** When forests on a tropical island are cut down, the soil is more easily eroded. Explain how this could affect a coral reef near the island.

Check Your Progress   CHAPTER PROJECT 5

By now you should have selected an organism to model. Research your organism to determine its size and other physical characteristics. How does the organism survive in its marine habitat? Check your plan for constructing the organism with your teacher. Your group should also begin building your model habitat. Make sure you have collected all the necessary materials before you begin building.

Program Resources

◆ **Teaching Resources** 5-3 Review and Reinforce, p. 137; 5-3 Enrich, p. 138

Media and Technology

Interactive Student Tutorial CD-ROM H-5

Resources From the Ocean

DISCOVER •••••••••••••••••••••••••••••••••••• ACTIVITY••••

Is It From the Ocean?

1. Your teacher will give you some labels from common house-hold products. Read the ingredient information on each label.
2. Divide the products into two piles—those you think include substances that come from the ocean and those that do not.

Think About It

Classifying For each product that you classified as coming from the ocean, name the item from the ocean that is used to produce it. In what ocean zone is it found?

W hen European explorers began sailing to North America, they were astounded by the huge number of codfish that lived off its eastern coast. One traveler reported that this area was so "swarming with fish that they could be taken not only with a net but in baskets let down and weighted with a stone." Others reported sailing through schools of cod so thick they slowed the boats down!

This cod fishery stretched from Newfoundland to a hook of land appropriately named Cape Cod. For more than 400 years, the seemingly endless supply of "King Cod" supported a thriving fishing industry. But beginning in the early 1900s, fishing crews had to work harder to catch the same amount of cod. As the fishing grew more difficult each year, it became clear that the cod were disappearing. With the price of cod rising, there was more competition to catch the fewer fish available. In 1992, the Canadian government had to declare the fishery closed.

No one knows for sure how long it will take the cod population to fully recover. Scientists are studying cod and other fisheries to learn how to preserve them for future generations.

Living Resources

Cod are just one example of a living resource from the ocean. How many other kinds of seafood

GUIDE FOR READING

◆ How does the supply of fish in a fishery change from year to year?

◆ Who controls and protects ocean resources?

Reading Tip Before you read, rewrite the headings in the section as how, why, or what questions. As you read, look for answers to those questions.

Figure 17 Big catches of cod like this one from Georges Bank, off the New England coast, have become less common since the early 1900s.

Objectives

After completing the lesson, students will be able to
◆ explain how the supply of fish in a fishery changes from year to year and list sources of water pollution;
◆ identify the ocean's living and nonliving resources and how they can be protected.

Key Terms aquaculture, nodules

1 Engage/Explore

Activating Prior Knowledge

Ask: **What kinds of foods do people obtain from the ocean?** (*Students should name a variety of fishes, shellfish, and other marine organisms.*) **Besides food, what other ocean resources do people use?** (*Students may have difficulty naming other resources. Accept all responses without comment.*)

•••••••• DISCOVER ••••••••

Skills Focus classifying
Materials *labels from common household products, including thickeners used in cooking, foods, abrasives, polishes, shampoos, and spice mixes containing sea salt*
Time 15 minutes
Tips If students seem confused about which substances come from the ocean, suggest that they consider both the living and nonliving things that can be found in the ocean.
Expected Outcome Students should be able to identify some substances that come from the ocean, especially seafoods and sea salt. They may not be able to identify other substances from the ocean at this time, such as stabilizers made from algae and abrasives made from diatoms.
Think It Over Answers will vary depending on the labels you use. Sample answers of products containing ocean resources: clam chowder—clams, intertidal zone; metal polish—diatoms, neritic and open-ocean zones; chocolate milk—kelp, neritic zone.

169 ◆ H

Reading Tip Tell students they should use the five main headings from the section. Provide an example for students, such as "What are some living resources from the ocean?" At the conclusion of the section, give students an opportunity to share their questions and answers by reading them aloud.

Program Resources

◆ **Teaching Resources** 5-4 Lesson Plan, p. 139; 5-4 Section Summary, p. 140

Media and Technology

 Audiotapes English-Spanish Summary 5-4

2 Facilitate

Living Resources

Real-Life Learning

Suggest that students visit a fish market or the seafood section of a super-market at a time when the store is not busy. Tell them to list the names of all the fish and other food items on display. Also have them interview the manager or clerk to obtain the answers to these questions: **Which of the foods are obtained from the ocean? From what source(s) does the store buy the items? What country or region is each item from originally? Does the store buy each item fresh, frozen, or dried? Are any items hard to obtain, and why?** Encourage students to add questions of their own. Provide an opportunity for students to report and compare their findings in class.
learning modality: verbal

Using the Visuals: Figure 18

Have students review the map key and look for the locations of the various ocean resources. Then ask: **Where on this map is the cod fishing area you read about on the previous page?** *(Off the northeastern coast of North America)* **Besides fish, what other resources can be found in that area of the ocean?** *(mineral resources/nodule deposits, oil and natural gas)* **What other areas have both fisheries and deposits of oil and gas?** *(Off the coasts of Alaska and California, eastern and southeastern South America, western Africa, Great Britain, Southeast Asia, Indonesia, and western Australia, and in the Gulf of Mexico and the Mediterranean Sea)* **What problems might drilling for oil or gas in the same ocean area where fisheries operate cause?** *(Sample answers: Building and operating the drilling rigs could disturb the fish and frighten them away; oil spills could kill the fish.)* **learning modality: visual**

have you tasted: tuna, shrimp, flounder, lobster, clams, squid, oysters, seaweed, or mussels? These foods and the many others that come from the ocean make up about five percent of the world's total food supply.

Harvesting Fish Just six species make up the majority of fishes harvested for eating: herring, sardine, anchovy, cod, pollock, and mackerel. Locate the world's major fisheries in Figure 18. You can see that they are all located close to coasts. Nearly all fishes caught are harvested from coastal waters or areas of upwelling. These waters contain nutrients and plankton on which they feed.

If used wisely, fisheries naturally renew themselves each year. **New fish are born, replacing those that are caught, but only as long as the fishery is not overfished. Overfishing causes the supply of fish to decrease.** Overfishing has become a problem as better technology has enabled people to catch large numbers of fish very quickly. For example, some fishing fleets have electronic equipment that allows them to locate schools of fish precisely. They can be caught faster than they can reproduce. Once this occurs, it begins a cycle that leads to fewer and fewer fish each season. Eventually, the fishery may be depleted, like the cod fishery you read about earlier.

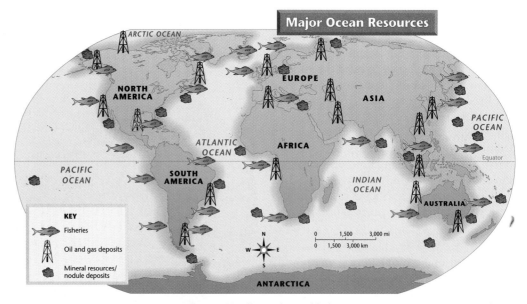

Figure 18 All over the world, the oceans are an important source of food, oil and gas, and minerals. *Interpreting Maps Where are Africa's major fisheries located?*

Background

Facts and Figures Today most of the world's commercial fish harvest is caught with huge nets, of which there are three main types. Seines are used to surround schools of fish. One end of a seine is attached to a large vessel, and the other end is pulled by a small, high-powered boat. After the school is surrounded, the bottom of the net is pulled tight, trapping the fish. Trawls are funnel-shaped nets with a large, open mouth and a small, closed tail. Fish are caught as the trawl is pulled through the water. Gill nets are long, rectangular nets used to form a wall of webbing that entangles fish when they swim into it. A fourth type of net, called a drift net, is about 5.5 km long and used mainly in open waters. Its use is controversial because whales, dolphins, marine birds, sea turtles, and other animals are also sometimes caught.

Aquaculture As fish stocks become depleted, **aquaculture,** the

 INTEGRATING TECHNOLOGY farming of saltwater and freshwater organisms, is likely to become more common. Aquaculture has been practiced in some Asian countries for centuries. This process involves creating an environment for the organisms and controlling nutrient levels, water temperature, light, and other factors to help them thrive. Oysters, abalone, and shrimp have successfully been farmed in artificial saltwater ponds and protected bays. Even landlocked regions can produce seafood using aquaculture. For example, salmon are now being raised in Nebraska fields that once were cattle ranches.

Other Ocean Products People harvest ocean organisms for many purposes besides food. For example, algae is an ingredient in many household products. Its gelatin-like texture makes it an ideal base for detergents, shampoos, cosmetics, paints, and even ice cream! Sediments containing the hard fragments of diatoms are used for abrasives and polishes. Many researchers believe that other marine organisms may be important sources of chemicals for medicines in the future.

☑ *Checkpoint* *How are fisheries naturally renewed each year?*

Mineral Resources

In addition to living organisms, the ocean contains valuable nonliving resources. Some of these are found within ocean water itself. Chapter 3 described how fresh water can be extracted from ocean water in the process of desalination. Desalination provides fresh water for many dry areas and islands. When the fresh water is removed from ocean water, the salts that are left behind are also a valuable resource. Over half of the world's supply of magnesium, a strong, light metal, is obtained from seawater in this way.

A second source of nonliving resources is the ocean floor. From the layer of sediments covering the continental shelves, gravel and sand are mined for use in building construction. In some areas of the world diamonds and gold are mined from sand deposits. Metals such as manganese also accumulate on the ocean floor. The metals concentrate around pieces of shell, forming black lumps called **nodules** (NAHJ oolz). Because they sometimes occur in waters as deep as 5,000 meters, recovering the nodules is a difficult process. The technology to gather them is still being developed.

Not all nations have agreed on who owns the rights to nodules and other resources on the deep ocean floor. Some feel the

Seaweed Candy

Make this Asian dessert **ACTIVITY** to discover one way to eat algae. Remember to prepare food only in a non-science classroom. Be sure to get permission before using a stove.

2 blocks of agar (one 0.5-ounce package)
1 cup sugar
4 cups guava juice or other fruit juice
food coloring

1. Rinse the agar, a substance obtained from algae.
2. Break agar into cubes and place them in a saucepan.
3. 🥽 Put on your goggles. Add the sugar and juice to the pan. Bring the mixture to a boil. Turn down the heat and cook, stirring, until the agar dissolves.
4. Remove pan from heat and stir in a few drops of food coloring. Pour the mixture into a shallow pan. Let cool.
5. Refrigerate candy until firm.
6. Cut into blocks and serve.

Inferring What purpose does the agar serve in this recipe? What purposes do the sugar and juice serve?

 Integrating Technology

Explain that oysters are farmed not only for food but for the pearls they produce. Other farmed organisms include mussels, clams, fish, and algae. Encourage interested students to find out more about marine aquaculture and report to the class. **learning modality: verbal**

TRY THIS

Skills Focus inferring **ACTIVITY**
Materials *2 blocks of agar, 1 cup sugar, 4 cups guava juice or other fruit juice, food coloring, water, saucepan, shallow pan, knife*
Time 20 minutes to prepare, several hours to set, 5 minutes to serve
Safety Supervise students closely when they work with the heated mixture. Make sure they wear goggles and mitts. Be careful when slicing the candy into blocks. *CAUTION: Check for food allergies before allowing students to taste the candy.*
Expected Outcome The mixture will set in a gelatinlike consistency.
Answers The agar binds the ingredients together in a smooth gel. The sugar and juice simply add flavor.
Extend Let students make the candy without agar to see what happens.

Mineral Resources

Building Inquiry Skills: Inferring

Explain that nodules were first found by HMS *Challenger*. During the time of HMS *Challenger,* technology did not exist to recover the nodules on a commercial scale. Today, deep-sea robots could be used to collect them. Ask: **Why do you think no companies are recovering the ocean nodules now?** (*Students may infer that existing technology is too expensive or inefficient to recover the nodules profitably.*) **learning modality: logical/mathematical**

Fuels From the Ocean Floor

Figure 19 Lit up like a city at night, this Norwegian oil-drilling platform rises above the icy waters of the North Sea. Hundreds of people may live and work aboard such an oil rig.

nations who find and recover the minerals should own them. Others feel that this is unfair to nations who cannot yet afford the technology to obtain a share of these resources.

Fuels From the Ocean Floor

Another type of nonliving resource forms from the remains of dead marine organisms. These remains sink to the bottom of the ocean, where they are buried by sediments. As more sediments accumulate, the buried remains decompose. Over hundreds of thousands of years, the heat and pressure from the overlying layers gradually transform the remains into oil and natural gas.

As you know, many organisms live in the part of the ocean above the continental shelf. The thick sediments on the continental shelves bury the remains of living things. As a result, the richest deposits of oil and gas are often located on the continental shelves.

Oil rigs like the one in Figure 19 drill the rocky ocean floor as much as 300 meters below the surface. Imagine trying to dig a hole in the concrete bottom of a swimming pool, while standing on a raft floating on the surface of the water. You can see why drilling the ocean floor is very difficult! Ocean drilling is made even harder by strong currents, winds, and violent storms.

Checkpoint **What is the source of the oil and gas deposits on the ocean floor?**

Ocean Pollution

It was once thought that the ocean was so vast that people could not damage it by throwing wastes into it. This is partially true—the ocean is a self-cleaning system that can absorb some wastes without permanent damage. But dumping large amounts of wastes into the ocean threatens many marine organisms.

Recall that water pollution is the addition of any substance that has a negative effect on the living things that depend on the water. Most ocean pollution comes from the land. Although some is the result of natural occurrences, most pollution is related to human activities.

Natural Sources Some pollution is the result of weather. For example, heavy rains wash fresh water into estuaries and out into the water offshore. This surge of fresh water pollutes the ocean by lowering its salinity. A sudden change in salinity may kill ocean animals that are unable to adjust to it.

Human Sources Pollutants related to human activities include sewage, chemicals, and trash dumped into coastal waters. Chemicals that run off fields and roads often end up in the ocean. These substances can harm ocean organisms directly. The pollutants can also build up in their bodies and poison other animals, including people, that feed on them. Trash can cause serious problems, too. Seals, otters, and other marine mammals that need to breathe air can get tangled in old fishing lines or nets and drown. Other animals are harmed when they swallow plastic bags that block their stomachs.

Oil Spills One major threat to ocean life is oil pollution. When an oil tanker or drilling platform is damaged, oil leaks into the surrounding ocean. Oil is harmful to many organisms. It coats the bodies of marine mammals and birds. This destroys their natural insulation and affects their ability to float. The oil is also harmful to animals that swallow it.

Figure 20 Removing oil from a beach is a difficult, messy chore. This cleanup worker is using absorbent mops to remove oil from the sand. In the closeup, two more workers try to clean oil from a bird's beak and feathers. *Inferring What might have caused this oil pollution?*

Program Resources

◆ **Interdisciplinary Explorations Series**
"Where River Meets Sea," pp. 35–37, 38, 39–42

Answers to Self-Assessment

☑ *Checkpoint*
The oil and gas deposits were formed from the remains of living organisms.

Caption Question
Figure 20 It probably was spilled by an oil tanker or drilling platform that was damaged.

Building Inquiry Skills: Applying Concepts

Have students refer back to the Arctic food-web diagram in Figure 15. Then pose the following problem: **Suppose that an oil spill killed many of the plankton in an area of the Arctic Ocean. What effect would this have on the food web in that area?** (*The small fish, which depend entirely on plankton, would die. Without animal plankton and small fish, Arctic cod would die. Arctic terns, which feed on small fish, would not survive. Animals that depend on the cod and small fish—beluga whales and loons—would die if they did not move to another area. Only the seals and sea ducks, which eat benthic invertebrates as well as fish, might survive in the area—but only if there were enough invertebrates to sustain their populations. If the seals did not survive in the area, the polar bears would also have to move to another area.*) **learning modality: logical/mathematical**

Including All Students

Ask students: **What kinds of chemicals might run off fields and roads into coastal waters?** (*Fertilizers, pesticides, and weed killers from fields; salt and oil from roads*) If students have read Chapter 3, ask: **Are these pollutants from point sources or nonpoint sources? Explain.** (*Nonpoint sources, because you cannot pinpoint their origin*) Challenge students to make a flowchart to show how these substances get to the ocean. **learning modality: logical/mathematical**

Ongoing Assessment

Concept Mapping Have each student draw a concept map showing the two major forms of ocean pollution (natural and human), their sources, and examples of the damage they cause.

Protecting Earth's Oceans

Building Inquiry Skills: Communicating

Have students imagine they are delegates to the United Nations, and they are meeting to discuss a major mineral deposit recently discovered in the mid-Atlantic Ocean. Have student teams represent the nation that discovered the deposit, the nation with the technology to mine it, and the closest nations to the deposit. With you serving as moderator, let students debate the issue of who owns the deposit and has the right to mine it. **learning modality: verbal**

3 Assess

Section 4 Review Answers

1. The supply of fish decreases because more fish are harvested than can be naturally replaced.

2. The world ocean is a continuous body of water with no boundaries, so no one nation owns it. All nations have an interest in it.

3. Any one: Fresh water from desalination, magnesium, gravel, sand, shells, diamonds, gold, manganese and other metals, oil, natural gas; answers regarding location and use will vary depending on which resource is chosen.

4. Accept either viewpoint so long as students support it with specific details and reasonable arguments.

Science at Home

Materials *rubber band*
Tips Let students do the activity themselves in class before they try it with a family member at home. Give students an opportunity to present their responses to the question in a class discussion.

Performance Assessment

Writing Have each student describe one way that a nation could prevent overfishing in its waters.

Figure 21 Flags fly outside the United Nations headquarters in New York City. The United Nations develops policies on the use of the oceans by countries. *Applying Concepts Why can't each nation make its own laws regarding ocean resources?*

Interestingly, there is a natural cleaning process that slowly takes place after oil spills. Certain bacteria that live in the ocean feed on the oil and multiply. It takes many years, but eventually an oil-covered beach can become clean again. This has happened even in the portions of the Prince William Sound in Alaska that were blanketed with oil from the 1989 wreck of the oil tanker *Exxon Valdez.*

Protecting Earth's Oceans

Who owns the ocean and its resources? Who has the responsibility of protecting them? These are questions that nations have been struggling to answer for hundreds of years. **Because the world ocean is a continuous body of water that has no boundaries, it is difficult to determine who, if anyone, should control portions of it. Nations must cooperate to manage and protect the oceans.**

The United Nations has established different boundaries in the oceans. According to one treaty, a nation now controls the first 22 kilometers out from its coasts. The nation also controls resources in the waters or on the continental shelf within 370 kilometers of shore. This treaty leaves approximately half of the ocean's surface waters as "high seas," owned by no nation. Ownership of the ocean floor beneath the high seas is still under debate.

Other international efforts have resulted in cooperation aimed at reducing ocean pollution. Examples include the establishment of marine refuges and regulations for building safer oil tankers.

Section 4 Review

1. How can overfishing affect a fishery?
2. Explain why international cooperation is necessary to solve many problems related to ocean resources.
3. Name a nonliving resource found in the ocean. Where is it located? How is it obtained and used?
4. **Thinking Critically Making Judgments** Should mineral resources on the ocean floor belong to whomever finds them, or to the closest nation? Consider each position and write a short paragraph stating your opinion.

Science at Home

Have a family member hook one end of a rubber band around his or her wrist. Stretch the rubber band across the back of the hand and hook the free end over three fingers as shown. Now ask the person to try to re-move the rubber band without using the other hand. Explain that this shows how difficult it is for seals or dolphins to free themselves from a plastic beverage ring or piece of net. Can you propose any ways to reduce this threat to marine mammals?

Answers to Self-Assessment

Caption Question

Figure 21 Different nations' laws might conflict. No nation owns the "high seas."

Program Resources

◆ **Teaching Resources** 5-4 Review and Reinforce, p. 141; 5-4 Enrich, p. 142

Media and Technology

 Interactive Tutorial CD-ROM H-5

SCIENCE AND SOCIETY

Shrimp Farms—At What Cost to the Environment?

About one quarter of the world's shrimp are raised on shrimp farms. Many shrimp farms are created by clearing trees from mangrove forests and digging shallow, fenced-in ponds. Farmers then fill the ponds with ocean water and shrimp larvae. After about six months, when the shrimp are big enough to sell, the farmers drain the pond water back into the ocean.

To grow healthy shrimp, farmers often add fertilizers, medicines, and pesticides to the ponds. When the pond water is released to the ocean, these chemicals can harm other animals. The United Nations has estimated that 25 percent of the world's mangrove forests have been destroyed as a result of shrimp farming. As awareness of the environmental impact of shrimp farms has grown, the industry has come under attack.

▲ Shrimp farmer in Malaysia

The Issues

How Important Is Shrimp Farming? For many people in the world, shrimp is more than luxury food: It is a staple of their diet and their main source of animal protein. The demand for shrimp currently is greater than the natural supply in Earth's oceans. To meet the demand, many countries, including the United States, have turned to shrimp farming. Shrimp farms provide needed food and jobs that some people believe are worth a certain amount of damage to the environment. They feel it is not possible to have shrimp farms that are both highly productive and environmentally safe.

Can the Pollution Be Reduced? Shrimp farmers are exploring ways to reduce the impact of their farms on the coastal environment. Better pond construction can help stop chemicals from leaking into the surrounding waters. Some governments recognize the importance of mangrove forests in providing a habitat for many species and in protecting the shoreline. These governments have passed laws regulating where shrimp farms may be built. Farmers must investigate the impact their ponds will have on nearby mangrove forests and get approval before choosing a location. These methods of reducing environmental damage, however, are expensive and time-consuming for the shrimp farmers.

Should Farmers Use Alternative Methods? In some parts of Asia, a less destructive method of shrimp farming has been practiced for centuries. Raising shrimp in ditches dug around clusters of mangroves provides the young shrimp with a natural nutrient supply that includes debris from the trees. A gate keeps the shrimp from escaping into the ocean and also allows the motion of the tides to replenish the water in the ditches. The disadvantage of this method is that it is much less profitable than the constructed shrimp ponds. Many shrimp farmers could not afford to switch to this method. If they did, the price of shrimp worldwide would rise.

You Decide

1. Identify the Problem

In your own words, summarize the problem facing shrimp farmers.

2. Analyze the Options

Make a list of the solutions mentioned. List the advantages and drawbacks of each. Who would benefit from each plan? Who might suffer?

3. Find a Solution

Write a brochure or pamphlet for shrimp farmers that states your proposed solution to their problem. After you have written the text, illustrate your brochure.

SCIENCE AND SOCIETY

Shrimp Farms—At What Cost to the Environment?

Purpose
Identify ways in which shrimp farming affects the environment, and propose a solution that addresses shrimp farmers' needs as well as environmental concerns.

Role-Play

Time 80–90 minutes

◆ After students have read the introductory text and the three paragraphs under The Issues, ask: **If you were a shrimp farmer who used the usual farming methods, would you want to change your methods? Why or why not?** Let students discuss this question freely until opposing viewpoints are clear.

◆ Divide the class into small groups, with each group member representing a different viewpoint—for example, a shrimp farmer who does not want to change his or her methods, another farmer who thinks new methods should be tried, an owner of a seafood company that sells shrimp, and a science advisor or government official who wants to protect the mangrove forests. Tell students that each group's goal is to arrive at an *agreement* on how shrimp farming should be done.

Extend Students could survey a local supermarket to see whether fresh, frozen, and/or canned shrimp are available and, if so, how much they cost. Suggest that students talk with the seafood department's manager or clerk to find out whether any fresh shrimp are obtained from shrimp farms in this country or overseas. Students can also check the labels on canned or frozen shrimp to find the country of origin.

You Decide

◆ Students' responses to Identify the Problem and Analyze the Options should be based on the concepts and issues presented in the text. In response to Find a Solution, however, students may suggest solutions based on their small-group discussions.

◆ Students can share their solutions by displaying the brochures or pamphlets on a bulletin board.

Cleaning Up an Oil Spill

Preparing for Inquiry

Key Concept Oil is difficult to remove from water, beaches, and organisms.

Skills Objectives Students will be able to
◆ model oil-spill cleanup using a variety of materials;
◆ form operational definitions of what clean water is and what a clean beach is.

Time 40 minutes

Advance Planning Obtain a feather for each group. Pillow feathers may be used if you cannot obtain larger ones.

Guiding Inquiry

Invitation Give each group a small paper cup containing a little dark molasses. Tell students that molasses is very similar in consistency to crude oil—the type of oil carried by tankers. Encourage students to examine the molasses by tilting the cup to see how it coats the sides and by dipping an index finger into it and rubbing it against their thumb to feel its consistency.

Introducing the Procedure

Have students read the newspaper article at the top of the page. Ask: **If you were one of the volunteers, what things would you expect to help clean?** *(Birds, sea otters, and any other animals coated with oil; rocks, sand, gravel, and plants on the beach)* **What kinds of cleanup materials do you think you'd use?** *(Accept all reasonable suggestions.)*

Troubleshooting the Experiment

◆ If necessary, remind students to record their observations in steps 5 and 6.
◆ Tell students to put any oil they recover (Step 6) in the clean paper cup.

CLEANING UP AN OIL SPILL

Oil Spill in Bay

An oil tanker hit a reef yesterday, spilling thousands of barrels of crude oil into the water. Cleanup efforts will begin today. Workers must race against time to save birds and sea otters. With stormy weather forecasted, however, scientists expect considerable damage. Volunteers are needed to help clean up.

Imagine that you are a volunteer helping to clean up an oil spill. In this activity, you will use a variety of materials to remove as much oil as possible from the water and to keep oil from reaching the beach. You will also see how oil affects animals that are exposed to a spill.

Problem

How can an oil spill be cleaned up?

Skills Focus

making models, forming operational definitions

Materials

water	shallow pan	vegetable oil
feather	paper cup	plastic dropper
paper towels	cotton balls	wooden sticks
marking pen	graduated cylinder, 100 mL	

Procedure

1. Place a pan on a table or desk covered with newspaper. Label one end of the pan "Beach" and the other end "Open Ocean."
2. Pour water into the pan to a depth of 2 cm.
3. Gently pour 20 mL of vegetable oil into the center of the pan. Record your observations.
4. Dip a feather and your finger into the oil. Observe how each is affected by the oil.
5. Try to wipe oil off the feather and your finger using paper towels. Record whether any oil is left on the feather or your skin.
6. Now try to clean up the spill. Record your observations with each step. First, using the wooden sticks, try to keep the oil from reaching the "beach." Next, gently blow across the surface of the water from the "open ocean" side to simulate wind and waves. Then use the cotton balls, paper towels, and dropper to recover as much of the oil as possible.
7. When you are finished, dispose of the oil and used items in the paper cup. Wash your hands.

Analyze and Conclude

1. How successful were you in cleaning up the oil? Is the water as clean as it was at the start?
2. How well were you able to keep the oil from reaching the beach? Describe how useful the different materials were in cleaning up the oil.
3. Describe what happened when you cleaned the feather and your finger. What might happen to fish, birds, and other animals if they were coated with oil as a result of an oil spill?
4. Predict how storms with strong winds and waves would affect the cleanup of an oil spill.
5. **Apply** Look at the used cleanup materials in the paper cup. What additional problems for cleanup crews does this suggest?

Getting Involved

One way to reduce the threat of oil spills is to transport less oil across the oceans. To make that possible, people would need to use less oil in their daily lives. Oil is used to heat homes, to produce gasoline, and to make products such as plastics and textiles. List at least three ways to reduce the amount of oil you and your family use.

Safety

Students should wear safety goggles and lab aprons during this lab to protect their eyes and clothing. At the conclusion of the lab, make sure students dispose of all oil and cleanup materials in an appropriate container and wash their hands thoroughly. Review the safety guidelines in Appendix A.

Program Resources

◆ **Teaching Resources** Chapter 5 Real-World Lab, pp. 146–147

SECTION 1 Exploring the Ocean

Key Ideas

◆ Technology such as sonar enables scientists to study the deep ocean floor despite the darkness, cold, and extreme pressure there.

◆ The ocean floor has features similar to those found on the continents, including plains, mountain ranges, volcanoes, and trenches. These landforms are all formed by the interactions of Earth's moving plates.

◆ In the process of sea-floor spreading, new rock forms at the edges of diverging plates, and old rock sinks between converging plates.

Key Terms

sonar	continental shelf	continental slope
seamount	abyssal plain	mid-ocean ridge
trench	magma	plates
sea-floor spreading		

SECTION 2 Life at the Ocean's Edge

INTEGRATING LIFE SCIENCE

Key Ideas

◆ Physical factors that affect marine organisms include salinity, water temperature, light, dissolved gases, nutrients, and wave action.

◆ Organisms in the rocky intertidal zone must be able to tolerate the pounding of the waves, as well as being both underwater and exposed to the air for long periods of time.

◆ Coastal wetlands include salt marshes and mangrove forests.

Key Terms

plankton	nekton	benthos
food web	intertidal zone	estuary
brackish		

SECTION 3 The Neritic Zone and Open Ocean

INTEGRATING LIFE SCIENCE

Key Ideas

◆ The neritic zone receives sunlight and nutrients washed from the land. Habitats in this zone include kelp forests and coral reefs.

◆ The thin layer of sunlit water at the surface is the only part of the open ocean that can support algae, which need the sunlight to produce food. Other marine organisms depend on the food made by algae.

◆ The chemical nutrients in the hot water around a hydrothermal vent support the organisms that live around the vent.

Key Terms

neritic zone	open-ocean zone
holdfast	atoll
bioluminescence	hydrothermal vent

SECTION 4 Resources From the Ocean

Key Ideas

◆ If used wisely, fisheries are a renewable resource. New fish will replace those that are caught, but only if overfishing does not reduce the population too severely.

◆ Nonliving resources from the ocean include dissolved substances in seawater and minerals and fuels from the ocean floor.

◆ Nations must cooperate to manage and protect the oceans.

Key Terms

aquaculture nodules

USING THE INTERNET

www.science-explorer.phschool.com

CHAPTER 5 REVIEW

Expected Outcome

Students will be unable to clean all the oil from their fingers and the feather and will be able to recover only a small amount of the oil floating on the water. Remind students of the molasses and how much thicker and stickier crude oil is than cooking oil.

Analyze and Conclude

1. Few, if any, students will be completely successful in cleaning up the oil. An observable film of oil will remain.

2. Students' success in keeping the oil from reaching the beach will vary. The wooden sticks will create barriers to prevent some oil from washing onto the beach. The paper towels and cotton balls will soak up some, but not all of the oil. The dropper will remove some oil but will also suction up water.

3. A light film of oil remains on the finger and feather. Heavily coated animals cannot survive. The insulation that fur and feathers provide is destroyed by the oil coating. Heavily coated birds cannot fly.

4. Winds and waves would wash the oily water onto the beach and would scatter it more widely on the water.

5. Cleanup materials are coated or saturated with oil and have to be disposed of in a way that they will not create more pollution.

Extending the Inquiry

Getting Involved Make sure students understand that they should not consider *vegetable* oil—the type of oil they used in this lab. Suggest that students first determine various uses of petroleum (fuel oil) by their families, then look for ways to reduce uses—for example, turning down the thermostat to use less heating oil and car-pooling to use less gasoline.

Program Resources

◆ **Teaching Resources** Chapter 5 Project Scoring Rubric, p. 126; Chapter 5 Performance Assessment Teacher Notes, pp. 188–189; Chapter 5 Performance Assessment Student Worksheet, p. 190; Chapter 5 Test, pp. 191–194.

Media and Technology

Interactive Student Tutorial CD-ROM H-5

Computer Test Bank Chapter 5 Test

177 ◆ H

Reviewing Content: Multiple Choice

1. b **2.** c **3.** d **4.** d **5.** b

Reviewing Content: True or False

6. diverge **7.** intertidal **8.** true **9.** atoll
10. true

Checking Concepts

11. Students may cite methods used by the HMS *Challenger* (pp. 146, 148–149), methods described in the text and the Science & History time line on pages 148–149, or methods used by *Glomar Challenger* (p. 152).

12. Any three: They must be able to tolerate the pounding of waves, changes in salinity and temperature, and alternating periods of being underwater and exposed to air.

13. The rivers that flow into estuaries can carry pollutants such as pesticides, sewage, and industrial wastes.

14. Hydrothermal vents occur in the deepest parts of the ocean far from sunlight, where food is scarce and organisms tend to be small, slow-moving, and of limited variety. Around the vents, however, the number, size, and variety of organisms is unusually large.

15. Students' descriptions of the ocean floor should include all the major features identified in the text on pages 150–152 and the accompanying visual essay (continental shelf, continental slope, trenches, abyssal plain, mid-ocean ridge, volcanic island, seamount) and organisms typically found in each area, drawn from Sections 2 and 3.

Thinking Visually

16. Sample title: Ocean Habitats;
a. varying salinity, exposure, temperature, rough wave action **b.** barnacles, mussels, sea stars, sea urchins, sponges, sea anemones **c.** neritic zone **d.** shallow water, warm temperatures, receives sunlight and a steady supply of nutrients, may have upwelling currents **e.** receives sunlight, dissolved nutrients less abundant than in the neritic zone
f. microscopic algae, copepods, krill,

Reviewing Content

 For more review of key concepts, see the Interactive Student Tutorial CD-ROM.

Multiple Choice
Choose the letter of the best answer.

1. Earth's crust is made up of moving
  a. magma.   **b.** plates.
  c. trenches.   **d.** abyssal plains.

2. An area where rivers flow into the ocean and fresh water and salt water mix is a(n)
  a. tide pool.
  b. hydrothermal vent.
  c. estuary.
  d. kelp forest.

3. A tropical ocean community made by tiny animals that have algae growing in their tissues is a
  a. mangrove forest.   **b.** salt marsh.
  c. intertidal zone.   **d.** coral reef.

4. In the open-ocean zone, organisms depend directly or indirectly on food that is made by
  a. marine mammals.
  b. nekton in the water column.
  c. plants growing on the deep ocean floor.
  d. algae near the surface.

5. Most ocean pollutants come from
  a. marine organisms.
  b. the land.
  c. the atmosphere.
  d. Earth's core.

True or False
If the statement is true, write true. If it is false, change the underlined word or words to make the statement true.

6. The mid-ocean ridge is formed where two plates <u>converge</u>.

7. The area between the high and low tide lines is the <u>neritic</u> zone.

8. Water that is partly salty and partly fresh is <u>brackish</u>.

9. A ring-shaped coral reef surrounding a lagoon is called a <u>seamount</u>.

10. Many deep-sea fishes use their <u>bioluminescence</u> to attract prey.

Checking Concepts

11. Describe one method that has been used to study the ocean floor.

12. Describe three physical factors that organisms in the rocky intertidal zone must overcome.

13. Explain why estuaries are especially vulnerable to pollution.

14. Explain why scientists were surprised to discover the variety of organisms living around hydrothermal vents.

15. **Writing to Learn** Imagine that you are an "aquanaut" on a voyage of discovery across the ocean floor. Write a logbook entry that summarizes your observations as you travel from one continent to another. Include details about the shape of the ocean floor, as well as some organisms you encounter along your journey.

Thinking Visually

16. **Compare/Contrast Table** Copy the table about ocean habitats onto a separate sheet of paper. Then fill in the empty spaces and add a title. (See the Skills Handbook for more on compare/contrast tables.)

Habitat	Zone	Conditions	Organisms
Tide pool	Intertidal	a. _?_	b. _?_
Coral reef	c. _?_	d. _?_	Coral, fishes, shrimp, eels
Surface zone	Open ocean	e. _?_	f. _?_
Hydrothermal vent	g. _?_	High pressure, dark, warm	h. _?_

---

young of many ocean animals (crabs, mollusks, fish, squid), jellyfish **g.** deep zone **h.** crabs, clams, tube worms, bacteria

Applying Skills

17. *A:* about 4,000 m; *C:* about 3,500 m
18. *Between A and B:* abyssal plain; *at point D:* trench
19. The distance between each point and the closest continental slope or the age of the rock on the seafloor at each point

Thinking Critically

20. *plankton:* microscopic algae *nekton:* squid, whales, sea otters, anglerfish *benthos:* sea stars, giant clams

21. The neritic zone lies above the continental shelf. Here, the water is shallower, warmer, and contains more nutrients than the deep zone. These conditions support a large number and wide variety of fish.

22. Populations of animals that feed directly on plankton would decline as their food supply decreased. In turn, populations of

Applying Skills

Use the diagram of a portion of the ocean floor to answer Questions 17–19.

17. **Interpreting Diagrams** What is the approximate depth of the ocean floor at point A? At point C?

18. **Inferring** What might the feature between locations A and B be? The feature at point D?

19. **Posing Questions** What other information would help you determine whether point A or point E is closer to the mid-ocean ridge? Explain.

Thinking Critically

20. **Classifying** Classify each of the following organisms as plankton, nekton, or benthos: squid, sea stars, microscopic algae, whales, sea otters, anglerfish, and giant clams.

21. **Making Generalizations** Explain why many of the world's fisheries are located in the neritic zone.

22. **Predicting** Suppose the number of plankton in the ocean suddenly decreased to half their current number. Predict how this would affect other marine organisms.

23. **Relating Cause and Effect** How might fertilizers used on farmland result in ocean pollution near shore?

Performance Assessment

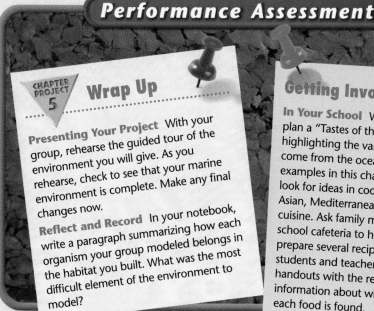

Wrap Up

Presenting Your Project With your group, rehearse the guided tour of the environment you will give. As you rehearse, check to see that your marine environment is complete. Make any final changes now.

Reflect and Record In your notebook, write a paragraph summarizing how each organism your group modeled belongs in the habitat you built. What was the most difficult element of the environment to model?

Getting Involved

In Your School With your classmates, plan a "Tastes of the Sea" exhibition highlighting the variety of foods that come from the ocean. Besides the examples in this chapter, you might look for ideas in cookbooks featuring Asian, Mediterranean, and Caribbean cuisine. Ask family members and your school cafeteria to help your class prepare several recipes for other students and teachers to sample. Make handouts with the recipes and information about where in the ocean each food is found.

Chapter 5 **H** ◆ **179**

Performance Assessment

Wrap Up
Presenting Your Project
Allow 10–15 minutes for each group to give a "guided tour" of its marine habitat. Prompt each group member to express his or her knowledge of the habitat and its inhabitants. Each student should also describe the characteristics of the particular organism that he or she modeled, including its specific physical and behavior adaptations to that habitat and, possibly, the organism's role in the food web. Allow time for questions and discussion after each group's presentation. Be sure to provide all students with positive feedback about their models.

Reflect and Record Emphasize that each group member is responsible for discussing conditions in the group's habitat, as well as his or her own organism. After students have described any difficulties they encountered in building the habitat, ask them to suggest other methods or materials they could have used.

animals that feed on the plankton-eaters would also decline.

23. Runoff on land could wash fertilizers into streams and rivers, which would eventually carry them into the ocean. Near land, the fertilizers would cause excess growth of plants and algae, upsetting the natural balance in coastal habitats.

Program Resources

◆ **Inquiry Skills Activity Book** Provides teaching and review of all inquiry skills

Getting Involved

This activity could be done as a cooperative learning project, with each small group looking for recipes, selecting one recipe, gathering the ingredients, and preparing the dish. Review the groups' recipe choices to ensure variety and to avoid ingredients that would be difficult or impossible to locate in your area. *CAUTION: Check for food allergies before allowing students to taste any foods. Also make sure students identify all ingredients in their handouts in case teachers and students in other classes have allergies. Never prepare food or eat in the lab room.*

The Mississippi

This interdisciplinary feature presents the central theme of transportation on the Mississippi River by connecting four different disciplines: science, social studies, mathematics, and language arts. The four explorations are designed to capture students' interest and help them see how the content they are studying in science relates to other school subjects and to real-world events. The unit is particularly suitable for team teaching.

1 Engage/Explore

Activating Prior Knowledge

Help students recall what they learned in Chapter 2, Fresh Water, by asking questions such as: **What are the parts of a river system?** *(The main river, its tributaries, and lakes, ponds, and wetlands along the river)* and **How does a river change as it flows from its source to its mouth?** *(Students should identify differences in the river's speed, width, and depth and features such as the flood plain and delta.)* Then ask: **What do you know about the Mississippi River?** *(Accept all responses without comment at this time.)*

Introducing the Unit

Display a large map of the United States, and invite a volunteer to point out the Mississippi River. Ask: **In which direction does the Mississippi flow?** *(From north to south)* Draw students' attention to the map on this page, and have them trace the river's route from its headwaters to its mouth. Ask: **Which states have the Mississippi River as a natural boundary?** *(Minnesota, Wisconsin, Iowa, Illinois, Missouri, Kentucky, Tennessee, Arkansas, Mississippi, and Louisiana)* **What are some of the Mississippi's major tributaries?** *(the Minnesota, Wisconsin, Illinois, Missouri, Ohio, Arkansas, Yazoo, and Red rivers)* **How large is the Mississippi River watershed?** *(It drains about 40 percent of the United States.)*

THE MISSISSIPPI

What would you name a river that—

◆ *carries about 420 million metric tons of cargo a year,*

◆ *drains 31 states and 2 Canadian provinces,*

◆ *looks like a tree that has a thin top trunk and 2 strong branches,*

◆ *flows at about 18,100 cubic meters of water per second?*

Native Americans called the river *misi sipi,* **an Algonquin name meaning "big water," or "father of waters."**

H ave you ever traveled on a river or lake that feeds into the mighty Mississippi River? Perhaps you have but never realized it. The map below shows the watershed of this great river. From the west, the Missouri River — the "Big Muddy"— carries soft silt eroded from the Great Plains. The Missouri joins the Mississippi near St. Louis, turning the river's clear water to muddy brown. From the east, the Ohio River flows in from the rocky Appalachian plateau, nearly doubling the volume of water in the river. In all, the huge Mississippi watershed drains about 40 percent of the United States.

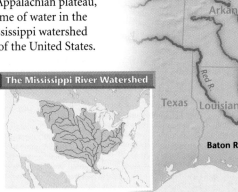

The Mississippi River Watershed

The Mississippi River starts at Lake Itasca and flows through 10 states to the Gulf of Mexico. The river is a drainage point for hundreds of tributaries in the vast Mississippi watershed. ▶

180 ◆ H

Program Resources

◆ **Teaching Resources** Interdisciplinary Explorations, Social Studies, pp. 148–151; Science, pp. 152–154; Mathematics, pp. 155–157; Language Arts, pp. 158–159

A National Trade Route

Since Native Americans settled in villages along the Mississippi around 1,200 years ago, the river has served as a water highway for trade and travel.

▲ St. Anthony Falls is the northernmost point of navigation on the Mississippi.

In the late 1600s, French explorers, fur traders, and soldiers arrived in the Mississippi Valley. They chose strategic sites for forts and fur-trading posts — Prairie du Chien, St. Louis, and St. Genevieve. At first, traders used canoes, rafts, and flatboats to carry goods downstream. But traveling up the river was difficult. Crews had to use long poles to push narrow keelboats upstream against the current.

▲ Crews in flatboats rode the river currents, steering with long oars.

In 1811, the arrival of *The New Orleans,* the first steamboat on the Mississippi River, changed the river forever. Within 40 years, there were hundreds more steamboats and many new river towns. On the upper Mississippi, the city of Minneapolis grew up around flour mills near the falls. Farther downstream, Memphis became a center for transporting cotton. Later, it was a stopping point for showboats and musicians. New Orleans quickly became a world port. It received cotton, tobacco, and sugar cane from southern plantations and exported corn, wheat and indigo to Europe. Imported luxury items, such as soap, coffee, shoes, and textiles, traveled upstream from the port of New Orleans. Up and down the river townspeople eagerly waited for the cry, "Steamboat comin'!"

▲ New Orleans has been a major trading port since its founding in 1718.

Social Studies Activity

Use the map to choose a city on the Mississippi River to learn about. Imagine that you are an early settler in the city. Write a letter to convince relatives to move to your city. Before writing, learn about the history, founding, and trade of the city. Look for answers to the following questions:

◆ Who founded the city? When was the city founded? Why did settlers decide to move there? Where did they come from?

◆ What part did the Mississippi River play in the city's founding?

◆ What other physical features were important to the city?

◆ Where did the city's name come from?

◆ What products were grown, bought, or sold there?

H ◆ 181

2 Facilitate

◆ Have students refer to the map on the previous page to find each settlement named in the text. Ask: **Why do you think people chose these places to settle and build a town?** *(The locations provided easy access to the river for travel and transporting goods.)* **How did steamboats change the river?** *(People no longer had to depend on their own strength to move boats.)*

◆ Encourage interested students to create a bulletin board display showing the various types of boats used on the river from earliest times to today.

◆ To extend this exploration, students could construct a time line of important events that have occurred in the Mississippi River valley since early times.

Social Studies Activity

Let students work individually. To provide more choices of cities, suggest that they consult other, more detailed maps of the area. Caution students to choose cities that are large enough to merit entries in encyclopedias or other readily available reference books. If time allows, let students read their letters aloud. **Teaching Resources** The following worksheets correlate with this page: Finding Places in the Mississippi Valley, page 148; Reading a Data Table, page 149; Making a Bar Graph, page 150; and Finding Your Way Around New Orleans, page 151.

3 Assess

Activity Assessment

Evaluate students' research procedures, particularly note-taking and outlining. Make sure their reports are in the form of letters and that they include the type of information that answers the questions on the student page.

Background

History When Europeans began to explore and settle North America, the Mississippi River played a major role. The first European to see the river was a Spaniard, Hernando de Soto, in 1541. French explorer and fur trader René-Robert Cavelier, Sieur de La Salle, canoed down the length of the river to the Gulf of Mexico. In 1682, he claimed the entire area for France and named it "Louisiana" in honor of the French king.

Early French settlements on the river included New Orleans (1717), St. Louis (1764), and Memphis (1819). In the late 1700s, France, Spain, and the United States fought for control of navigation on the Mississippi, including the right to use the port of New Orleans. In the Louisiana Purchase of 1803, the U.S. purchased from France all the land from the Mississippi River westward to the Rockies.

2 Facilitate

- Discuss the hazards involved in boating on a river. Ask: **Have you ever gone canoeing on a river or seen a movie of people rafting through river rapids? What can people do to make a river safer for travel and transportation?** *(Accept all reasonable answers. Point out that this page describes one way of "taming" rivers.)*

- Review the diagrams step by step to make sure they understand how a lock operates. You could choose volunteers to read the captions aloud as students examine the illustrations.

- To extend this exploration, suggest that students research the building of the Panama Canal, which includes six pairs of locks. Encourage students to focus on the construction problems posed by the terrain and how engineers solved them. Also have students compare and contrast the locks on the Panama Canal with those on the Mississippi River.

Science Activity

Tell students that the four "L" shapes on the drawing represent modeling wax, which makes the model lock watertight. Teaching Resources page 154 provides complete instructions for building the model.

Teaching Resources The following worksheets correlate with this page: Traveling the Upper Mississippi, pages 152–153, and Making a Model Lock, page 154.

3 Assess

Activity Assessment

Schedule time for students to demonstrate and explain their models. During these presentations, focus on evaluating students' understanding of the "locking through" process rather than on their skill in building models that operate without flaws such as leaks or sticky gates.

Taming the River

Navigating the sandbars, shallow water, and rocky rapids on the upper Mississippi River was treacherous for captains of ships and barges in the 1800s. To make traveling easier, engineers in the early 1900s built a "water staircase," a series of 29 locks and dams between Minneapolis, Minnesota, and Alton, Illinois, above St. Louis. A lock is an enclosed basin, with gates at each end. Locks allow engineers to raise or lower the water level in a certain area of the river. Between the locks on the upper Mississippi, the river forms wide pools of quiet water, maintaining a channel deep enough for large boats.

Use the diagrams to trace how a boat "locks through" as it travels upstream. This technology allowed boats to travel to cities on the upper Mississippi. ▶

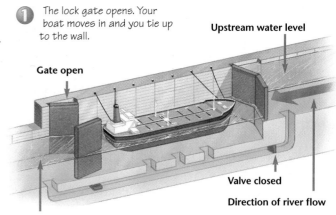

① The lock gate opens. Your boat moves in and you tie up to the wall.

Upstream water level

Gate open

Valve closed

Direction of river flow

Downstream water level

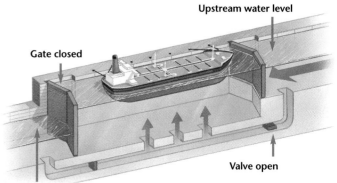

Gate closed

Upstream water level

Valve open

Downstream water level

② The gate closes, and water pours in. As water fills the lock—like a bathtub filling—it lifts the boat a meter or more. When the water in the lock is even with the water level upstream, the gates at the upstream end open. You untie your boat and move out into the river.

If you were going downstream, you would "lock through" in reverse. The water would empty out of the lock, lowering the water level to match the level downstream.

Science Activity

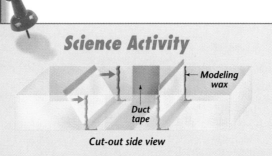

Modeling wax

Duct tape

Cut-out side view

Use a cardboard milk container to build a working model of a lock. Set up your lock following the illustration. Then demonstrate how your lock works, using a cork or pen cap as your ship and sailing it through the lock.

182 ◆ H

Background

Facts and Figures Some students may wonder why the natural topography of the upper Mississippi differed so markedly from that of the lower Mississippi before the locks and dams were constructed. The answer lies in the river's ancient history.

The upper Mississippi is much older than the lower Mississippi. Many thousands of years ago, the mouth of the Mississippi was located near what is today Cape Girardeau, Missouri. The river deposited silt in the ocean gulf, over time creating a delta stretching southward more than 1,900 km to the Gulf of Mexico. As the delta built up, the river created a channel through the new land. Today's lower Mississippi winds through this ancient delta.

All Aboard

The whistle blows. The gleaming white steamboat pulls away from the dock just below Fort Snelling, Minnesota. You head downstream toward New Orleans. As you watch the paddlewheel splashing in the water, you think of the old-time steamboats that carried passengers up and down the Mississippi River in the 1800s.

Today you are cruising at a speed of 11.3 kilometers per hour. You want to stay awake until you enter Lock 3 at Red Wing, Minnesota. It's 4:30 P.M. on Monday now. You know that it's about 78.8 kilometers to Red Wing. It should take about 7 hours to reach the lock. So you'll be there at 11:30 P.M. and through the lock by midnight.

As your boat travels along the river, it will follow the schedule you see on this page. The highlight of your trip will be Mark Twain's hometown of Hannibal, Missouri. You will arrive there on Friday.

Look at the Upper Mississippi River schedule to answer the questions below. Distances are given from Fort Snelling.

- What is your average speed between Dubuque and Hannibal? Use the following equation:

$$speed = \frac{distance}{time}$$

Round to the nearest tenth.

- How long will you spend in Prairie du Chien?
- About how long does it take to travel from Prairie du Chien to Dubuque?

MISSISSIPPI RIVERBOAT SCHEDULE
MAY to SEPTEMBER

UPPER MISSISSIPPI RIVERBOAT SCHEDULE

Port	Arrival Time	Departure Time	Distance From Fort Snelling
Fort Snelling, MN		4:30 P.M. Mon.	0 km
Lock 3, Red Wing, MN	11:30 P.M. Mon.	12:00 midnight	78.8 km
Prairie du Chien, WI	11:00 P.M. Tues.	10:30 A.M. Wed.	337.8 km
Dubuque, IA	6:30 P.M. Wed.	7:00 P.M. Wed.	426.3 km
Hannibal, MO	1:00 A.M. Fri.	———	863.9 km

LOWER MISSISSIPPI RIVERBOAT SCHEDULE

Port	Arrival Time	Departure Time	Distance From Fort Snelling
Hannibal, MO		6 P.M. Fri.	863.9 km
Lock 26 at Alton, IL	a. ?	b. ?	1033 km
St. Louis, MO	c. ?	d. ?	1070.7 km
Cape Girardeau, MO	6:30 A.M. Sun.	———	e. ?

Math Activity

Now complete the riverboat schedule for the Lower Mississippi. Your boat will leave Hannibal at 6 P.M. Friday and will travel at a speed of 14.7 kilometers per hour for the rest of the journey.

- When will you arrive at Lock 26?
- You spend 34 minutes in the lock. When will you depart from Lock 26? Your boat travels on. When will it arrive in St. Louis?
- The boat will spend 4 hours in St. Louis and head to Cape Girardeau, arriving at 6:30 A.M. Sunday. How far is it from St. Louis to Cape Girardeau?

H ◆ 183

---

2 Facilitate

- Have students find the ports listed in the schedule on the map on page 180 and trace the riverboat's route. (Cape Girardeau, not shown on the map, is at the river's bend above Cairo.) Point out that on the schedule, each segment of the journey lasts from the departure time listed for one port to the arrival time listed for the next port. Also emphasize that the distances listed in the right column are all from the original departure point at Fort Snelling. To determine whether students understand how to read the schedule, ask: **How far is it from Dubuque to Hannibal?** (863.9–426.3m, or 437.6 km) **How long does that part of the trip take?** (30 hours–from 7:00 P.M. Wednesday to 1:00 A.M. Friday)

- As a whole-class activity, have students work through the three questions in the left column. (Average speed between Dubuque and Hannibal, 437.6 km ÷ 30 hrs = 14.6 km/hr; time spent in Prairie du Chien, 11.5 hrs; travel time from Prairie du Chien to Dubuque, 8 hrs)

Math Activity

Let students complete the activity on their own. Remind them that to convert parts of hours expressed as decimal fractions, they must multiply the fraction by 60.
Teaching Resources The following worksheets correlate with this page: Calculating Distances Between Locks, page 155; Graphing Population Changes, page 156; and Paddlewheel Steamboat Cruises, page 157.

3 Assess

Activity Assessment

a. 5:30 A.M. Saturday (169.1 km ÷ 14.7 km/hr = 11.5 hrs from 6 P.M. Friday)
b. 6:04 A.M. Saturday (5:30 + 34 min)
c. 8:40 A.M. Saturday (37.7 km ÷ 14.7 km/hr = 2.6 hrs from 6:04 A.M.)
d. 12:40 P.M. Saturday
e. 1332.4 km from Fort Snelling (261.7 km from St. Louis to Cape Girardeau)

Background

Integrating Science and Technology
Today, modern versions of the fabled steamboats offer cruises on the Mississippi and several of its major tributaries, including the Illinois, Ohio, Tennessee, and Arkansas rivers. The *Delta Queen, Mississippi Queen,* and *American Queen* offer cruises with a variety of itineraries on the upper and lower Mississippi.

Today's steamboats look like those of Mark Twain's day, but they have hulls of welded steel (not wood), air conditioning, elevators between decks, and electronic navigation aids. They are powered in part by steam engines that turn their colorful paddlewheels. They also have powerful auxiliary diesel engines as well as devices that make steering the big boats much easier than it was 100 years ago.

2 Facilitate

- Ask students if they are familiar with Mark Twain and have read any of his books or stories. If so, let them describe the plots and characters briefly.
- After students have read the excerpt, ask: **Have you ever had to walk around your home in the dark? How did you keep from running into things?** *(Students will probably say they already knew the layout from seeing it so many times in the light.)* **Why did Mr. Bixby use the image of a dark hall?** *(To relate the new task to a familiar experience)*

Language Arts Activity

Encourage students to share their responses to the questions posed in the text. *(A river pilot must know the river's shape so well that he can navigate safely even when he cannot see the shore. Mr. Bixby respects the river and is proud of his knowledge of it. You can tell by what he says.)* Ask: **Based on this excerpt, how would you describe Mr. Bixby?** *(Experienced, tough, no-nonsense, forceful, insistent)* **How would you describe the young Mark Twain?** *(Nervous, overwhelmed, unsure of himself, reluctant, somewhat negative)*

- Before students begin writing, ask: **How do you think the excerpt should end?** *(Since students know that Twain did become a river pilot, they should realize that the excerpt would end on a positive note, with Twain resolving to do his best.)* Remind students of the following points: (1) The characters should talk as people would in Mark Twain's time; (2) the dialogue should move the story along and bring it to a natural conclusion; (3) every time the speaker changes, a new paragraph should begin; and (4) the speaker's words should be set off with quotation marks.
  Teaching Resources The following worksheets correlate with this page: Mississippi River Vocabulary, page 158, and The Mound Builders, page 159.

Mark Three! Mark Twain!

To steer a boat on the Mississippi, early riverboat pilots had to memorize landmarks at every bend and curve of the river, going both upstream and down. They had to know where the channel was deep enough for the boat, where the current was strong, where there were sandbars or sunken logs.

When Samuel Clemens was growing up in the small river town of Hannibal, Missouri, his ambition was to become a Mississippi River steamboat pilot. He was a pilot for a while. Later he became one of America's most famous writers, using the pen name Mark Twain. In the passage below from his book *Life on the Mississippi*, Twain describes a lesson he learned from an experienced pilot, Mr. Bixby.

What's in a Name?
Mark Twain's name comes from a term that steamboat crews used to measure the depth of river water. *Twain* means "two." Dropping a weighted line, they would call out the depth: "Mark twain!"—2 fathoms deep; "Mark three!"—3 fathoms deep. (Note: One fathom equals 1.8 meters.)

"**M**y boy," [Bixby said] "you've got to know the shape of the river perfectly. It is all there is left to steer by on a very dark night. Everything else is blotted out and gone. But mind you, it hasn't the same shape in the night that it has in the daytime."

"How on earth am I ever going to learn it, then?"

"How do you follow a hall at home in the dark? Because you know the shape of it. You can't see it."

"Do you mean to say that I've got to know all the million trifling variations of shape in the banks of this interminable [endless] river as well as I know the shape of the front hall at home?"

"On my honor, you've got to know them better than any man ever did know the shapes of the halls in his own house."

"I wish I was dead!"

"Now I don't want to discourage you, but —. . . . You see, this has got to be learned; there isn't any getting around it. . .

The river is a very different shape on a pitch-dark night from what it is on a starlight night. All shores seem to be straight lines, then, and mighty dim ones, too; and you'd run them for straight lines, only you know better. . . . Then there's your gray mist. You take a night when there's one of these grisly, drizzly gray mists, and then there isn't any particular shape to a shore. A gray mist would tangle the head of the oldest man that ever lived. Well, then, different kinds of moonlight change the shape of the river in different ways. You see —"

"Oh, don't say any more, please! Have I got to learn the shape of the river according to all these five hundred thousand different ways? If I tried to carry all that cargo in my head, it would make me stoop-shouldered."

"No! You only learn the shape of the river; and you learn it with such absolute certainty that you can always steer by the shape that's in your head, and never mind the one that's before your eyes."

History "Mark Twain" is one of the literary world's most famous pen names. Twain himself—in *Life on the Mississippi*, written in 1883—claimed that an older riverboat pilot had used the name for a series of articles and that he (Twain) had borrowed it for a parody. However, most editors and critics do not accept this account, particularly since Clemens first used the pen name 20 years earlier when he was working as a reporter for the Virginia City (Nevada) *Territorial Enterprize*.

Twain never forgot the Mississippi River and his years as a river pilot. As a journalist, humorist, and lecturer, he traveled throughout the United States and abroad. His most popular works for young people are *The Adventures of Tom Sawyer*, *The Adventures of Huckleberry Finn*, and "The Celebrated Jumping Frog of Calaveras County."

Language Arts Activity

Read the excerpt, focusing on what the dialogue tells you about the characters of Mark Twain and Mr. Bixby.

◆ What lesson does Mark Twain learn?

◆ How does Mr. Bixby feel about the Mississippi River? How can you tell?

Now, use dialogue to write an ending to this riverboat excerpt. Before you begin writing, think carefully about the characters, setting, and your conclusion.

Riverboat captains were licensed to navigate the river. ▶

Activity Assessment

Let each student read his or her ending aloud to the rest of the class or role-play the dialogue with a partner. Evaluate students' written work based on the four points identified above.

Tie It Together

Time 1 week (2 days for research, 2 days for preparing the brochure and booth, 1 day for the fair)

Tips Have students work in groups of four or five. Encourage groups to choose a city that can be researched easily with readily available resource materials. If necessary, help each group divide up the tasks and work out a plan for researching and compiling information. Guide students through the writing process as follows:

◆ In the research stage, suggest that they narrow the topics by listing all their ideas and then selecting the ones that are most interesting.

◆ In the drafting stage, remind students to begin the brochure with a general introduction, followed by topic-specific sections such as Key Attractions, Famous People, and Historic Sites.

◆ In the editing stage, remind students to read the draft carefully, looking for errors and ways to improve the brochure.

Extend Groups could choose one cultural aspect to research across different cities. For example, one group could find out about (and possibly prepare for class tasting) foods representing different ethnic and regional groups—a Cajun dish for Louisiana, Scandinavian food for Minnesota, and so on. Another group could research the music in river cities, including jazz and ragtime in New Orleans, country and rock in Memphis, and bluegrass in Kentucky. Still another group could explore various types of arts and crafts characteristic of different cities and regions along the river.

Tie It Together

Celebrate the River

Plan a class fair featuring cities on the Mississippi River today, such as St. Louis (above). Set up a booth for each city and create a travel brochure to persuade people to visit.

As a team, choose a city to represent. Then divide up tasks so different members find information on the following topics:

◆ Interesting attractions and events that your city offers— zoos, museums, parks, sports events, music festivals, and so on.

◆ Influences of different groups on the city's food, customs, music, and architecture.

◆ Physical features of the area around the city.

◆ Famous people—writers, political figures, entertainers—who lived there.

◆ Historic places to visit, such as monuments, houses, battlefields, and statues.

◆ Illustrations and pictures of special attractions.

◆ Maps of walking tours and historic areas.

◆ Native plants and animals in the area.

Before starting your brochure, decide which attractions to highlight. Think of a slogan for your travel campaign. If you wish, make a poster. Celebrate life on the river today.

Developing scientific thinking in students is important for a solid science education. To learn how to think scientifically, students need frequent opportunities to practice science process skills, critical thinking skills, as well as other skills that support scientific inquiry. The *Science Explorer* Skills Handbook introduces the following key science skills:

◆ Science Process Skills
◆ SI Measuring Skills
◆ Skills for Conducting a Scientific Investigation
◆ Critical Thinking Skills
◆ Information Organizing Skills
◆ Data Table and Graphing Skills

The Skills Handbook is designed as a reference for students to use whenever they need to review a science skill. You can use the activities provided in the Skills Handbook to teach or reinforce the skills.

Think Like a Scientist

Observing

Before students look at the photograph, remind them that an observation is only what they can see, hear, smell, taste, or feel. Ask: **Which senses will you use to make observations from this photograph?** *(Sight is the only sense that can be used to make observations from the photograph.)* **What are some observations you can make from the photograph?** *(Answers may vary. Sample answers: The boy is wearing sneakers, sport socks, shorts, and a tee shirt; the boy is sitting in the grass holding something blue against his knee; the boy is looking at his knee; there is a soccer ball laying beside the boy.)* List the observations on the chalkboard. If students make any inferences or predictions about the boy at this point, ask: **Can you be sure your statement is factual and accurate from just observing the photograph?** Help students understand how observations differ from inferences and predictions.

Inferring

Review students' observations from the photograph. Then ask: **What inferences can you**

Think Like a Scientist

*A*lthough you may not know it, you think like a scientist every day. Whenever you ask a question and explore possible answers, you use many of the same skills that scientists do. Some of these skills are described on this page.

Observing

When you use one or more of your five senses to gather information about the world, you are **observing**. Hearing a dog bark, counting twelve green seeds, and smelling smoke are all observations. To increase the power of their senses, scientists sometimes use microscopes, telescopes, or other instruments that help them make more detailed observations.

An observation must be factual and accurate—an exact report of what your senses detect. It is important to keep careful records of your observations in science class by writing or drawing in a notebook. The information collected through observations is called evidence or data.

Inferring

When you explain or interpret an observation, you are **inferring**, or making an inference. For example, if you hear your dog barking, you may infer that someone is at your front door. To make this inference, you combine the evidence—the barking dog—and your experience or knowledge—you know that your dog barks when strangers approach—to reach a logical conclusion.

Notice that an inference is not a fact; it is only one of many possible explanations for an observation. For example, your dog may be barking because it wants to go for a walk. An inference may turn out to be incorrect even if it is based on accurate observations and logical reasoning. The only way to find out if an inference is correct is to investigate further.

Predicting

When you listen to the weather forecast, you hear many predictions about the next day's weather—what the temperature will be, whether it will rain, and how windy it will be. Weather forecasters use observations and knowledge of weather patterns to predict the weather. The skill of **predicting** involves making an inference about a future event based on current evidence or past experience.

Because a prediction is an inference, it may prove to be false. In science class, you can test some of your predictions by doing experiments. For example, suppose you predict that larger paper airplanes can fly farther than smaller airplanes. How could you test your prediction?

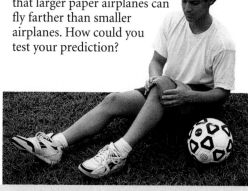

 ACTIVITY Use the photograph to answer the questions below.

Observing Look closely at the photograph. List at least three observations.

Inferring Use your observations to make an inference about what has happened. What experience or knowledge did you use to make the inference?

Predicting Predict what will happen next. On what evidence or experience do you base your prediction?

make from your observations? *(Students may say that the boy hurt his knee playing soccer and is holding a coldpack against his injured knee.)* **What experience or knowledge helped you make this inference?** *(Students may have experienced knee injuries from playing soccer, and they may be familiar with coldpacks like the one the boy is using.)* **Can anyone suggest another possible explanation for these observations?** *(Answers may vary. Sample answer: The boy hurt his knee jogging, and he just happened to sit beside a soccer ball his sister*

left in the yard.) **How can you find out whether an inference is correct?** *(by further investigation)*

Predicting

After coming to some consensus about the inference that the boy hurt his knee, encourage students to make predictions about what will happen next. *(Students' predictions may vary. Sample answers: The boy will go to the doctor. A friend will help the boy home. The boy will get up and continue playing soccer.)*

Classifying

Could you imagine searching for a book in the library if the books were shelved in no particular order? Your trip to the library would be an all-day event! Luckily, librarians group together books on similar topics or by the same author. Grouping together items that are alike in some way is called **classifying**. You can classify items in many ways: by size, by shape, by use, and by other important characteristics.

Like librarians, scientists use the skill of classifying to organize information and objects. When things are sorted into groups, the relationships among them become easier to understand.

ACTIVITY Classify the objects in the photograph into two groups based on any characteristic you choose. Then use another characteristic to classify the objects into three groups.

Making Models

Have you ever drawn a picture to help someone understand what you were saying? Such a drawing is one type of model. A model is a picture, diagram, computer image, or other representation of a complex object or process. **Making models** helps people understand things that they cannot observe directly.

Scientists often use models to represent things that are either very large or very small, such as the planets in the solar system, or the parts of a cell. Such models are physical models—drawings or three-dimensional structures that look like the real thing. Other models are mental models—mathematical equations or words that describe how something works.

ACTIVITY This student is using a model to demonstrate what causes day and night on Earth. What do the flashlight and the tennis ball in the model represent?

Communicating

Whenever you talk on the phone, write a letter, or listen to your teacher at school, you are communicating. **Communicating** is the process of sharing ideas and information with other people. Communicating effectively requires many skills, including writing, reading, speaking, listening, and making models.

Scientists communicate to share results, information, and opinions. Scientists often communicate about their work in journals, over the telephone, in letters, and on the Internet. They also attend scientific meetings where they share their ideas with one another in person.

ACTIVITY On a sheet of paper, write out clear, detailed directions for tying your shoe. Then exchange directions with a partner. Follow your partner's directions exactly. How successful were you at tying your shoe? How could your partner have communicated more clearly?

On what did you base your prediction? (*Scientific predictions are based on knowledge and experience.*) Point out that in science, predictions can often be tested with experiments.

Classifying

ACTIVITY

Encourage students to think of other common things that are classified. Then ask: **What things at home are classified?** (*Clothing might be classified by placing it in different dresser drawers; glasses, plates, and silverware are grouped in different parts of the kitchen; screws, nuts, bolts, washers, and nails might be separated into small containers.*) **What are some things that scientists classify?** (*Scientists classify many things they study, including organisms, geological features and processes, and kinds of machines.*) After students have classified the different fruits in the photograph, have them share their criteria for classifying them. (*Some characteristics students might use include shape, color, size, and where they are grown.*)

Making Models

ACTIVITY

Ask students: **What are some models you have used to study science?** (*Students may have used human anatomical models, solar system models, maps, stream tables.*) **How did these models help you?** (*Models can help you learn about things that are difficult to study, either because they are too big, too small, or complex.*) Be sure students understand that a model does not have to be three-dimensional. For example, a map in a textbook is a model. Ask: **What do the flashlight and tennis ball represent?** (*The flashlight represents the sun, and the ball represents Earth.*) **What quality of each item makes this a good model?** (*The flashlight gives off light, and the ball is round and can be rotated by the student.*)

Communicating

ACTIVITY

Challenge students to identify the methods of communication they've used today. Then ask: **How is the way you communicate with a friend similar to and different from the way scientists communicate about their work to other scientists?** (*Both may communicate using various methods, but scientists must be very detailed and precise, whereas communication between friends may be less detailed and precise.*) Encourage students to communicate like a scientist as they carry out the activity. (*Students' directions should be detailed and precise enough for another person to successfully follow.*)

Making Measurements

Measuring in SI

Review SI units in class with students. Begin by providing metric rulers, graduated cylinders, balances, and Celsius thermometers. Use these tools to reinforce that the meter is the unit of length, the liter is the unit of volume, the gram is the unit of mass, and the degree Celsius is the unit for temperature. Ask: **If you want to measure the length and width of your classroom, which SI unit would you use?** *(meter)* **Which unit would you use to measure the amount of matter in your textbook?** *(gram)* **Which would you use to measure how much water a drinking glass holds?** *(liter)* **When would you use the Celsius scale?** *(To measure the temperature of something)* Then use the measuring equipment to review SI prefixes. For example, ask: **What are the smallest units on the metric ruler?** *(millimeters)* **How many millimeters are there in 1 cm?** *(10 mm)* **How many in 10 cm?** *(100 mm)* **How many centimeters are there in 1 m?** *(100 cm)* **What does 1,000 m equal?** *(1 km)*

Length (Students

![ACTIVITY]

should state that the shell is 4.6 centimeters, or 46 millimeters, long.) If students need more practice measuring length, have them use meter sticks and metric rulers to measure various objects in the classroom.

Liquid Volume

![ACTIVITY]

(Students should state that the volume of water in the graduated cylinder is 62 milliliters.) If students need more practice measuring liquid volume, have them use a graduated cylinder to measure different volumes of water.

Making Measurements

When scientists make observations, it is not sufficient to say that something is "big" or "heavy." Instead, scientists use instruments to measure just how big or heavy an object is. By measuring, scientists can express their observations more precisely and communicate more information about what they observe.

Measuring in SI

The standard system of measurement used by scientists around the world is known as the International System of Units, which is abbreviated as SI (in French, *Système International d'Unités*). SI units are easy to use because they are based on multiples of 10. Each unit is ten times larger than the next smallest unit and one tenth the size of the next largest unit. The table lists the prefixes used to name the most common SI units.

Common SI Prefixes

Prefix	Symbol	Meaning
kilo-	k	1,000
hecto-	h	100
deka-	da	10
deci-	d	0.1 (one tenth)
centi-	c	0.01 (one hundredth)
milli-	m	0.001 (one thousandth)

Length To measure length, or the distance between two points, the unit of measure is the **meter (m)**. One meter is the approximate distance from the floor to a doorknob. Long distances, such as the distance between two cities, are measured in kilometers (km). Small lengths are measured in centimeters (cm) or millimeters (mm). Scientists use metric rulers and meter sticks to measure length.

Common Conversions

1 km = 1,000 m
1 m = 100 cm
1 m = 1,000 mm
1 cm = 10 mm

The larger lines on the metric ruler in the picture show centimeter divisions, while the smaller, unnumbered lines show millimeter divisions. How many centimeters long is the shell? How many millimeters long is it?

![ACTIVITY]

Liquid Volume To measure the volume of a liquid, or the amount of space a liquid takes up, you will use a unit of measure known as the **liter (L)**. One liter is the approximate volume of a medium-sized carton of milk. Smaller volumes are measured in milliliters (mL). Scientists use graduated cylinders to measure liquid volume.

Common Conversion

1 L = 1,000 mL

The graduated cylinder in the picture is marked in milliliter divisions. Notice that the water in the cylinder has a curved surface. This curved surface is called the *meniscus*. To measure the volume, you must read the level at the lowest point of the meniscus. What is the volume of water in this graduated cylinder?

![ACTIVITY]

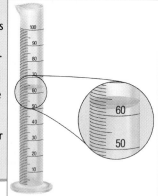

Mass To measure mass, or the amount of matter in an object, you will use a unit of measure known as the **gram (g)**. One gram is approximately the mass of a paper clip. Larger masses are measured in kilograms (kg). Scientists use a balance to find the mass of an object.

Common Conversion

1 kg = 1,000 g

The electronic balance displays the mass of an apple in kilograms. What is the mass of the apple? Suppose a recipe for applesauce called for one kilogram of apples. About how many apples would you need?

Temperature
To measure the temperature of a substance, you will use the **Celsius scale**. Temperature is measured in degrees Celsius (°C) using a Celsius thermometer. Water freezes at 0°C and boils at 100°C.

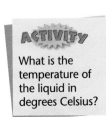

What is the temperature of the liquid in degrees Celsius?

Mass (Students should state that the mass of the apple is 0.1 kilograms. They would need 10 apples to make 1 kilogram.) If students need practice determining mass, have them use a balance to determine the mass of various common objects, such as coins, paper clips, and books.

Temperature (Students should state that the temperature of the liquid is 35°C.) If students need practice measuring temperature, have them use a Celsius thermometer to measure the temperature of various water samples.

Converting SI Units

Review the steps for converting SI units and work through the example with students. Then ask: **How many millimeters are in 80 centimeters?** (Students should follow the steps to calculate that 80 centimeters is equal to 800 millimeters.)

Have students do the conversion problems in the activity. (**1.** 600 millimeters = 0.6 meters; **2.** 0.35 liters = 350 milliliters; **3.** 1,050 grams = 1.05 kilograms) If students need more practice converting SI units, have students make up conversion problems and trade with a partner.

Converting SI Units

To use the SI system, you must know how to convert between units. Converting from one unit to another involves the skill of **calculating**, or using mathematical operations. Converting between SI units is similar to converting between dollars and dimes because both systems are based on multiples of ten.

Suppose you want to convert a length of 80 centimeters to meters. Follow these steps to convert between units.

1. Begin by writing down the measurement you want to convert—in this example, 80 centimeters.
2. Write a conversion factor that represents the relationship between the two units you are converting. In this example, the relationship is *1 meter = 100 centimeters*. Write this conversion factor as a fraction, making sure to place the units you are converting from (centimeters, in this example) in the denominator.

3. Multiply the measurement you want to convert by the fraction. When you do this, the units in the first measurement will cancel out with the units in the denominator. Your answer will be in the units you are converting to (meters, in this example).

Example

80 centimeters = ___?___ meters

$$80 \text{ centimeters} \times \frac{1 \text{ meter}}{100 \text{ centimeters}} = \frac{80 \text{ meters}}{100}$$

$$= 0.8 \text{ meters}$$

Convert between the following units.
1. 600 millimeters = _?_ meters
2. 0.35 liters = _?_ milliliters
3. 1,050 grams = _?_ kilograms

H ◆ 189

Conducting a Scientific Investigation

Posing Questions

Before students do the activity on the next page, walk them through the steps of a typical scientific investigation. Begin by asking: **Why is a scientific question important to a scientific investigation?** *(It is the reason for conducting a scientific investigation and how every investigation begins.)* **What is the scientific question in the activity at the bottom of the next page?** *(Is a ball's bounce affected by the height from which it is dropped?)*

Developing a Hypothesis

Emphasize that a hypothesis is a prediction about the outcome of a scientific investigation, but it is *not* a guess. Ask: **On what information do scientists base their hypotheses?** *(Their observations and previous knowledge or experience)* Point out that a hypothesis does not always turn out to be correct. Ask: **In that case, do you think the scientist wasted his or her time? Explain your answer.** *(No, because the scientist probably learned from the investigation and maybe could develop another hypothesis that could be supported.)*

Designing an Experiment

Have a volunteer read the Experimental Procedure in the box. Then call on students to identify the manipulated variable *(amount of salt added to water)*, the variables that are kept constant *(amount and starting temperature of water, placing containers in freezer)*, the responding variable *(time it takes water to freeze)*, and the control *(Container 3)*.

Ask: **How might the experiment be affected if Container 1 had only 100 mL of water?** *(It wouldn't be a fair comparison with the containers that have more water.)* **What if Container 3 was not included in the experiment?** *(You wouldn't have anything to compare the other two containers to know if their freezing times were faster or slower than normal.)* Help students understand the importance of

Conducting a Scientific Investigation

In some ways, scientists are like detectives, piecing together clues to learn about a process or event. One way that scientists gather clues is by carrying out experiments. An experiment tests an idea in a careful, orderly manner. Although all experiments do not follow the same steps in the same order, many follow a pattern similar to the one described here.

Posing Questions

Experiments begin by asking a scientific question. A scientific question is one that can be answered by gathering evidence. For example, the question "Which freezes faster— fresh water or salt water?" is a scientific question because you can carry out an investigation and gather information to answer the question.

Developing a Hypothesis

The next step is to form a hypothesis. A **hypothesis** is a prediction about the outcome of the experiment. Like all predictions, hypotheses are based on your observations and previous knowledge or experience. But, unlike many predictions, a hypothesis must be something that can be tested. A properly worded hypothesis should take the form of an *If... then* statement. For example, a hypothesis might be *"If I add salt to fresh water, then the water will take longer to freeze."* A hypothesis worded this way serves as a rough outline of the experiment you should perform.

keeping all variables constant except the manipulated variable. Also be sure they understand the role of the control. Then ask: **What operational definition is used in this experiment?** *("Frozen" means the time at which a wooden stick can no longer move in a container.)*

Designing an Experiment

Next you need to plan a way to test your hypothesis. Your plan should be written out as a step-by-step procedure and should describe the observations or measurements you will make.

Two important steps involved in designing an experiment are controlling variables and forming operational definitions.

Controlling Variables In a well-designed experiment, you need to keep all variables the same except for one. A **variable** is any factor that can change in an experiment. The factor that you change is called the **manipulated variable.** In this experiment, the manipulated variable is the amount of salt added to the water. Other factors, such as the amount of water or the starting temperature, are kept constant.

The factor that changes as a result of the manipulated variable is called the responding variable. The **responding variable** is what you measure or observe to obtain your results. In this experiment, the responding variable is how long the water takes to freeze.

An experiment in which all factors except one are kept constant is a **controlled experiment**. Most controlled experiments include a test called the control. In this experiment, Container 3 is the control. Because no salt is added to Container 3, you can compare the results from the other containers to it. Any difference in results must be due to the addition of salt alone.

Forming Operational Definitions
Another important aspect of a well-designed experiment is having clear operational definitions. An **operational definition** is a statement that describes how a particular variable is to be measured or how a term is to be defined. For example, in this experiment, how will you determine if the water has frozen? You might decide to insert a stick in each container at the start of the experiment. Your operational definition of "frozen" would be the time at which the stick can no longer move.

EXPERIMENTAL PROCEDURE

1. Fill 3 containers with 300 milliliters of cold tap water.

2. Add 10 grams of salt to Container 1; stir. Add 20 grams of salt to Container 2; stir. Add no salt to Container 3.

3. Place the 3 containers in a freezer.

4. Check the containers every 15 minutes. Record your observations.

Interpreting Data

The observations and measurements you make in an experiment are called data. At the end of an experiment, you need to analyze the data to look for any patterns or trends. Patterns often become clear if you organize your data in a data table or graph. Then think through what the data reveal. Do they support your hypothesis? Do they point out a flaw in your experiment? Do you need to collect more data?

Drawing Conclusions

A conclusion is a statement that sums up what you have learned from an experiment. When you draw a conclusion, you need to decide whether the data you collected support your hypothesis or not. You may need to repeat an experiment several times before you can draw any conclusions from it. Conclusions often lead you to pose new questions and plan new experiments to answer them.

Is a ball's bounce affected by the height from which it is dropped? Using the steps just described, plan a controlled experiment to investigate this problem.

ACTIVITY

Interpreting Data

Emphasize the importance of collecting accurate and detailed data in a scientific investigation. Ask: **What if the students forgot to record the times that they made their observations in the experiment?** *(They wouldn't be able to completely analyze their data to draw valid conclusions.)* Then ask: **Why are data tables and graphs a good way to organize data?** *(They often make it easier to compare and analyze data.)* You may wish to have students review the Skills Handbook pages on Creating Data Tables and Graphs at this point.

Drawing Conclusions

Help students understand that a conclusion is not necessarily the end of a scientific investigation. A conclusion about one experiment may lead right into another experiment. Point out that in scientific investigations, a conclusion is a summary and explanation of the results of an experiment.

Tell students to suppose that for the Experimental Procedure described on this page, they obtained the following results: Container 1 froze in 45 minutes, Container 2 in 80 minutes, and Container 3 in 25 minutes. Ask: **What conclusions can you draw about this experiment?** *(Students might conclude that the more salt that is added to fresh water, the longer it takes the water to freeze. The hypothesis is supported, and the question of which freezes faster is answered—fresh water.)*

You might wish to have students work in pairs to plan the controlled experiment. *(Students should develop a hypothesis, such as "If I increase the height from which a ball is dropped, then the height of its bounce will increase." They can test the hypothesis by dropping balls from varying heights (the manipulated variable). All trials should be done with the same kind of ball and on the same surface (constant variables). For each trial, they should measure the height of the bounce (responding variable).)* After students have designed the experiment, provide rubber balls and invite them to carry out the experiment so they can collect and interpret data and draw conclusions.

ACTIVITY

Thinking Critically

Comparing and Contrasting

Emphasize that the skill of comparing and contrasting often relies on good observation skills, as in this activity. *(Students' answers may vary. Sample answer: Similarities—both are dogs and have four legs, two eyes, two ears, brown and white fur, black noses, pink tongues; Differences—smooth coat vs. rough coat, more white fur vs. more brown fur, shorter vs. taller, long ears vs. short ears.)*

Applying Concepts

Point out to students that they apply concepts that they learn in school in their daily lives. For example, they learn to add, subtract, multiply, and divide in school. If they get a paper route or some other part-time job, they can apply those concepts. Challenge students to practice applying concepts by doing the activity. *(Antifreeze lowers the temperature at which the solution will freeze, and thus keep the water in the radiator from freezing.)*

Interpreting Illustrations

Again, point out the need for good observation skills. Ask: **What is the difference between "interpreting illustrations" and "looking at the pictures"?** *("Interpreting illustrations" requires thorough examination of the illustration, caption, and labels, while "looking at the pictures" implies less thorough examination.)* Encourage students to thoroughly examine the diagram as they do the activity. *(Students' paragraphs may vary, but should describe the internal anatomy of an earthworm, including some of the organs in the earthworm.)*

Thinking Critically

Has a friend ever asked for your advice about a problem? If so, you may have helped your friend think through the problem in a logical way. Without knowing it, you used critical-thinking skills to help your friend. Critical thinking involves the use of reasoning and logic to solve problems or make decisions. Some critical-thinking skills are described below.

Comparing and Contrasting

When you examine two objects for similarities and differences, you are using the skill of **comparing and contrasting**. Comparing involves identifying similarities, or common characteristics. Contrasting involves identifying differences. Analyzing objects in this way can help you discover details that you might otherwise overlook.

ACTIVITY
Compare and contrast the two animals in the photo. First list all the similarities that you see. Then list all the differences.

Applying Concepts

When you use your knowledge about one situation to make sense of a similar situation, you are using the skill of **applying concepts**. Being able to transfer your knowledge from one situation to another shows that you truly understand a concept. You may use this skill in answering test questions that present different problems from the ones you've reviewed in class.

ACTIVITY
You have just learned that water takes longer to freeze when other substances are mixed into it. Use this knowledge to explain why people need a substance called antifreeze in their car's radiator in the winter.

Interpreting Illustrations

Diagrams, photographs, and maps are included in textbooks to help clarify what you read. These illustrations show processes, places, and ideas in a visual manner. The skill called **interpreting illustrations** can help you learn from these visual elements. To understand an illustration, take the time to study the illustration along with all the written information that accompanies it. Captions identify the key concepts shown in the illustration. Labels point out the important parts of a diagram or map, while keys identify the symbols used in a map.

Blood vessels
Reproductive organs
Hearts
Brain
Mouth
Bristles
Digestive tract
Nerve cord
Waste-removal organs
Intestine

▲ Internal anatomy of an earthworm

ACTIVITY
Study the diagram above. Then write a short paragraph explaining what you have learned.

Relating Cause and Effect

If one event causes another event to occur, the two events are said to have a cause-and-effect relationship. When you determine that such a relationship exists between two events, you use a skill called **relating cause and effect**. For example, if you notice an itchy, red bump on your skin, you might infer that a mosquito bit you. The mosquito bite is the cause, and the bump is the effect.

It is important to note that two events do not necessarily have a cause-and-effect relationship just because they occur together. Scientists carry out experiments or use past experience to determine whether a cause-and-effect relationship exists.

ACTIVITY
You are on a camping trip and your flashlight has stopped working. List some possible causes for the flashlight malfunction. How could you determine which cause-and-effect relationship has left you in the dark?

Making Generalizations

When you draw a conclusion about an entire group based on information about only some of the group's members, you are using a skill called **making generalizations**. For a generalization to be valid, the sample you choose must be large enough and representative of the entire group. You might, for example, put this skill to work at a farm stand if you see a sign that says, "Sample some grapes before you buy." If you sample a few sweet grapes, you may conclude that all the grapes are sweet—and purchase a large bunch.

ACTIVITY
A team of scientists needs to determine whether the water in a large reservoir is safe to drink. How could they use the skill of making generalizations to help them? What should they do?

Making Judgments

When you evaluate something to decide whether it is good or bad, or right or wrong, you are using a skill called **making judgments**. For example, you make judgments when you decide to eat healthful foods or to pick up litter in a park. Before you make a judgment, you need to think through the pros and cons of a situation, and identify the values or standards that you hold.

ACTIVITY
Should children and teens be required to wear helmets when bicycling? Explain why you feel the way you do.

Problem Solving

When you use critical-thinking skills to resolve an issue or decide on a course of action, you are using a skill called **problem solving**. Some problems, such as how to convert a fraction into a decimal, are straightforward. Other problems, such as figuring out why your computer has stopped working, are complex. Some complex problems can be solved using the trial and error method—try out one solution first, and if that doesn't work, try another. Other useful problem-solving strategies include making models and brainstorming possible solutions with a partner.

Relating Cause and Effect

Emphasize that not all events that occur together have a cause-and-effect relationship. For example, tell students that you went to the grocery and your car stalled. Ask: **Is there a cause-and-effect relationship in this situation? Explain your answer.** (*No, because going to the grocery could not cause a car to stall. There must be another cause to make the car stall.*) Have students do the activity to practice relating cause and effect. (*Students should identify that the flashlight not working is the effect. Some possible causes include dead batteries, a burned-out light bulb, or a loose part.*)

Making Generalizations

Point out the importance of having a large, representative sample before making a generalization. Ask: **If you went fishing at a lake and caught three catfish, could you make the generalization that all fish in the lake are catfish? Why or why not?** (*No, because there might be other kinds of fish you didn't catch because they didn't like the bait or they may be in other parts of the lake.*) **How could you make a generalization about the kinds of fish in the lake?** (*By having a larger sample*) Have students do the activity to practice making generalizations. (*The scientists should collect and test water samples from a number of different parts of the reservoir.*)

Making Judgments

Remind students that they make a judgment almost every time they make a decision. Ask: **What steps should you follow to make a judgment?** (*Gather information, list pros and cons, analyze values, make judgment*) Invite students to do the activity, and then to share and discuss the judgments they made. (*Students' judgments will vary, but should be supported by valid reasoning. Sample answer: Children and teens should be required to wear helmets when bicycling because helmets have been proven to save lives and reduce head injuries.*)

Problem Solving

ACTIVITY
Challenge student pairs to solve a problem about a soapbox derby. Explain that their younger brother is building a car to enter in the race. The brother wants to know how to make his soapbox car go faster. After student pairs have considered the problem, have them share their ideas about solutions with the class. (*Most will probably suggest using trial and error by making small changes to the car and testing the car after each change. Some students may suggest making and manipulating a model.*)

Organizing Information

Organizing Information

As you read this textbook, how can you make sense of all the information it contains? Some useful tools to help you organize information are shown on this page. These tools are called *graphic organizers* because they give you a visual picture of a topic, showing at a glance how key concepts are related.

Concept Maps

Concept maps are useful tools for organizing information on broad topics. A concept map begins with a general concept and shows how it can be broken down into more specific concepts. In that way, relationships between concepts become easier to understand.

A concept map is constructed by placing concept words (usually nouns) in ovals and connecting them with linking words. The most general concept word is placed at the top, and the words become more specific as you move downward. The linking words, which are written on a line extending between two ovals, describe the relationship between the two concepts they connect. If you follow any string of concepts and linking words down the map, it should read like a sentence.

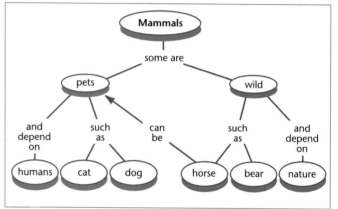

Some concept maps include linking words that connect a concept on one branch of the map to a concept on another branch. These linking words, called cross-linkages, show more complex interrelationships among concepts.

Compare/Contrast Tables

Compare/contrast tables are useful tools for sorting out the similarities and differences between two or more items. A table provides an organized framework in which to compare items based on specific characteristics that you identify.

To create a compare/contrast table, list the items to be compared across the top of a table. Then list the characteristics that will form the basis of your comparison in the left-hand

Characteristic	Baseball	Basketball
Number of Players	9	5
Playing Field	Baseball diamond	Basketball court
Equipment	bat, baseball, mitts	basket, basketball

column. Complete the table by filling in information about each characteristic, first for one item and then for the other.

Venn Diagrams

Another way to show similarities and differences between items is with a Venn diagram. A Venn diagram consists of two or more circles that partially overlap. Each circle represents a particular concept or idea. Common characteristics, or similarities, are written within the area of overlap between the two circles. Unique characteristics, or differences, are written in the parts of the circles outside the area of overlap.

To create a Venn diagram, draw two overlapping circles. Label the circles with the names of the items being compared. Write the unique characteristics in each circle outside the area of overlap. Then write the shared characteristics within the area of overlap.

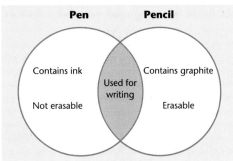

Pen **Pencil**

Contains ink

Used for writing

Contains graphite

Not erasable

Erasable

Flowcharts

A flowchart can help you understand the order in which certain events have occurred or should occur. Flowcharts are useful for outlining the stages in a process or the steps in a procedure.

To make a flowchart, write a brief description of each event in a box. Place the first event at the top of the page, followed by the second event, the third event, and so on. Then draw an arrow to connect each event to the one that occurs next.

Preparing Pasta

Boil water
↓
Cook pasta
↓
Drain water
↓
Add sauce

Cycle Diagrams

A cycle diagram can be used to show a sequence of events that is continuous, or cyclical. A continuous sequence does not have an end because, when the final event is over, the first event begins again. Like a flowchart, a cycle diagram can help you understand the order of events.

To create a cycle diagram, write a brief description of each event in a box. Place one event at the top of the page in the center. Then, moving in a clockwise direction around an imaginary circle, write each event in its proper sequence. Draw arrows to connect each event to the one that occurs next to form a continuous circle.

Steps in a Science Experiment

Pose a question
→ Develop a hypothesis
→ Design an experiment
→ Interpret data
→ Draw conclusions
→ (back to Pose a question)

H ◆ 195

Venn Diagrams

ACTIVITY

Students can use the same information from their compare/contrast tables to create a Venn diagram. Make sure students understand that the overlapping area of the circles is used to list similarities and the parts of the circles outside the overlap area are used to show differences. If students want to list similarities and differences among three activities, show them how to add a third circle that overlaps each of the other two circles and has an area of overlap for all three circles. (*Students' Venn diagrams will vary. Make sure they have accurately listed similarities in the overlap area and differences in the parts of the circles that do not overlap.*)

Flowcharts

ACTIVITY

Encourage students to create a flowchart to show the things they did this morning as they got ready for school. Remind students that a flowchart should show the correct order in which events occurred or should occur. (*Students' flowcharts will vary somewhat. A typical flowchart might include: got up → ate breakfast → took a shower → brushed teeth → got dressed → gathered books and homework → put on jacket.*)

Cycle Diagrams

ACTIVITY

Review that a cycle diagram shows a sequence of events that is continuous. Then challenge students to create a cycle diagram that shows how the weather changes with the seasons where they live. (*Students' cycle diagrams may vary, though most will include four steps, one for each season.*)

Creating Data Tables and Graphs

Data Tables

Have students create a data table to show how much time they spend on different activities during one week. Suggest that students first list the main activities they do every week. Then they should determine the amount of time they spend on each activity each day. Remind students to give this data table a title. *(Students' data tables will vary. A sample data table is shown below.)*

Bar Graphs

Students can use the data from their data table above to make a bar graph showing how much time they spend on different activities during a week. The vertical axis should be divided into units of time, such as hours. Remind students to label both axes and give their graph a title. *(Students' bar graphs will vary. A sample bar graph is shown below.)*

Creating Data Tables and Graphs

How can you make sense of the data in a science experiment? The first step is to organize the data to help you understand them. Data tables and graphs are helpful tools for organizing data.

Data Tables

You have gathered your materials and set up your experiment. But before you start, you need to plan a way to record what happens during the experiment. By creating a data table, you can record your observations and measurements in an orderly way.

Suppose, for example, that a scientist conducted an experiment to find out how many Calories people of different body masses burn while doing various activities. The data table shows the results.

Notice in the data table that the manipulated variable (body mass) is the heading of one column. The responding variable (for Experiment 1, the number of Calories burned while bicycling) is the heading of the next column. Additional columns were added for related experiments.

CALORIES BURNED IN 30 MINUTES OF ACTIVITY			
Body Mass	Experiment 1 Bicycling	Experiment 2 Playing Basketball	Experiment 3 Watching Television
30 kg	60 Calories	120 Calories	21 Calories
40 kg	77 Calories	164 Calories	27 Calories
50 kg	95 Calories	206 Calories	33 Calories
60 kg	114 Calories	248 Calories	38 Calories

Bar Graphs

To compare how many Calories a person burns doing various activities, you could create a bar graph. A bar graph is used to display data in a number of separate, or distinct, categories. In this example, bicycling, playing basketball, and watching television are three separate categories.

To create a bar graph, follow these steps.

1. On graph paper, draw a horizontal, or *x*-, axis and a vertical, or *y*-, axis.
2. Write the names of the categories to be graphed along the horizontal axis. Include an overall label for the axis as well.
3. Label the vertical axis with the name of the responding variable. Include units of measurement. Then create a scale along the axis by marking off equally spaced numbers that cover the range of the data collected.
4. For each category, draw a solid bar using the scale on the vertical axis to determine the appropriate height. For example, for bicycling, draw the bar as high as the 60 mark on the vertical axis. Make all the bars the same width and leave equal spaces between them.
5. Add a title that describes the graph.

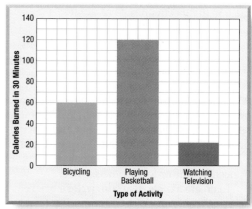

Calories Burned by a 30-kilogram Person in Various Activities

Time Spent on Different Activities in a Week				
	Going to Classes	Eating Meals	Playing Soccer	Watching Television
Monday	6	2	2	0.5
Tuesday	6	1.5	1.5	1.5
Wednesday	6	2	1	2
Thursday	6	2	2	1.5
Friday	6	2	2	0.5
Saturday	0	2.5	2.5	1
Sunday	0	3	1	2

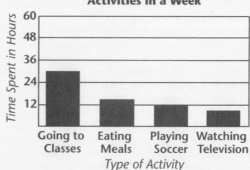

Time Spent on Different Activities in a Week

Line Graphs

To see whether a relationship exists between body mass and the number of Calories burned while bicycling, you could create a line graph. A line graph is used to display data that show how one variable (the responding variable) changes in response to another variable (the manipulated variable). You can use a line graph when your manipulated variable is *continuous*, that is, when there are other points between the ones that you tested. In this example, body mass is a continuous variable because there are other body masses between 30 and 40 kilograms (for example, 31 kilograms). Time is another example of a continuous variable.

Line graphs are powerful tools because they allow you to estimate values for conditions that you did not test in the experiment. For example, you can use the line graph to estimate that a 35-kilogram person would burn 68 Calories while bicycling.

To create a line graph, follow these steps.

1. On graph paper, draw a horizontal, or *x*-, axis and a vertical, or *y*-, axis.
2. Label the horizontal axis with the name of the manipulated variable. Label the vertical axis with the name of the responding variable. Include units of measurement.
3. Create a scale on each axis by marking off equally spaced numbers that cover the range of the data collected.
4. Plot a point on the graph for each piece of data. In the line graph above, the dotted lines show how to plot the first data point (30 kilograms and 60 Calories). Draw an imaginary vertical line extending up from the horizontal axis at the 30-kilogram mark. Then draw an imaginary horizontal line extending across from the vertical axis at the 60-Calorie mark. Plot the point where the two lines intersect.

Effect of Body Mass on Calories Burned While Bicycling

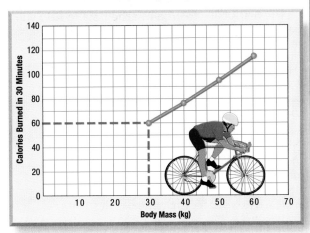

5. Connect the plotted points with a solid line. (In some cases, it may be more appropriate to draw a line that shows the general trend of the plotted points. In those cases, some of the points may fall above or below the line.)
6. Add a title that identifies the variables or relationship in the graph.

> Create line graphs to display the data from Experiment 2 and Experiment 3 in the data table. **ACTIVITY**

> You read in the newspaper that a total of 4 centimeters of rain fell in your area in June, 2.5 centimeters fell in July, and 1.5 centimeters fell in August. What type of graph would you use to display these data? Use graph paper to create the graph. **ACTIVITY**

Line Graphs

Walk students through the steps involved in creating a line graph using the example illustrated on the page. For example, ask: **What is the label on the horizontal axis? On the vertical axis?** *(Body Mass (kg); Calories Burned in 30 Minutes)* **What scales are used on each axis?** *(3 squares per 10 kg on the x-axis and 2 squares per 20 Calories on the y-axis)* **What does the second data point represent?** *(77 Calories burned for a body mass of 40 kg)* **What trend or pattern does the graph show?** *(The number of Calories burned in 30 minutes of cycling increases with body mass.)*

Have students follow the steps to carry out the first activity. *(Students should make a different graph for each experiment with different y-axis scales to practice making scales appropriate for data. See sample graphs below.)*

Have students carry out the second activity. **ACTIVITY** *(Students should conclude that a bar graph would be best to display the data. A sample bar graph for these data is shown below.)*

Rainfall in June, July, and August

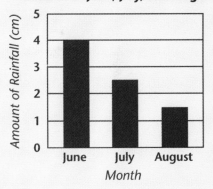

Effect of Body Mass on Calories Burned While Playing Basketball

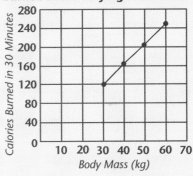

Effect of Body Mass on Calories Burned While Watching Television

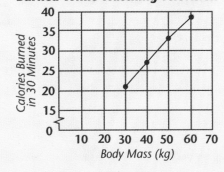

Circle Graphs

Emphasize that a circle graph has to include 100 percent of the categories for the topic being graphed. For example, ask: **Could the data in the bar graph titled "Calories Burned by a 30-kilogram Person in Various Activities" (on the previous page) be shown in a circle graph? Why or why not?** (*No, because it does not include all the possible ways a 30-kilogram person can burn Calories.*) Then walk students through the steps for making a circle graph. Help students to use a compass and a protractor. Use the protractor to illustrate that a circle has 360 degrees. Make sure students understand the mathematical calculations involved in making a circle graph.

You might wish to have students work in pairs to complete the activity. (*Students' circle graphs should look like the graph below.*)

ACTIVITY

Circle Graphs

Like bar graphs, circle graphs can be used to display data in a number of separate categories. Unlike bar graphs, however, circle graphs can only be used when you have data for *all* the categories that make up a given topic. A circle graph is sometimes called a pie chart because it resembles a pie cut into slices. The pie represents the entire topic, while the slices represent the individual categories. The size of a slice indicates what percentage of the whole a particular category makes up.

The data table below shows the results of a survey in which 24 teenagers were asked to identify their favorite sport. The data were then used to create the circle graph at the right.

Sports That Teens Prefer

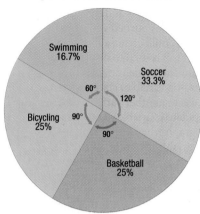

FAVORITE SPORTS	
Sport	Number of Students
Soccer	8
Basketball	6
Bicycling	6
Swimming	4

To create a circle graph, follow these steps.

1. Use a compass to draw a circle. Mark the center of the circle with a point. Then draw a line from the center point to the top of the circle.
2. Determine the size of each "slice" by setting up a proportion where x equals the number of degrees in a slice. (NOTE: A circle contains 360 degrees.) For example, to find the number of degrees in the "soccer" slice, set up the following proportion:

$$\frac{\text{students who prefer soccer}}{\text{total number of students}} = \frac{x}{\text{total number of degrees in a circle}}$$

$$\frac{8}{24} = \frac{x}{360}$$

Cross-multiply and solve for x.

$$24x = 8 \times 360$$
$$x = 120$$

The "soccer" slice should contain 120 degrees.

3. Use a protractor to measure the angle of the first slice, using the line you drew to the top of the circle as the 0° line. Draw a line from the center of the circle to the edge for the angle you measured.
4. Continue around the circle by measuring out the size of each slice with the pro-tractor. Start measuring from the edge of the previous slice so the wedges do not overlap. When you are done, the entire circle should be filled in.
5. Determine the percentage of the whole circle that each slice represents. To do this, divide the number of degrees in a slice by the total number of degrees in a circle (360), and multiply by 100%. For the "soccer" slice, you can find the percentage as follows:

$$\frac{120}{360} \times 100\% = 33.3\%$$

6. Use a different color to shade in each slice. Label each slice with the name of the category and with the percentage of the whole it represents.
7. Add a title to the circle graph.

In a class of 28 students, 12 students take the bus to school, 10 students walk, and 6 students ride their bicycles. Create a circle graph to display these data. **ACTIVITY**

Ways Students Get to School

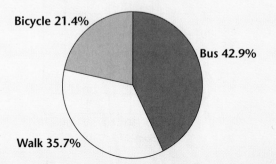

Laboratory Safety

Safety Symbols

These symbols alert you to possible dangers in the laboratory and remind you to work carefully.

Safety Goggles Always wear safety goggles to protect your eyes in any activity involving chemicals, flames or heating, or the possibility of broken glassware.

Lab Apron Wear a laboratory apron to protect your skin and clothing from damage.

Breakage You are working with materials that may be breakable, such as glass containers, glass tubing, thermometers, or funnels. Handle breakable materials with care. Do not touch broken glassware.

Heat-resistant Gloves Use an oven mitt or other hand protection when handling hot materials. Hot plates, hot glassware, or hot water can cause burns. Do not touch hot objects with your bare hands.

Heating Use a clamp or tongs to pick up hot glassware. Do not touch hot objects with your bare hands.

Sharp Object Pointed-tip scissors, scalpels, knives, needles, pins, or tacks are sharp. They can cut or puncture your skin. Always direct a sharp edge or point away from yourself and others. Use sharp instruments only as instructed.

Electric Shock Avoid the possibility of electric shock. Never use electrical equipment around water, or when the equipment is wet or your hands are wet. Be sure cords are untangled and cannot trip anyone. Disconnect the equipment when it is not in use.

Corrosive Chemical You are working with an acid or another corrosive chemical. Avoid getting it on your skin or clothing, or in your eyes. Do not inhale the vapors. Wash your hands when you are finished with the activity.

Poison Do not let any poisonous chemical come in contact with your skin and do not inhale its vapors. Wash your hands when you are finished with the activity.

Physical Safety When an experiment involves physical activity, take precautions to avoid injuring yourself or others. Follow instructions from your teacher. Alert your teacher if there is any reason you should not participate in the activity.

Animal Safety Treat live animals with care to avoid harming the animals or yourself. Working with animal parts or preserved animals also may require caution. Wash your hands when you are finished with the activity.

Plant Safety Handle plants in the laboratory or during field work only as directed by your teacher. If you are allergic to certain plants, tell your teacher before doing an activity in which those plants are used. Avoid touching harmful plants such as poison ivy, poison oak, or poison sumac, or plants with thorns. Wash your hands when you are finished with the activity.

Flames You may be working with flames from a lab burner, candle, or matches. Tie back loose hair and clothing. Follow instructions from your teacher about lighting and extinguishing flames.

No Flames Flammable materials may be present. Make sure there are no flames, sparks, or other exposed heat sources present.

Fumes When poisonous or unpleasant vapors may be involved, work in a ventilated area. Avoid inhaling vapors directly. Only test an odor when directed to do so by your teacher, and use a wafting motion to direct the vapor toward your nose.

Disposal Chemicals and other laboratory materials used in the activity must be disposed of safely. Follow the instructions from your teacher.

Hand Washing Wash your hands thoroughly when finished with the activity. Use antibacterial soap and warm water. Lather both sides of your hands and between your fingers. Rinse well.

General Safety Awareness You may see this symbol when none of the symbols described earlier appears. In this case, follow the specific instructions provided. You may also see this symbol when you are asked to develop your own procedure in a lab. Have your teacher approve your plan before you go further.

Laboratory Safety

Laboratory safety is an essential element of a successful science class. It is important for you to emphasize laboratory safety to students. Students need to understand exactly what is safe and unsafe behavior, and what the rationale is behind each safety rule.

Review with students the Safety Symbols and Science Safety Rules listed on this and the next two pages. Then follow the safety guidelines below to ensure that your classroom will be a safe place for students to learn science.

◆ Post safety rules in the classroom and review them regularly with students.

◆ Familiarize yourself with the safety procedures for each activity before introducing it to your students.

◆ Review specific safety precautions with students before beginning every science activity.

◆ Always act as an exemplary role model by displaying safe behavior.

◆ Know how to use safety equipment, such as fire extinguishers and fire blankets, and always have it accessible.

◆ Have students practice leaving the classroom quickly and orderly to prepare them for emergencies.

◆ Explain to students how to use the intercom or other available means of communication to get help during an emergency.

◆ Never leave students unattended while they are engaged in science activities.

◆ Provide enough space for students to safely carry out science activities.

◆ Keep your classroom and all science materials in proper condition. Replace worn or broken items.

◆ Instruct students to report all accidents and injuries to you immediately.

Laboratory Safety

Additional tips are listed below for the Science Safety Rules discussed on these two pages. Please keep these tips in mind when you carry out science activities in your classroom.

General Precautions

◆ For open-ended activities like Chapter Projects, go over general safety guidelines with students. Have students submit their procedures or design plans in writing and check them for safety considerations.

◆ In an activity where students are directed to taste something, be sure to store the material in clean, *nonscience* containers. Distribute the material to students in *new* plastic or paper dispensables, which should be discarded after the tasting. Tasting or eating should never be done in a lab classroom.

◆ During physical activity, make sure students do not overexert themselves.

◆ Remind students to handle microscopes and telescopes with care to avoid breakage.

Heating and Fire Safety

◆ No flammable substances should be in use around hot plates, light bulbs, or open flames.

◆ Test tubes should be heated only in water baths.

◆ Students should be permitted to strike matches to light candles or burners *only* with strict supervision. When possible, you should light the flames, especially when working with sixth graders.

◆ Be sure to have proper ventilation when fumes are produced during a procedure.

◆ All electrical equipment used in the lab should have GFI switches.

Using Chemicals Safely

◆ When students use both chemicals and microscopes in one activity, microscopes should be in a separate part of the room from the chemicals so that when students remove their goggles to use the microscopes, their eyes are not at risk.

Science Safety Rules

To prepare yourself to work safely in the laboratory, read over the following safety rules. Then read them a second time. Make sure you understand and follow each rule. Ask your teacher to explain any rules you do not understand.

Dress Code

1. To protect yourself from injuring your eyes, wear safety goggles whenever you work with chemicals, burners, glassware, or any substance that might get into your eyes. If you wear contact lenses, wear your safety goggles and notify your teacher.
2. Wear a lab apron or coat whenever you work with corrosive chemicals or substances that can stain.
3. Tie back long hair to keep it away from any chemicals, flames, or equipment.
4. Remove or tie back any article of clothing or jewelry that can hang down and touch chemicals, flames, or equipment. Roll up or secure long sleeves.
5. Never wear open shoes or sandals.

General Precautions

6. Read all directions for an experiment several times before beginning the activity. Carefully follow all written and oral instructions. If you are in doubt about any part of the experiment, ask your teacher for assistance.
7. Never perform activities that are not assigned or authorized by your teacher. Obtain permission before "experimenting" on your own. Never handle any equipment unless you have specific permission.
8. Never perform lab activities without direct supervision.
9. Never eat or drink in the laboratory.
10. Keep work areas clean and tidy at all times. Bring only notebooks and lab manuals or written lab procedures to the work area. All other items, such as purses and backpacks, should be left in a designated area.
11. Do not engage in horseplay.

First Aid

12. Always report all accidents or injuries to your teacher, no matter how minor. Notify your teacher immediately about any fires.
13. Learn what to do in case of specific accidents, such as getting acid in your eyes or on your skin. (Rinse acids from your body with lots of water.)
14. Be aware of the location of the first-aid kit, but do not use it unless instructed by your teacher. In case of injury, your teacher should administer first aid. Your teacher may also send you to the school nurse or call a physician.
15. Know the location of emergency equipment, such as the fire extinguisher and fire blanket, and know how to use it.
16. Know the location of the nearest telephone and whom to contact in an emergency.

Heating and Fire Safety

17. Never use a heat source, such as a candle, burner, or hot plate, without wearing safety goggles.
18. Never heat anything unless instructed to do so. A chemical that is harmless when cool may be dangerous when heated.
19. Keep all combustible materials away from flames. Never use a flame or spark near a combustible chemical.
20. Never reach across a flame.
21. Before using a laboratory burner, make sure you know proper procedures for lighting and adjusting the burner, as demonstrated by your teacher. Do not touch the burner. It may be hot. And never leave a lighted burner unattended!
22. Chemicals can splash or boil out of a heated test tube. When heating a substance in a test tube, make sure that the mouth of the tube is not pointed at you or anyone else.
23. Never heat a liquid in a closed container. The expanding gases produced may blow the container apart.
24. Before picking up a container that has been heated, hold the back of your hand near it. If you can feel the heat on the back of your hand, the container is too hot to handle. Use an oven mitt to pick up a container that has been heated.

Using Glassware Safely

◆ Use plastic containers, graduated cylinders, and beakers whenever possible. If using glass, students should wear safety goggles.

◆ Use only nonmercury thermometers with anti-roll protectors.

◆ Check all glassware periodically for chips and scratches, which can cause cuts and breakage.

Using Chemicals Safely

25. Never mix chemicals "for the fun of it." You might produce a dangerous, possibly explosive substance.
26. Never put your face near the mouth of a container that holds chemicals. Never touch, taste, or smell a chemical unless you are instructed by your teacher to do so. Many chemicals are poisonous.
27. Use only those chemicals needed in the activity. Read and double-check labels on supply bottles before removing any chemicals. Take only as much as you need. Keep all containers closed when chemicals are not being used.
28. Dispose of all chemicals as instructed by your teacher. To avoid contamination, never return chemicals to their original containers. Never simply pour chemicals or other substances into the sink or trash containers.
29. Be extra careful when working with acids or bases. Pour all chemicals over the sink or a container, not over your work surface.
30. If you are instructed to test for odors, use a wafting motion to direct the odors to your nose. Do not inhale the fumes directly from the container.
31. When mixing an acid and water, always pour the water into the container first and then add the acid to the water. Never pour water into an acid.
32. Take extreme care not to spill any material in the laboratory. Wash chemical spills and splashes immediately with plenty of water. Immediately begin rinsing with water any acids that get on your skin or clothing, and notify your teacher of any acid spill at the same time.

Using Glassware Safely

33. Never force glass tubing or thermometers into a rubber stopper or rubber tubing. Have your teacher insert the glass tubing or thermometer if required for an activity.
34. If you are using a laboratory burner, use a wire screen to protect glassware from any flame. Never heat glassware that is not thoroughly dry on the outside.
35. Keep in mind that hot glassware looks cool. Never pick up glassware without first checking to see if it is hot. Use an oven mitt. See rule 24.
36. Never use broken or chipped glassware. If glassware breaks, notify your teacher and dispose of the glassware in the proper broken-glassware container. Never handle broken glass with your bare hands.
37. Never eat or drink from lab glassware.
38. Thoroughly clean glassware before putting it away.

Using Sharp Instruments

39. Handle scalpels or other sharp instruments with extreme care. Never cut material toward you; cut away from you.
40. Immediately notify your teacher if you cut your skin when working in the laboratory.

Animal and Plant Safety

41. Never perform experiments that cause pain, discomfort, or harm to mammals, birds, reptiles, fishes, or amphibians. This rule applies at home as well as in the classroom.
42. Animals should be handled only if absolutely necessary. Your teacher will instruct you as to how to handle each animal species brought into the classroom.
43. If you know that you are allergic to certain plants, molds, or animals, tell your teacher before doing an activity in which these are used.
44. During field work, protect your skin by wearing long pants, long sleeves, socks, and closed shoes. Know how to recognize the poisonous plants and fungi in your area, as well as plants with thorns, and avoid contact with them.
45. Never eat any part of an unidentified plant or fungus.
46. Wash your hands thoroughly after handling animals or the cage containing animals. Wash your hands when you are finished with any activity involving animal parts, plants, or soil.

End-of-Experiment Rules

47. After an experiment has been completed, clean up your work area and return all equipment to its proper place.
48. Dispose of waste materials as instructed by your teacher.
49. Wash your hands after every experiment.
50. Always turn off all burners or hot plates when they are not in use. Unplug hot plates and other electrical equipment. If you used a burner, check that the gas-line valve to the burner is off as well.

Using Sharp Instruments

◆ Always use blunt-tip safety scissors, except when pointed-tip scissors are required.

Animal and Plant Safety

◆ When working with live animals or plants, check ahead of time for students who may have allergies to the specimens.
◆ When growing bacteria cultures, use only disposable petri dishes. After streaking, the dishes should be sealed and not opened again by students. After the lab, students should return the unopened dishes to you. Students should wash their hands with antibacterial soap.
◆ Two methods are recommended for the safe disposal of bacteria cultures. *First method:* Autoclave the petri dishes and discard without opening. *Second method:* If no autoclave is available, carefully open the dishes (never have a student do this) and pour full-strength bleach into the dishes and let stand for a day. Then pour the bleach from the petri dishes down a drain and flush the drain with lots of water. Tape the petri dishes back together and place in a sealed plastic bag. Wrap the plastic bag with a brown paper bag or newspaper and tape securely. Throw the sealed package in the trash. Thoroughly disinfect the work area with bleach.
◆ To grow mold, use a new, sealable plastic bag that is two to three times larger than the material to be placed inside. Seal the bag and tape it shut. After the bag is sealed, students should not open it. To dispose of the bag and mold culture, make a small cut near an edge of the bag and cook in a microwave oven on high setting for at least 1 minute. Discard the bag according to local ordinance, usually in the trash.
◆ Students should wear disposable nitrile, latex, or food-handling gloves when handling live animals or nonliving specimens.

End-of Experiment Rules

◆ Always have students use antibacterial soap for washing their hands.

abyssal plain A smooth, nearly flat region of the deep ocean floor. (p. 151)

acid rain Rain that is more acidic than normal, caused by the release of molecules of sulfur dioxide and nitrogen oxide into the air. (p. 101)

aquaculture The farming of saltwater and freshwater organisms. (p. 171)

aquifer An underground layer of rock or soil that holds water. (p. 72)

artesian well A well in which water rises because of pressure within the aquifer. (p. 73)

atoll A ring-shaped coral island. (p. 164)

benthos Organisms that live on the bottom of the ocean or other body of water. (p. 157)

bioluminescence The production of light by living things. (p. 167)

brackish Water that is partly salty and partly fresh, characteristic of estuaries. (p. 160)

capillary action The combined force of attraction among water molecules and with the molecules of surrounding materials. (p. 25)

climate The pattern of temperature and precipitation typical of an area over a long period of time. (p. 136)

coagulation The process by which particles in a liquid clump together; a step in the water treatment process. (p. 85)

concentration The amount of one substance in a certain volume of another substance. (p. 84)

condensation The process by which a gas changes to a liquid. (p. 27)

conservation The process of using a resource wisely so it will not be used up. (p. 92)

continental shelf A gently sloping, shallow area of the ocean floor that extends outward from the edge of a continent. (p. 150)

continental slope A steep incline leading down from the edge of the continental shelf. (p. 150)

controlled experiment An experiment in which all factors except one are kept constant. (p. 191)

Coriolis effect The effect of Earth's rotation on the direction of winds and currents. (p. 135)

crest The highest point of a wave. (p. 116)

current A large stream of moving water that flows through the ocean. (p. 135)

delta The area of sediment deposits that build up near a river's mouth. (p. 50)

deposition The process by which soil and fragments of rock are deposited in a new location. (p. 45)

desalination The process of obtaining fresh water from salt water by removing the salt. (p. 94)

divide A ridge of land that separates one watershed from another. (p. 45)

drought A water shortage caused by scarce rainfall in a particular area. (p. 91)

El Niño An abnormal climate event that occurs every 2 to 7 years in the Pacific Ocean, causing changes in winds, currents, and weather patterns. (p. 139)

erosion The process by which fragments of soil and rock are broken off from the ground surface and carried away. (p. 45)

estuary A coastal inlet or bay where fresh water from rivers mixes with salty ocean water. (p. 160)

eutrophication The process by which nutrients in a lake build up over time, causing an increase in the growth of algae. (p. 57)

evaporation The process by which molecules at the surface of a liquid absorb enough energy to change to the gaseous state. (p. 27)

filtration The process of passing water through a series of screens that allow the water through, but not larger solid particles. (p. 85)

flocs Sticky globs created by adding a chemical such as alum during water treatment. (p. 85)

flood plain A broad, flat valley through which a river flows. (p. 50)

food web The feeding relationships in a habitat. (p. 157)

frequency The number of waves that pass a specific point in a given amount of time. (p. 116)

G

geyser A type of hot spring in which the water is under pressure and bursts periodically into the air. (p. 74)

glacier A huge mass of ice and snow that moves slowly over the land. (p. 65)

groin A stone or concrete wall built out from a beach to reduce erosion. (p. 119)

groundwater Water that fills the cracks and pores in underground soil and rock layers. (p. 22)

H

habitat The place where an organism lives and that provides the things it needs to survive. (p. 20)

hardness The level of the minerals calcium and magnesium in water. (p. 84)

headwaters The many small streams that come together at the source of the river. (p. 48)

holdfast A bundle of rootlike strands that attaches algae to the rocks. (p. 164)

hydroelectric power Electricity produced by the kinetic energy of water moving over a waterfall or dam. (p. 106)

hydrothermal vent An area where ocean water sinks through cracks in the ocean floor, is heated by the underlying magma, and rises again through the cracks. (p. 168)

hypothesis A prediction about the outcome of an experiment. (p. 190)

impermeable Characteristic of materials through which water does not easily pass, such as clay and granite. (p. 69)

intertidal zone The area that stretches from the highest high-tide line on land out to the point on the continental shelf exposed by the lowest low tide. (p. 158)

irrigation The process of supplying water to areas of land to make them suitable for growing crops. (p. 17)

kinetic energy The form of energy that an object has when it is moving. (p. 106)

leach field The ground area around a septic tank through which wastewater filters after leaving the tank. (p. 89)

levee A long ridge formed by deposits of sediments alongside a river channel. (p. 52)

longshore drift The movement of sand along a beach; caused by waves coming into shore at an angle. (p. 118)

magma Hot, liquid substance that makes up part of Earth's mantle. (p. 153)

manipulated variable The one factor that a scientist changes during an experiment. (p. 191)

meander A looping curve formed in a river as it winds through its flood plain. (p. 50)

mid-ocean ridge The continuous range of mountains on the ocean floor that winds around Earth. (p. 151)

mouth The point where a river flows into another body of water. (p. 50)

neap tide A tide with the least difference between low and high tide that occurs when the sun and moon pull at right angles to each other. (p. 125)

nekton Free-swimming animals that can move throughout the water column. (p. 157)

neritic zone The part of the ocean that extends from the low-tide line out to the edge of the continental shelf. (p. 163)

nodule A lump formed when metals such as manganese build up around pieces of shell on the ocean floor. (p. 171)

nonpoint source A widely spread source of pollution that is difficult to link to a specific point of origin, such as road runoff. (p. 99)

open-ocean zone The area of the ocean beyond the edge of the continental shelf. (p. 163)

operational definition A statement that describes how a particular variable is to be measured or a term is to be defined. (p. 191)

oxbow lake The crescent-shaped, cutoff body of water that remains after a river carves a new channel. (p. 50)

permeable Characteristic of materials that allow water to easily pass through them, such as sand and gravel. (p. 69)

pesticide A chemical intended to kill insects and other organisms that damage crops. (p. 102)

pH How acidic or basic a substance is, measured on a scale of 1 (very acidic) to 14 (very basic). (p. 83)

photosynthesis The process by which plants use water, plus carbon dioxide and energy from the sun, to make food. (p. 19)

plankton Tiny algae and animals that float in water and are carried by waves and currents. (p. 157)

plate One of the major pieces that make up Earth's upper layer. (p. 153)

point source A specific source of pollution that can be identified, such as a pipe. (p. 99)

polar molecule A molecule that has electrically charged areas. (p. 24)

pores Tiny openings in and between particles of rock and soil which may contain air or water. (p. 69)

potential energy Energy that is stored and waiting to be used. (p. 106)

precipitation Water that falls to Earth as rain, snow, sleet, or hail. (p. 34)

recharge New water that enters an aquifer from the surface. (p. 73)

reservoir A natural or artificial lake that stores water for human use. (p. 56)

responding variable The factor that changes as a result of changes to the manipulated variable in an experiment. (p. 191)

rip current A rush of water that flows rapidly back to sea through a narrow opening. (p. 118)

runoff Water that flows over the ground surface rather than soaking into the ground. (p. 43)

salinity The total amount of dissolved salts in a water sample. (p. 127)

sandbar A ridge of sand deposited by waves as they slow down near shore. (p. 118)

saturated zone A layer of permeable rock or soil in which the cracks and pores are totally filled with water. (p. 69)

sea-floor spreading The process by which new material is added to the ocean floor along the boundary between diverging plates. (p. 154)

seamount A mountain on the ocean floor that is completely underwater. (p. 151)

sediments The particles of rock and soil that are moved by water or wind, resulting in erosion and deposition. (p. 45)

septic tank An underground tank containing bacteria that treat wastewater as it passes through. (p. 89)

sewage Water containing human wastes. (p. 87)

sludge Deposits of fine solids that settle out from wastewater during the treatment process. (p. 88)

solution A mixture that forms when one substance dissolves another. (p. 25)

solvent A substance that dissolves another substance, forming a solution. (p. 25)

sonar A system that uses sound waves to calculate the distance to an object, which gets its name from **so**und **na**vigation and **r**anging. (p. 149)

specific heat The amount of heat needed to increase the temperature of a certain mass of substance by 1°C. (p. 29)

spring A place where groundwater bubbles or flows out of cracks in the rocks. (p. 74)

spring tide A tide with the greatest difference between high and low tide that occurs when the sun and the moon are aligned in a line with Earth. (p. 124)

state A form of matter; solid, liquid, or gas. (p. 26)

submersible An underwater vehicle built of strong materials to resist pressure at depth. (p. 131)

surface tension The tightness across the surface of water that is caused by the polar molecules pulling on each other. (p. 24)

tides The daily rise and fall of Earth's waters on shores. (p. 123)

transpiration The process by which plants release water vapor through their leaves. (p. 33)

trench A deep canyon in the ocean floor. (p. 152)

tributary A smaller stream or river that feeds into a main river. (p. 44)

trough The lowest point of a wave. (p. 117)

tsunami A giant wave caused by an earthquake on the ocean floor. (p. 121)

unsaturated zone A layer of rocks and soil above the water table in which the pores contain air as well as water. (p. 69)

upwelling An upward flow of cold water from the ocean depths. (p. 137)

variable Any factor that can change as part of an experiment. (p. 191)

water cycle The continuous process by which water moves through the living and nonliving parts of the environment. (p. 32)

water pollution The addition of any substance that has a negative effect on water or the living things that depend on the water. (p. 97)

water quality The degree of purity of water, determined by measuring the substances in water, besides water molecules. (p. 82)

watershed The land area that supplies water to a river system. (p. 44)

water table The top of the saturated zone, or depth to the groundwater in an aquifer. (p. 69)

water vapor The invisible, gaseous form of water. (p. 20)

wave The movement of energy through a body of water. (p. 115)

wave height The vertical distance from the crest of a wave to the trough. (p. 117)

wavelength The horizontal distance between two wave crests. (p. 116)

wetland An area of land that is covered with a shallow layer of water during some or all of the year. (p. 59)

Acknowledgments

Illustration

Patrice Rossi Calkin: 50, 58
Warren Cutler: 6, 7, 54–55, 62–63, 158–159
John Edwards & Associates: 99, 116, 117, 118, 121, 123, 125, 137, 154, 163
GeoSystems Global Corporation: 21, 44, 63 t, 135, 153, 170
Andrea Golden: 8, 24, 25, 27, 34, 36, 37, 61, 72
Martucci Design: 20, 179, 196, 197, 198
Paul Mirocha: 167
Morgan Cain & Associates: 86, 93, 102, 106, 188 bl, 188 br, 189 tl, 189 bl
Morgan Cain & Associates (Chris Forsey): 148, 150–151, 165
Matt Myerchak: 76, 110, 142, 195
Ortelius Design Inc.: 16, 18, 19, 57, 96, 122, 139, 147, 155
Matthew Pippin: 22, 33, 48–49, 69, 73, 77, 85, 88, 89, 107, 130
J/B Woolsey Associates (Mark Desman): 166, 192
Rose Zgodzinski: 128

Photography

Photo Research Paula Wehde

Cover Design Bruce Bond
Cover Image ©Tony Rostron/Panoramic Images

Nature of Science
Page 10, 11, 12 b, Courtesy of Cindy Lee Van Dover; **12 t,** Emory Kristof/National Geographic Image Collection; **13,** Woods Hole Oceanographic Institution.

Chapter 1
Pages 14-15, Randy Linchs/Sharpshooters; **16 b,** Uniphoto; **17 tl,** Peter Menzel/Stock Boston; **17 tr,** Foodpix; **18 t,** O. Louis Mazzatenta/National Geographic Image Collection; **18 b,** Liba Taylor/Corbis; **19 t,** Tom Bean/TSI; **19 b,** Gianni Dagli Orti/Corbis; **23,** Russ Lappa; **24 b,** Stephen Dalton/Photo Researchers; **25 inset** Tom Bean/The Stock Market; **25 b,** Mark & Audry Gibson/The Stock Market; **27 l,** Steven C. Kaufman/Peter Arnold; **27 m,** Chris Soresen/the Stock Market; **27 r,** Japack/Leo de Wys; **28 b,** Neal Mishler/Natural Selection; **29 t,** D. Adams/Picture Perfect Images; **29 b,** Russ Lappa; **31 b, 32 t,** Richard Haynes; **32 b,** Michael Giannechini/Photo Researchers; **34 t,** John Shaw/Tom Stack & Associates; **35 t, 37 t,** Japack/Leo de Wys.

Chapter 2
Pages 40-41, Dave Johnston/Picture Cube; **42 t,** Russ Lappa; **42 inset** Wernher Krutein/Gamma-Liaison; **42 m,** Superstock; **43,** Paul Barton/The Stock Market; **45,** Jacques Jangoux/TSI; **47,** Mark Thayer; **48 l,** Michael Durham/ENP; **48 b,** Darrell Gulin/TSI; **49 l,** Harry Engels/Animals Animals; **49 r,** Hal Horwitz/Corbis; **51 inset,** Gregory Foster/Gamma-Liaison; **51 b** Bill Gillette/Gamma-Liaison; **52,** Les Stone/Sygma; **53 t,** Russ Lappa; **53 b,** Annie Griffiths Belt/Aurora; **56 l,** David L. Brown/The Stock Market; **56 r,** John Shaw/Tom Stack & Associates; **57,** George Holton/Photo Researchers; **59 t,** Russ Lappa; **59 b,** Helen Cruickshank/Photo Researchers; **60 l,** Breck P. Kent/Animals Animals; **60 r, 204,** Greg Vaughn/Tom Stack & Associates; **61,** John Eastcott/Yva Momatiuk/Earth Scenes; **64,** Patrick M. Rose/Save the Manatee; **65 t,** Richard Haynes; **65 b,** Ralph A. Clevenger/Westlight; **66 t,** Don Pitcher/Stock Boston; **66 bl,** Hulton Getty/TSI; **66 br,** Superstock; **67,** Ralph A. Clevenger/Westlight; **68 t,** Richard Haynes; **68 b,** Tim Olive/Sharpshooters; **71,** Mark Thayer; **74,** Barbara Filet/TSI; **75,** R. Clevenger/Westlight.

Chapter 3
Pages 78-79, Jeremy Horner/Corbis; **80,** Russ Lappa; **81,** Guy Marche/TSI; **82,** Michael Newman/Photo Edit; **87 b,** Deborah Davis/Photo Edit; **87 t,** Ted Horowitz/The Stock Market; **90 t,** Russ Lappa; **90 b,** Laura Sikes/Sygma; **91,** Calvin Larsen/Photo Researchers; **92,** Russ Lappa; **94 t,** Peter Skinner/Photo Researchers; **94 b, 95, 97t,** Russ Lappa; **97,** Seth Resnick/Stock Boston; **100,** Corbis/Bettmann; **101 t,** Mugshots/The Stock Market; **101 b,** Wayne Eastep/TSI; **103 t,** Carson Baldwin/Earth Scenes; **103 b,** John Eastcott/Yva Momatiuk/Stock Boston; **104,** Peter Essick/Aurora; **105 t,** Russ Lappa; **105 b,** I. Burgum/P. Boorman/TSI; **107 b,** Robert K. Grubbs/Photo Network; **108,** George Gerster/Photo Researchers; **109 b,** Deborah David/Photo Edit; **109 t,** Mugshots/Stock Market.

Chapter 4
Pages 112-113, Seigried Layda/TSI; **114 t,** Richard Haynes; **114-115 b,** Aaron Chang/The Stock Market; **119 t,** ©1996 The Art Institute of Chicago, Clarence Buckingham Collection; **119 b,** Russ Lappa; **120 t,** Eric Horan/Gamma Liaison; **120 b,** Grace Davies/New England Stock; **122, 123,** Gene Ahrens/Bruce Coleman; **126,** Maher Attar/Sygma; **127 t,** Richard Haynes; **127 b,** Russ Lappa; **128,** Alon Reininger/The Stock Market; **129,** Corel; **131,** Russ Lappa; **133,** Mark Thayer; **134 b,** Russ Lappa; **134 t,** Richard Haynes; **136,** Raven/Explorer/Photo Researchers; **137 br,** Carol Roessler/Animals Animals; **140,** Ryan Ott/AP Photo.

Chapter 5
Pages 144-145, Fred Bavendam; **146 t,** Russ Lappa; **146 b,** The Granger Collection; **147,** Courtesy, Peabody Essex Museum, Salem, MA; **148,** Norbert Wu/The Stock Market; **149 t,** Scripps Oceanographic Institution; **149 b,** Scott Camanzine/Photo Researchers; **152,** Ted Streshinsky/Corbis; **154,** Russ Lappa; **156,** Richard Dunoff/The Stock Market; **157 tr,** E.R. Degginger/Photo Researchers; **157 mr,** Tim Heller/Mo Yung Productions; **157 br,** Doug Perrine/Innerspace Visions; **157 bl,** F. Stuart Westmorland/Photo Researchers; **160 bl,** Maresa Pryor, **br,** Peter Weiman **both** Earth Scenes; **161 t,** Lynda Richardson/Corbis; **161 b,** Andy Mertinez/Photo Researchers; **162 t,** Richard Haynes; **162 b,** Jeff Foott/Tom Stack & Associates; **164 l,** Chuck Davis/TSI; **164 r,** Randy Morse/Tom Stack & Associates; **165,** Mike Bacon/Tom Stack & Associates; **166,** Norbert Wu; **168,** D. Foster/WHOI/Visuals Unlimited; **169 t,** Richard Haynes; **169 b,** Nathan Benn/Stock Boston; **171,** Russ Lappa; **172,** Arnulf Husmo/TSI; **173 l,** Bob Torrez/TSI; **173 r,** Bill Nation/Sygma; **174 t,** Jake Evans/TSI; **174 b,** Richard Haynes; **175,** Tim Hauf/Visuals Unlimited; **177 l,** Doug Perrine/Innerspace Visions; **177 r,** Randy Morse/Tom Stack & Associates.

Interdisciplinary Exploration
Page 181 t, The Granger Collection; **181 m,** North Wind Picture Archives; **181 b,** University Art Collection, Tulane; **183,** Richard Pasley/Liaison International; **184,** Art Resource; **185 t,** North Wind Picture Archives; **185 b,** Chromo Sohm/Photo Researchers.

Skills Handbook
Page 186, Mike Moreland/Photo Network; **187 t,** Foodpix; **187 m,** Richard Haynes; **187 b,** Russ Lappa; **190,** Richard Haynes; **192,** Ron Kimball; **193,** Renee Lynn/Photo Researchers.